Elementary Introduction to
NUCLEAR
REACTOR
PHYSICS

S. E. LIVERHANT

Associate Professor of Physics
Maritime College
State University of New York

NEW YORK · LONDON, JOHN WILEY & SONS, INC.

Elementary Introduction to
NUCLEAR
REACTOR
PHYSICS

Preface

In less than a generation nuclear reactor physics has developed from esoteric beginnings to a branch of knowledge that has found its way into the college curriculum.

Although still taught primarily at the graduate level, there is already a significant number of colleges and institutions offering or planning to offer undergraduate degrees in nuclear science or engineering where courses in reactor physics are an integral part of the program. Undoubtedly, this trend will persist and interest in nuclear technology at the undergraduate level will continue to grow through the added stimulus of large-scale financial support of the U. S. Atomic Energy Commission.

This book is intended to serve as a textbook for an undergraduate course in nuclear reactor physics. It has been my aim to give an elementary but coherent account of that branch of physics involved in the study and design of nuclear reactors at a standard of presentation judged to be suitable for advanced undergraduate students. The book is the outcome of a course which was originally developed at New York Maritime College as early as 1951. During the last seven years I have been giving this course to selected groups of junior and senior engineering students who have previously had one semester of atomic and nuclear physics and one semester of differential equations.

I have attempted to follow a consistent and logical line of development of the subject matter, steering a middle course between a too detailed and rigorous mathematical treatment and a too shallow and purely descriptive exposition. The mathematical skill required by students using this book does not go beyond calculus and elementary differential equations and, when mathematical arguments are used to derive physically significant results which may not be immediately evident to the student, all necessary intermediate steps are shown in

v

detail. I have tried not to overemphasize and treat in excessive detail any one topic, so as to keep the book well-balanced and within the bounds of an undergraduate course.

Many of the concepts are introduced early in the book, and their more detailed description is reserved for the latter part of the book where the mathematical technique for their use and application is explained. This procedure has considerable pedagogic value since it separates the conceptual difficulty or novelty from the purely technical difficulty involved in the learning of a new concept. As the student later on encounters again a concept which he has already met earlier in his course, the sense of complete newness and sometimes overwhelming strangeness will be absent and, instead, the feeling of relative familiarity will be of great help to him in learning its practical use and application.

The first three chapters deal with some fundamental aspects of nuclear physics as far as they have a direct bearing on the physics of nuclear reactors. In this basic review course only those topics which are of immediate importance to the nuclear reactor physicist or engineer have been emphasized, whereas some others which may be indispensable to an over-all general understanding of nuclear phenomena have not been touched upon. Starting with the nucleus as a composite structure with inherent stability or the lack of it the logical line of development leads to a consideration of radioactivity, to the concept of binding energy, and to an examination of the character of nuclear forces which are responsible for it. The liquid drop model of the nucleus is next introduced and nuclear reactions are explained in terms of the formation of a compound nucleus. Neutron reactions representing the most important type of nuclear reactions for our purpose are then considered, which leads to the concept of neutron cross sections. The various neutron cross sections are subsequently examined and their energy dependence is described with some reference to neutron resonances and their relation to the compound nucleus. The neutron fission cross section leads to an examination of the physical aspects of nuclear fission and its explanation in terms of the previously described liquid drop model of the nucleus. It has been found that the consistent and systematic use of a nuclear model such as this is of tremendous help to students, especially engineering students, notwithstanding the shortcomings of such a model in some respects. The possibility of a chain-reacting system is subsequently presented and the necessary conditions for its satisfactory operation are examined. This material introduces the need for studying in some detail the interaction of neutrons with matter in bulk, the physics of thermal neutrons, and the thermalization of fission neutrons. This discussion is followed by an elementary exposition of neutron diffusion theory in a manner suitable for undergraduates, a consideration of the critical equation and of the spatial distribution of neutrons in finite reactor assemblies of simple geometries. Some aspects of the nonstationary reactor are then presented in an elementary manner together with some of the causes that lead to its nonstationary character. The concluding chapters deal with nuclear radiations that are associated with the operation of a nuclear reactor, their detection and measurement, and, finally, the need for protection against them and some elementary aspects of health physics.

It is hoped that this book will also be found helpful to graduate engineers, or scientists who want or need to familiarize themselves with some aspects of nuclear science as applied to reactors or allied fields, to those who require an intermediate textbook for their preparatory reading before embarking on a more advanced and intensive study of the subject, and to those who wish to gain a maximum of insight into the physical principles with a minimum of mathematical technique.

A large number of worked examples have been included which serve to illustrate the ideas developed in the book and to demonstrate their use for obtaining numerical answers to physical problems. Readers who are using this book for self-instruction should find these worked examples throughout the text especially helpful.

In conclusion I wish to express my indebtedness and gratitude to Captain J. Barton Hoag, U.S.C.G., Professor of Physics and Head of the Science Department of the U. S. Coast Guard Academy, for reviewing the entire manuscript, for his many helpful suggestions, constructive criticism, and encouraging comments, and to Dr. Meir H. Degani, Professor of Physics and Chairman of the Science Department at the State University of New York Maritime College, for his personal interest, valuable advice, and friendly encouragement throughout. I also wish to thank my students for working out the solutions to the problems at the end of each chapter and for their interest and enthusiasm which originally gave me the idea that it might be worth while to undertake the writing of a text such as is here presented.

S. E. LIVERHANT

May 1960

Contents

chapter **1**

The Atomic Nucleus

1.1 Introduction

Nuclear reactor physics is a branch of nuclear physics that deals with the large-scale interaction of neutrons with fissionable materials and with such other materials as are used in the construction of nuclear reactors.

Various types of nuclear reactors have been built for the purpose of studying nuclear fission and of phenomena associated with it, and for the purpose of utilizing the energy released in nuclear fission.

The energy obtained from the combustion of traditional fuels which has been used by man since almost the beginning of civilization can properly be called "atomic energy," since it is liberated during chemical processes which are essentially atomic or electronic rearrangements that do not involve the nuclei of the atoms.

In contrast with this process the energy released by nuclear fission is of an entirely different origin, since it arises as a result of a nuclear reaction in the course of which the constituents of a uranium or other fissionable nucleus are directly affected, with radically different nuclear arrangements emerging after the reaction. The energy liberated in this type of reaction is properly termed "nuclear energy" because its source are the nuclei of the atoms.

The practical importance of nuclear fission lies in the release of a large amount of energy accompanying this process, which occurs on a scale of about a million times larger as compared to the amount of energy obtained from the combustion of an atom of traditional fuel.

The study of reactors and reactor physics requires some familiarity with the principles of nuclear physics and the general properties of atomic nuclei. This information is presented in the first three chapters of this book, beginning with a general survey of the kinds of nuclear species and a description of some general features of nuclear structure.

The concept of nuclear stability is introduced and applied to the classification of nuclei according to their type of nuclear stability. The unstable nuclei, commonly called radioactive nuclei, have been an important source of information about nuclei in general and, because of this, the laws of radioactivity are described in some detail and are then applied to the important topic of isotope production.

1.2   Nuclear Structure

The constituents of atomic nuclei are collectively known as nucleons, of which there are two kinds, **protons** and **neutrons.** Each proton carries a positive charge that is numerically equal to that of the electron, whereas the neutron is an electrically neutral particle.

The masses of the proton and neutron are very nearly equal, although that of the neutron is somewhat larger than that of the proton.

The number of neutrons, N, inside an atomic nucleus together with the number of protons, Z, inside the same nucleus determine the **atomic mass number**, A, of the atom.

$$A = N + Z$$

The chemical properties of atoms are determined by the number of atomic electrons in the neutral atom, which must be equal to Z so as to result in an electrically neutral atom by exactly balancing the positive charge of an equal number of nuclear protons.

All atoms having the same number of nuclear protons, and therefore the same Z, are **isotopes** of the same element. Most elements occur in nature as a mixture of several isotopes (some even as many as 20), i.e., they all have the same characteristic Z, but differ in the number of their nuclear neutrons N. Consequently, their mass numbers A are different.

For example, $_8O^{16}$, $_8O^{17}$, $_8O^{18}$ are three isotopes of the same element oxygen ($Z = 8$) with atomic mass numbers 16, 17, 18, respectively, of which $_8O^{16}$ is the most abundant by far of the three isotopes.

The term **nuclide** is often used interchangeably with the term isotope. It is, however, a more general term and it denotes any species of atom without having reference to any particular nuclear property.

1.3   Distribution of Nuclides

Over 1300 different nuclei are presently known, of which only about one-fifth are stable, the rest being unstable and decaying spontaneously with the accompanying emission of particles or radiation.

Unstable nuclides occur both naturally and can also be obtained artificially by bombarding stable nuclei with high-energy particles.

If we include artificially created elements, a total of 102 different elements from $Z = 1$ to $Z = 102$ are known, with mass numbers ranging from 1 to about 260, with only the mass number $A = 5$ missing in an otherwise continuous chain of mass numbers.

All nuclides beyond bismuth ($Z = 83$) are unstable and disintegrate spontaneously with the emission of γ-rays or energetic particles.

By far the largest number of stable nuclei ($\sim 60\%$) have an even number of protons and an even number of neutrons. These are the even-even nuclei. The odd-even and even-odd nuclei, i.e., those having an odd number of protons and an even number of neutrons and vice versa, make up about 20% each of the total number of stable nuclei. Only four stable nuclei fall into the odd-odd category, namely, $_1H^2$, $_3Li^6$, $_5B^{10}$, $_7N^{14}$. (The odd-odd nuclei $_{19}K^{40}$, $_{71}Lu^{176}$, $_{23}V^{50}$, $_{57}La^{138}$ occur in minute quantities in nature, but all are radioactive.)

These facts seem to indicate that the even-even nuclei represent a more stable nuclear arrangement than do the odd-odd or even-odd arrangements. The reason for this preference is not yet fully understood, although it can be made plausible on the basis of the general properties of nuclear forces.

The neutron in the free state, when it is not bound inside a nucleus, is itself an unstable particle which decays spontaneously into a proton and an electron after an average lifetime of about 12 min.

$$n \longrightarrow p + e^-$$

When contained inside a nucleus, however, the neutron behaves as an indivisible fundamental particle and should then not be looked upon as a particle having a composite structure.

Certain nuclei having what is called a "magic" number of neutrons are especially stable. These numbers are 2, 8, 20, 28, 50, 82, and 126. The nuclei $_{36}Kr^{86}$ and $_{54}Xe^{136}$ are examples of this stability. The magic numbers of neutrons or protons correspond to the formation of closed shells in nuclei and can be pictured to be somewhat similar to the electron shells in the atomic structure of the elements. The most stable of all nuclei are the "doubly magic" nuclei which have a magic number of protons as well as a magic number of neutrons. Familiar examples of doubly magic nuclei are $_2He^4$, $_8O^{16}$, $_{20}Ca^{40}$, and $_{82}Pb^{208}$. (For additional information see M. G. Mayer and J. H. D. Jensen, *Elementary Theory of Nuclear Shell Structure*, John Wiley & Sons, 1955.)

1.4 Nuclear Stability

A nucleus can be considered stable if it does not undergo transformations spontaneously, i.e., of its own accord and without the addition of outside energy, such as by bombardment with high-energy nuclear projectiles or irradiation with γ-rays.

It is instructive to plot the known stable nuclei graphically in such a way that the neutron number $N = A - Z$ appears along the y-axis and the proton number Z along the x-axis (Fig. 1.1).

Such a graph shows that for stable nuclei the number of neutrons and the number of protons tend to be equal in the light nuclei, with a gradual increase in the number of neutrons over that of protons appearing as the atomic number of the nuclides goes up.

The graph also shows clearly that all stable nuclei fall within a narrow band which encloses the so-called line of stability.

The ratio of N/Z starts with the value 1 for $_1H^2$ and gradually increases to the maximum value of 1.52 for bismuth-209, the heaviest stable nuclide.

All unstable nuclei when plotted on the same diagram will be located outside the stability region. Those lying above and to the left of the stability zone are in the neutron excess region and will thus show a tendency to reduce their N/Z ratio. This can be achieved either (1) by β^--decay or (2) by the much rarer event of neutron emission.

1. A β^--decay is equivalent to the transformation of a neutron into a proton with the simultaneous creation of an electron and its ejection from the nucleus.

$$n \longrightarrow p + e^-$$

As an example of a β^--emission one has the decay of carbon-14 to nitrogen-14:

$$_6C^{14} \longrightarrow {_7N^{14}} + {_{-1}e^0}$$

2. A neutron emission occurs only from a highly excited nucleus and is, under ordinary circumstances, very infrequent. As an example of a neutron emission one has the transformation of Krypton-87 into the stable isotope Krypton-86, a reaction which is associated with a preceding nuclear fission in a significant number of cases.

$$_{36}Kr^{87} \longrightarrow {_{36}Kr^{86}} + {_0n^1}$$

All nuclei which are located below and to the right of the stability zone lie in a region of excess protons or neutron deficiency. They will tend to increase their N/Z ratio by such spontaneous processes as (1) β^+-emission (positron emission) or (2) electron capture (orbital or K-capture).

1. The β^+-emission, which is the emission of a positron from a nucleus, is preceded by the transformation of a proton into a neutron inside the nucleus with the simultaneous creation of a positive electron.

$$p \longrightarrow n + e^+$$

An example of this process is the transformation of nitrogen-12 into stable carbon-12:

$$_7N^{12} \longrightarrow _6C^{12} + _1e^0$$

2. The alternative possibility for reducing the excessive number of protons in a nucleus exists in the capture of an extra-nuclear electron by the nucleus, thereby bringing about a reduction in its net positive charge. This process would be equivalent to the fusion of a proton and an electron to form a neutron.

$$p + e^- \longrightarrow n$$

The electrons that are most likely to be captured are those closest to the nucleus of the atom, i.e., the two electrons in the K-shell of the atom. Because of this, orbital electron capture is commonly called **K-capture**, although electron captures from the higher L- and M-shells are also possible, but are much less probable than K-capture.

In heavy elements no positron emissions occur, and electron capture is the only mechanism for the reduction of the Z/N ratio in the heavy nuclei in Fig. 1.1 for which $Z < 83$.

A classical example of K-capture is the transformation of vanadium-49 into titanium-49.

$$_{23}V^{49} + _{-1}e^0 \longrightarrow _{22}Ti^{49}$$

1.5   Isobars

Transformations in nuclear configurations that imply the conversion of a proton into a neutron or a neutron into a proton such as occur with electron-capture or β-decay do not change the total number of nucleons in the nucleus and so leave the atomic mass number unchanged. Such transformations are known as *isobaric* transformations and the nuclei concerned are *isobars*.

For example,

$$_5B^{12} \longrightarrow _6C^{12} + _{-1}e^0 \quad \text{(electron emission)}$$
$$_7N^{12} \longrightarrow _6C^{12} + _{+1}e^0 \quad \text{(positron emission)}$$

are isobaric transformations and $_5B^{12}$, $_7N^{12}$, $_6C^{12}$ are three isobars with common atomic mass number $A = 12$.

Isobaric transitions are indicated in Fig. 1.1 as displacements along lines perpendicular to the line $N = Z$.

It appears to be well established that two isobars with Z differing only by one unit cannot both exist as stable nuclei. If there are such neighboring isobars, one will always decay into the other. Only if their charge numbers Z differ by two units can both isobars exist as stable entities, as for example, $_{16}S^{36}$ and $_{18}A^{36}$, or $_{20}Ca^{40}$ and $_{18}A^{40}$.

For odd values of A, there is generally only one stable isobar, with the notable exception of the odd mass numbers $A = 113$, $A = 115$, and $A = 123$, where we have the stable isobaric pairs (Cd^{113}, In^{113}), (In^{115}, Sn^{115}), and (Sb^{123}, Te^{123}).

1.6 Natural and Induced Radioactivity

We have seen that the region above and below the stability zone is occupied by unstable nuclides. These are the artificial or induced radio-nuclides, so-called because they have been obtained artificially by bombarding naturally occurring nuclei with high-energy nuclear particles such as neutrons, protons, deuterons, and α-particles.

When used as projectiles these high-energy particles can achieve nuclear disintegrations or transmutations of the target nuclei which result, in many cases, in radioactive product nuclei. These radioactive isotopes have become very prominent in industrial, medical, and biological research and their manufacture is an important function of nuclear reactors.

However, no new or previously unknown stable nuclides have ever been obtained as a result of nuclear transmutations by artificial means, such as bombardment with high-energy particles. (The elements Technetium, $Z = 43$, Promethium, $Z = 61$, and Astatine, $Z = 85$, which do not occur in nature, have been produced artificially, but they all are unstable.)

1. Neutron-induced reactions which result in the absorption of the neutron and so increase the N/Z ratio will, in general, yield nuclei that show β^--radioactivity. For example, [( )* denotes a radioactive nucleus.]

(n, α) $_{11}Na^{23} + {_0}n^1 \longrightarrow ({_9}F^{20})^* + {_2}He^4$

$({_9}F^{20})^* \longrightarrow {_{10}}Ne^{20} + \beta^-$

(n, p) $_{29}Cu^{65} + {_0}n^1 \longrightarrow ({_{28}}Ni^{65})^* + {_1}H^1$

$({_{28}}Ni^{65})^* \longrightarrow {_{29}}Cu^{65} + \beta^-$

(n, γ) $_{29}Cu^{65} + {_0}n^1 \longrightarrow ({_{29}}Cu^{66})^* + \gamma$

$({_{29}}Cu^{66})^* \longrightarrow {_{30}}Zn^{66} + \beta^-$

Nuclear reactions with deuterons, which are atomic nuclei of an isotope of hydrogen and consist of a neutron and a proton bound together to form a single nucleus, can also lead to an increase of the N/Z ratio and the formation of β^--radioactive product nucleus. Thus, in (d, p) reactions the target nucleus retains an extra neutron and re-emits the proton of the deuteron to form an unstable isotope that is β^--active, as for example

(d, p) $_{11}Na^{23} + {_1}H^2 \longrightarrow ({_{11}}Na^{24})^* + {_1}H^1$

$({_{11}}Na^{24})^* \longrightarrow {_{12}}Mg^{24} + \beta^-$

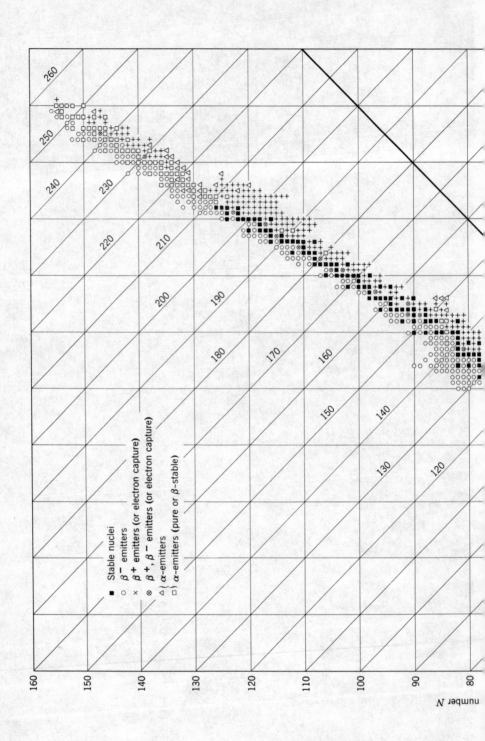

number N

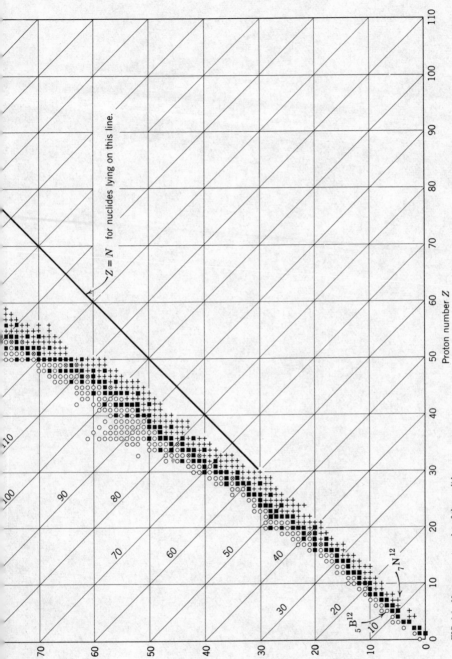

FIG. 1.1. Neutron-proton plot of the nuclides.

2. Nuclear reactions that lead to the emission of a neutron such as (p, n), (α, n), (d, n), or (γ, n) reactions result in a product nucleus with a decreased N/Z ratio and, commonly, yield β^+-radioactive nuclei. For example,

(p, n) $\qquad _{47}Ag^{107} + {}_1H^1 \longrightarrow ({}_{48}Cd^{107})^* + {}_0n^1$

$\qquad\qquad\qquad ({}_{48}Cd^{107})^* \longrightarrow {}_{47}Ag^{107} + \beta^+$

(α, n) $\qquad _{13}Al^{27} + {}_2He^4 \longrightarrow ({}_{15}P^{30})^* + {}_0n^1$

$\qquad\qquad\qquad ({}_{15}P^{30})^* \longrightarrow {}_{14}Si^{30} + \beta^+$

(d, n) $\qquad _6C^{12} + {}_1H^2 \longrightarrow ({}_7N^{13})^* + {}_0n^1$

$\qquad\qquad\qquad ({}_7N^{13})^* \longrightarrow {}_6C^{13} + \beta^+$

(γ, n) $\qquad _{15}P^{31} + \gamma \longrightarrow ({}_{15}P^{30})^* + {}_0n^1$

$\qquad\qquad\qquad ({}_{15}P^{30})^* \longrightarrow {}_{14}Si^{30} + \beta^+$

In addition, the (p, γ) reaction leads similarly to a reduction in the N/Z ratio and this generally results in the production of a β^+-emitter. Thus, for example,

(p, γ) $\qquad _6C^{12} + {}_1H^1 \longrightarrow ({}_7N^{13})^* + \gamma$

$\qquad\qquad\qquad ({}_7N^{13})^* \longrightarrow {}_6C^{13} + \beta^+$

The region beyond $Z = 83$, which so far has not been considered in this summary review, contains the naturally radioactive nuclides. Historically, these were the progenitors of nuclear physics and their exploration led to the formulation of the laws of radioactive decay which are valid for both natural and artificial radioactivity.

With the naturally radioactive nuclides, spontaneous transmutations occur in single nuclei, whereas with the manufactured radioactive nuclei, induced transmutations are first brought about by the collision and interaction of two nuclei.

The spontaneous decay of a heavy radioactive nucleus is caused by an inherent lack of stability of that nucleus and it occurs without any external physical stimulation.

In general, the decay product of a radioactive nucleus is another unstable nucleus, so that there results a whole chain of radioactive nuclei which finally terminates in a stable nucleus. Three such radioactive chains or series beginning, respectively, with uranium-238, uranium-235, and thorium-232 have been known for many years, and a fourth has recently been identified which starts with the artificial transuranium element plutonium-241. The series is known as the neptunium series because neptunium is the longest lived element of the series (Fig. 1.2 and Tables 1.1 to 1.4).

The stable end products of the naturally radioactive series are the lead isotopes Pb-206, Pb-207, and Pb-208 respectively, whereas the stable end

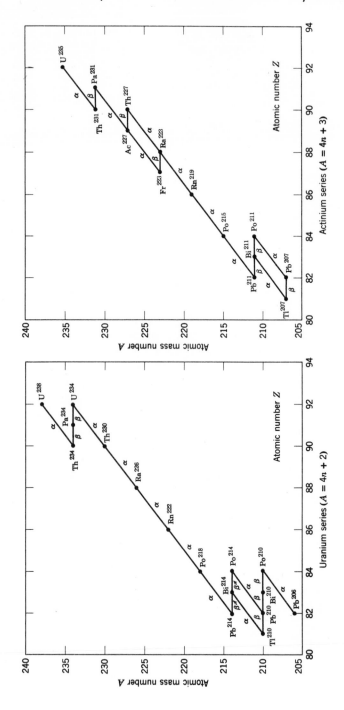

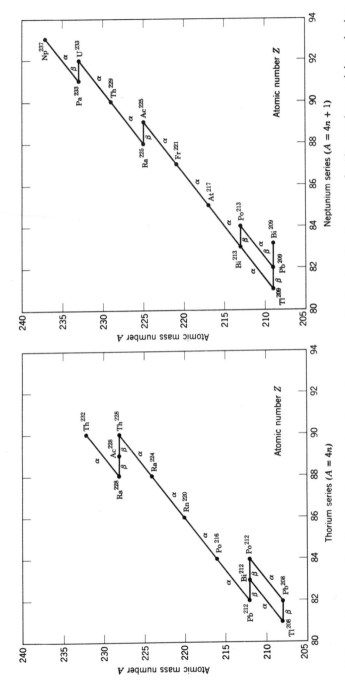

FIG. I.2. Diagrams of radioactive decay showing the main sequences of natural radioactive decay for the uranium, actinium, thorium, and neptunium series.

TABLE 1.1   Uranium Series

Radioelement (classical name)	Nuclide	Modern Name	Half-Life	Disintegration Mode and Energy (Mev)		
				α	β	γ
Uranium I (UI)	$_{92}U^{238}$	Uranium	4.51×10^9 yr	4.18		0.045
Uranium X$_1$	$_{90}Th^{234}$	Thorium	24.1 day		0.205	0.09
Uranium X$_2$	$_{91}Pa^{234}$	Protactinium	1.175 min		2.32	0.817
Uranium Z (UZ)	$_{91}Pa^{234}$	Protactinium	6.7 hr		1.2	
Uranium II (UII)	$_{92}U^{234}$	Uranium	2.48×10^5 yr	4.763		0.05; 0.117
Ionium (Io)	$_{90}Th^{230}$	Thorium	8.0×10^4 yr	4.68 4.61		0.068; 0.228
Radium (Ra)	$_{88}Ra^{226}$	Radium	1620 yr	4.777		0.186
Ra Emanation (Rn)	$_{86}Rn^{222}$	Radon	3.825 day	5.486		
Radium A (Ra A)	$_{84}Po^{218}$	Polonium	3.05 min	5.998		
Radium B (Ra B)	$_{82}Pb^{214}$	Lead	26.8 min		0.65	0.29 (many more)
Astatine-218	$_{85}At^{218}$	Astatine	2 sec	6.63		
Radium C (Ra C)	$_{83}Bi^{214}$	Bismuth	19.7 min	5.505	3.17	0.0625; 0.6091 (α)
Radium C' (Ra C')	$_{84}Po^{214}$	Polonium	1.64×10^{-4} sec	5.444		0.606; 2.42 (β)
Radium C" (Ra C")	$_{81}Tl^{210}$	Thallium	1.32 min	7.680	1.8	?
Radium D (Ra D)	$_{82}Pb^{210}$	Lead	19.4 yr		0.018	0.0465
Radium E (Ra E)	$_{83}Bi^{210}$	Bismuth	5.0 day		1.17	
Radium F (Ra F)	$_{84}Po^{210}$	Polonium	138.3 day	5.298		0.800
Thallium-206	$_{81}Tl^{206}$	Thallium	4.20 min		1.51	
Radium G (Ra G)	$_{82}Pb^{206}$	Lead	Stable			

0.02%   0.04% 5×10^{-5}%

TABLE 1.2 Actinium Series

Radioelement (classical name)	Nuclide	Modern Name	Half-Life	Disintegration Mode and Energy (Mev)		
				α	β	γ
Actinouranium (AcU)	$_{92}U^{235}$	Uranium	7.13×10^8 yr	4.58 4.40		Many groups
Uranium Y (UY)	$_{90}Th^{231}$	Thorium	25.64 hr		0.302	0.030 0.022
Protactinium (Pa)	$_{91}Pa^{231}$	Protactinium	3.43×10^4 yr	5.042 4.66		0.32 Many groups
Actinium (Ac)	$_{89}Ac^{227}$	Actinium	21.8 yr	4.94	0.04	0.37
Radioactinium (RdAc)	$_{90}Th^{227}$	Thorium	18.4 day	6.03 5.65		0.258 0.50
Actinium K (Ac K)	$_{87}Fr^{223}$	Francium	21 min		1.2	0.09
Actinium X (Ac X)	$_{88}Ra^{223}$	Radium	11.7 day	5.86 5.42		Many groups
Ac Emanation (An)	$_{86}Rn^{219}$	Radon	3.92 sec	6.824 6.56		Many groups
Actinium A (Ac A)	$_{84}Po^{215}$	Polonium	1.83×10^{-3} sec	7.365		
Actinium B (Ac B)	$_{82}Pb^{211}$	Lead	36.1 min		1.39	Many groups
Astatine-215	$_{85}At^{215}$	Astatine	10^{-4} sec	8.00		
Actinium C (Ac C)	$_{83}Bi^{211}$	Bismuth	2.16 min	6.618 6.272	?	0.350
Actinium C' (Ac C')	$_{84}Po^{211}$	Polonium	0.52 sec	7.434		
Actinium C" (Ac C")	$_{81}Tl^{207}$	Thallium	4.78 min		1.44	0.87
Actinium D (Ac D)	$_{82}Pb^{207}$	Lead	Stable			

1.2%
$5 \times 10^{-4}\%$
0.3%

TABLE 1.3 Thorium Series

Radioelement (classical name)	Nuclide	Modern Name	Half-Life	Disintegration Mode and Energy (Mev)		
				α	β	γ
Thorium (Th)	$_{90}Th^{232}$	Thorium	1.39×10^{10} yr	3.98		0.055
Mesothorium 1 (MsTh 1)	$_{88}Ra^{228}$	Radium	6.7 yr		0.012	0.03
Mesothorium 2 (MsTh 2)	$_{89}Ac^{228}$	Actinium	6.13 hr		2.18	Many groups
Radiothorium (RdTh)	$_{90}Th^{228}$	Thorium	1.90 yr	5.423 5.34		0.0843
Thorium X (Th X)	$_{88}Ra^{224}$	Radium	3.64 day	5.681		0.241
Thoron (Tn)	$_{86}Rn^{220}$	Radon	52 sec	6.282		
Thorium A (Th A)	$_{84}Po^{216}$	Polonium	0.16 sec	6.774	?	
Thorium B (Th B)	$_{82}Pb^{212}$	Lead	10.6 hr		0.589	0.115–0.299
Astatine-216	$_{85}At^{216}$	Astatine	3×10^{-4} sec	7.79		
Thorium C (Th C)	$_{83}Bi^{212}$	Bismuth	60.5 min	6.086– 5.48	2.25	0.04–0.47 (α) $\overline{0.72; 2.20\ (\beta)}$
Thorium C' (Th C')	$_{84}Po^{212}$	Polonium	3×10^{-7} sec	8.776		
Thorium C" (Th C")	$_{81}Tl^{208}$	Thallium	3.1 min		1.792	Many groups
Thorium D (Th D)	$_{82}Pb^{208}$	Lead	Stable			

0.014%

33.7%

66.3%

TABLE I.4 Neptunium Series

Radioelement	Nuclide	Half-Life	Disintegration Mode and Energy (Mev)		
			α	β	γ
Plutonium	$_{94}Pu^{241}$	13.2 yr		0.02	
Americium	$_{95}Am^{241}$	462 yr	5.546		0.062
Neptunium	$_{93}Np^{237}$	2.20×10^6 yr	4.77		
Protactinium	$_{91}Pa^{233}$	27.4 day		0.53	0.31
Uranium	$_{92}U^{233}$	1.62×10^5 yr	4.823		0.08; 0.04; 0.31
Thorium	$_{90}Th^{229}$	7340 yr	5.02		
Radium	$_{88}Ra^{225}$	14.8 day		0.3	
Actinium	$_{89}Ac^{225}$	10.0 day	5.80		
Francium	$_{87}Fr^{221}$	4.8 min	6.30		
Astatine	$_{85}At^{217}$	0.018 sec	7.02		
Bismuth	$_{83}Bi^{213}$	47 min	5.86	1.39	
Polonium	$_{84}Po^{213}$	4.2×10^{-6} sec	8.336		
Thallium	$_{81}Tl^{209}$	2.2 min		1.99	
Lead	$_{82}Pb^{209}$	3.32 hr		0.635	
Bismuth	$_{83}Bi^{209}$	Stable			

product of the neptunium series is bismuth-209. (There is some evidence that Bi^{209} too is an α-emitter with half-life $\sim 2 \times 10^{18}$ years.)

Each of the four radioactive series can be represented by a characteristic term which gives the atomic mass numbers of all the members of the series in terms of a variable integer n.

Thus, the series can be expressed by

Thorium series	$4n$	with n from 58 to 52
Neptunium series	$4n + 1$	with n from 60 to 52
Uranium-238 series	$4n + 2$	with n from 59 to 51
Uranium-235 series	$4n + 3$	with n from 58 to 51
(or Actinium series)		

Three types of emissions are known to occur with the naturally radioactive nuclei: (1) α-particle (i.e., $_2He^4$) emission, (2) β^--particle emission, and (3) γ-emission.

1. An α-decay leads to an element whose nuclear charge is reduced by 2 and whose atomic mass number is reduced by 4 as compared to the corresponding quantities of the parent nucleus.

$$_ZM^A \longrightarrow \, _{Z-2}M^{A-4} + \, _2He^4$$

2. A β^--decay results in a new daughter nucleus whose atomic number is increased by 1 with no change in the atomic mass number.

$$_ZM^A \longrightarrow \, _{Z+1}M^A + \, _{-1}e^0$$

3. A γ-emission has no effect on the atomic or on the mass number of the nucleus, but is indicative of a transition between two energy states of the same nucleus. The initially excited nucleus emits its excitation energy either in the form of a single γ-ray (or photon) or in the form of a series of γ-rays, called a cascade.

No positrons or protons are emitted by naturally radioactive nuclei. These nuclei apparently can eject positive charge only by emitting α-particles. This circumstance seems to indicate that α-particles must play a special role in the structure of heavy nuclei.

1.7   The Transuranium Elements

Induced or artificial radioactivity can be achieved not only with isotopes of one of the naturally occurring elements but also with those of the so-called **transuranium elements**, which are all elements of atomic number greater than 92. These elements have been generated by bombarding U-238 with neutrons or α-particles. By further bombarding some of the newly created elements with high-energy projectiles the range of artificially created elements has been pushed up to $Z = 106$.

As examples of nuclear transformations that lead to new elements consider the following reactions:

$$_{92}U^{238} + {_0}n^1 \longrightarrow ({_{92}}U^{239})^* + \gamma$$
$$({_{92}}U^{239})^* \longrightarrow ({_{93}}Np^{239})^* + \beta^-$$
$$({_{93}}Np^{239})^* \longrightarrow {_{94}}Pu^{239} + \beta^-$$

or

$$_{92}U^{238} + {_2}He^4 \longrightarrow ({_{94}}Pu^{241})^* + {_0}n^1$$
$$({_{94}}Pu^{241})^* \longrightarrow {_{95}}Am^{241} + \beta^-$$

All of the transuranium elements are radioactive, all are α-emitters, and some both α-emitters and β-emitters.

The most important of these elements from the point of view of nuclear engineering is plutonium-239 because of its usefulness as a nuclear fuel, and its production is the chief purpose of a particular type of nuclear reactor known as a production reactor. When the amount of Pu^{239} produced exceeds the amount of reactor fuel consumed, the reactor is generally termed a **breeder reactor**.

1.8   The Laws of Radioactive Decay

An empirical fact of fundamental significance is that **the probability of decay of a radioactive nucleus does not depend on its age.** Consequently, all nuclei of a radioactive element have at all times the same and equal probability of decay.

The decay probability per second is measured in terms of the fraction of nuclei of the total number present that decays per second.

If dN nuclei decay during the time interval dt out of N nuclei present at time t, the fractional number of decayed nuclei over the total number of nuclei is dN/N, so that the decay probability per second is

$$\text{Decay probability per second} = \frac{dN/N}{dt}$$

Experimental evidence has shown that this quantity has a constant value for a given nuclide and that it is a characteristic of this particular radioactive nuclide. It is called the **decay constant** of the nuclide and denoted by λ.

The fundamental law of radioactive decay can then be stated in the form

$$\frac{-dN}{N} = \lambda \, dt \tag{1.1}$$

Here, a minus sign has been introduced to take account of the fact that dN represents a decrease in the number of nuclei present during the positive time interval dt.

If this expression is rewritten in the slightly modified but equivalent form,

$$\frac{dN}{dt} = -\lambda N \tag{1.2}$$

it becomes clear that the number of nuclear decays per unit time, dN/dt, called the **activity** of the substance, is always proportional to the total number of nuclei, N, still present at time t.

If Eq. 1.1 is integrated between the times $t = 0$ and $t = t$, the number of nuclei N, which remain after a time t has elapsed, can be obtained in terms of the initial number of nuclei N_0, which were present at the time $t = 0$.

Integration gives

$$\int_{N_0}^{N} \frac{dN}{N} = -\int_{0}^{t} \lambda \, dt$$

Therefore

$$\log \frac{N}{N_0} = -\lambda t*$$

Therefore

$$N = N_0 \exp(-\lambda t) \tag{1.3}$$

showing that the number of surviving nuclei decreases exponentially as shown in Fig. 1.3.

---

* The natural logarithm (base e) will be denoted throughout by "log"; i.e., $\log \equiv \log_e$. The logarithm to the base 10 occurs only rarely and it will be written $\log_{10}$.

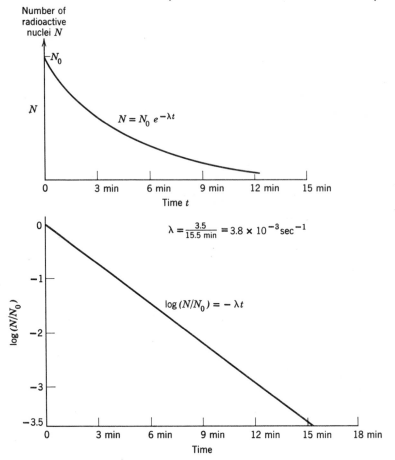

FIG. 1.3. Radioactive decay of Ra A ($_{84}Po^{218}$). The figure illustrates the exponential decay of a radioactive material (at top). The radioactive decay constant λ can be obtained from the slope of the straight line that results when N/N_0 is plotted on a logarithmic scale against the time t (at bottom).

Example 1.1. To find the number of α-decays that occur in a 1 gram sample of thorium-232 in one year, if the disintegration constant λ of thorium ($_{90}Th^{232}$) is 1.58×10^{-18} sec^{-1}.

If N_0 is the initial number of nuclei, N the number remaining after one year, and ΔN the number of decays during that period,

$$\Delta N = N_0 - N$$
$$= N_0 - N_0 \exp(-\lambda t)$$
$$= N_0 [1 - \exp(-\lambda t)]$$

$$\lambda t = 1.58 \times 10^{-18} \text{ sec}^{-1} \times 3.15 \times 10^7 \text{ sec}$$
$$= 5 \times 10^{-11}$$

This small value of the exponent allows us to expand the exponential term and to use

$$\exp(-\lambda t) \doteq 1 - \lambda t$$

and neglect higher terms.

Hence $$\Delta N = N_0 \lambda t$$

The number of nuclei in 1 gram, N_1, is

$$N_1 = \frac{\text{number of nuclei per mole}}{\text{weight per mole}}$$

$$= \frac{\text{Avogadro's number}}{\text{molecular weight}}$$

$$= \frac{6.02 \times 10^{23} \text{ atoms/mole}}{232 \text{ grams/mole}}$$

$$= 2.60 \times 10^{21} \text{ atoms or nuclei per gram}$$

Therefore, since the sample of thorium considered is 1 gram, initially, $N_0 = N_1$,

$$\Delta N = 2.60 \times 10^{21} \times 5 \times 10^{-11} \text{ nuclei}$$

$$= 13 \times 10^{10} \text{ nuclei}$$

This number is very large considered by itself. However, compared to the initial number of nuclei present it is only a minute fraction, namely, $(13 \times 10^{10})/(26 \times 10^{20}) = 5 \times 10^{-10}$. In fact, Th^{232} is the longest lived and, hence, the least unstable of the naturally occurring radioactive α-emitters (see Tables 1.1 to 1.4).

1.9 Activity

The activity A of a radioactive substance, as previously mentioned, is the rate of decay, or the number of disintegrations per second.

$$A \equiv \left| \frac{dN}{dt} \right|$$

$$= \lambda N \qquad (1.4)$$

It is this activity which is usually measured experimentally, rather than N.

The activity A_0, at time $t = 0$, is

$$A_0 = \left| \left(\frac{dN}{dt} \right)_{t=0} \right|$$

$$= \lambda N_0$$

Hence, combining this with Eq. 1.4,

$$\frac{A}{A_0} = \frac{N}{N_0}$$

$$= N_0 \frac{\exp(-\lambda t)}{N_0}$$

$$= \exp(-\lambda t)$$

so that the activity A is seen to have the same time dependence as N.

$$A = A_0 \exp(-\lambda t) \tag{1.5}$$

This conclusion can also be drawn directly from 1.4 which shows that A is proportional to N.

The unit of activity is the **curie** which is defined as that quantity of radioactive material which decays at the rate of 3.70×10^{10} disintegrations per second. Subunits in common use are the millicurie and the microcurie. The same unit is used to describe (1) activity and, (2) the associated amount of radioactive material. This is possible, once the modes of decay of the particular substance have been clearly established.

Example 1.2. Calculate the activity of 1 gram of Th^{232} using the data from Example 1.1.

$$A = \lambda N$$
$$= 1.58 \times 10^{-18} \text{ sec}^{-1} \times 2.60 \times 10^{21} \text{ nuclei}$$
$$= 4.1 \times 10^3 \text{ dis/sec}$$
$$= \frac{4.1 \times 10^3}{3.7 \times 10^{10}} \text{ curie} = 0.11 \text{ microcurie}$$

1.10 Average Lifetime

Since the decay constant λ has the dimensions of a reciprocal time (sec^{-1}), we can define a time T_A

$$T_A = \frac{1}{\lambda} \tag{1.6}$$

and in terms of it, rewrite the radioactive decay law 1.3

$$N = N_0 \exp\left(\frac{-t}{T_A}\right) \tag{1.7}$$

T_A is the average lifetime of a radioactive nucleus as can readily be seen by evaluating the average life of the nuclei for the radioactive sample under consideration, following the standard procedure of averaging. For this purpose, we take the sum of the combined lifetimes of all the nuclei and divide it by the total number of nuclei.

If ΔN is a small group of nuclei which decay during a time interval between t and $t + \Delta t$, (Fig. 1.4), the combined lifetime of this group is: $\Delta T = t\Delta N$. Adding all these lifetimes for the groups of nuclei that decay during the entire time interval from $t = 0$ to $t = \infty$, we get for the total combined lifetime of all the groups (using integral notation),

$$T = \int_0^\infty dT = \int_{N=N_0}^{N=0} t \, dN$$

Dividing this by all nuclei N_0, initially present, we get

$$
\begin{aligned}
T_A &= \frac{1}{N_0} \int_{N_0}^{0} t \, dN \\
&= \frac{1}{N_0} \int_{0}^{\infty} t(-\lambda N_0 \exp(-\lambda t)) \, dt \\
&= \lambda \int_{\infty}^{0} t \exp(-\lambda t) \, dt \\
&= \lambda \left[\left. \frac{t \exp(-\lambda t)}{-\lambda} \right|_{\infty}^{0} + \frac{1}{\lambda} \int_{\infty}^{0} \exp(-\lambda t) \, dt \right] \\
&= \int_{\infty}^{0} \exp(-\lambda t) \, dt \quad \text{(since the integrated part is zero at both limits)} \\
&= \frac{1}{\lambda}
\end{aligned}
$$

This proves that $1/\lambda$ is indeed equal to the average lifetime of the nuclei.

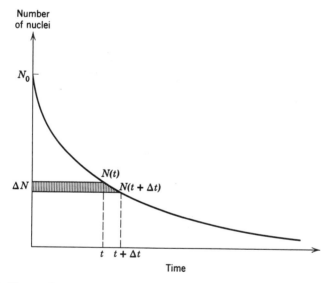

FIG. 1.4. The number of nuclei ΔN that decay spontaneously during the time interval Δt, (lying between the time t and $t + \Delta t$), have a combined lifetime of $t\Delta N$, which is represented in the Figure by the shaded area.

1.11 Half-Life

The usual way of describing the rate of nuclear disintegrations is to specify the **half-life** $T_{1/2}$, of the nuclear species. This is the time interval during which one-half of the total number of nuclei that were present at the beginning of the time interval have decayed.

If N_1 nuclei are present at time t_1 and one-half that number, $N_2 = \frac{1}{2} N_1$, have survived at time t_2, we can write

$$N_1 = N_0 \exp(-\lambda t_1)$$

$$N_2 = N_0 \exp(-\lambda t_2)$$

Hence,

$$\frac{N_1}{N_2} = \exp[\lambda(t_2 - t_1)] = 2$$

and

$$\left. \begin{array}{c} \dfrac{\log 2}{\lambda} = t_2 - t_1 = T_{\frac{1}{2}} \\[2mm] T_{\frac{1}{2}} = \dfrac{0.693}{\lambda} = 0.693 T_A \end{array} \right\} \qquad (1.8)$$

or

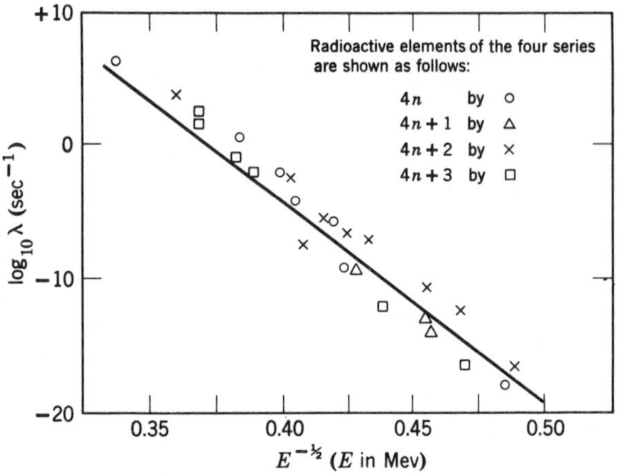

FIG. 1.5. The Geiger-Nuttall law.

The half-lives of radioactive nuclides vary considerably for different elements, from $\sim 10^{15}$ years for the longest lived to $\sim 10^{-11}$ sec for the shortest lived known nuclide.

In the case of α-decay the half-life of the emitter is related to the energy E of the emitted α-particles by

$$\log T_{\frac{1}{2}} = A \log E - B \qquad \text{(Geiger-Nuttall law)} \qquad (1.9)$$

with the constant A very nearly the same for the three natural radioactive series, and B being a different constant for each series. For the small range in E of available data an equally good fit is obtained with the relation $\log T_{\frac{1}{2}} = aE^{-\frac{1}{2}} + b$ which is illustrated in Fig. 1.5.

Example I.3. It is found that 46.3 mg of naturally occurring potassium show a β-activity of 1.5 dis per sec. The isotope responsible for this activity is K^{40} which makes up 0.012% of the natural mixture. Calculate the half-life of K^{40}.

The number of K^{40}-atoms in 46.3 mg of natural potassium is

$$N = \frac{0.012}{100} \times 46.3 \times 10^{-3} \text{ grams} \times \frac{6.02 \times 10^{23} \text{ atoms/mole}}{40 \text{ grams/mole}}$$

$$= 8.37 \times 10^{16} \text{ atoms}$$

$$
\begin{aligned}
T_{\frac{1}{2}} &= \frac{0.693}{\lambda} \\
&= \frac{0.693N}{dN/dt} \qquad \text{using 1.2} \\
&= \frac{0.693 \times 8.37 \times 10^{16} \text{ atoms}}{1.5 \text{ dis/sec}} \\
&= 5.8 \times 10^{16} \text{ sec} \\
&= 1.23 \times 10^{9} \text{ years}
\end{aligned}
$$

This long half-life explains why this unstable nuclide is still found to occur in nature. It is one of about a dozen such nuclides which, although radioactive, are still found in nature because of their long half-life, which is comparable to or greater than the estimated life of the earth.

I.12 Radioactive Equilibrium and Serial Transformations

We have seen that in many cases the product nuclei from radioactive decay are themselves radioactive as, for example, with the members of the radioactive series. If the product, or daughter nucleus, shows a characteristic activity of its own, the resultant activity of a sample of the material will, in general, be more complex than if there were only a single type of radioactive nuclide present in the sample.

Consider the decay of a parent nucleus a with decay constant λ_a into a daughter nucleus b which itself is unstable and which then decays to a nuclear species c with its own decay constant λ_b.

$$a \xrightarrow{\lambda_a} b \xrightarrow{\lambda_b} c$$

The rate at which the number of daughter nuclei, N_b, builds up is then equal to the rate of their formation from the decaying parent nuclei less the rate of their own decay into nuclei of type c.

If N_a and N_b are the number of parent and daughter nuclei, respectively, which are present at time t, and N_a^0 and N_b^0 the corresponding numbers of nuclei present at time $t = 0$, then the

rate of formation of b nuclei from a nuclei

$$= \left| \left(\frac{dN_a}{dt} \right)_{a \to b} \right| = \lambda_a N_a$$

and the

rate of decay of b nuclei into c nuclei

$$= \left| \left(\frac{dN_b}{dt} \right)_{b \to c} \right| = \lambda_b N_b$$

so that the

net rate of production of b-type nuclei is

$$\frac{dN_b}{dt} = \left| \left(\frac{dN_a}{dt} \right)_{a \to b} \right| - \left| \left(\frac{dN_b}{dt} \right)_{b \to c} \right|$$

$$= \lambda_a N_a - \lambda_b N_b$$

By 1.3, $N_a = N_a^0 \exp(-\lambda_a t)$ so that the previous equation becomes, with this substitution for N_a,

$$\frac{dN_b}{dt} = \lambda_a N_a^0 \exp(-\lambda_a t) - \lambda_b N_b$$

Integration of this equation gives the number of daughter nuclei of type b which are present at time t, Fig. 1.6, namely,

$$N_b = N_b^0 \exp(-\lambda_b t) + N_a^0 \frac{\lambda_a}{\lambda_b - \lambda_a} [\exp(-\lambda_a t) - \exp(-\lambda_b t)] \quad (1.10)$$

As an example of practical importance in reactor operation we can cite the build-up of Xe^{135} from I^{135} after reactor shutdown which follows this equation (Chapter 11).

Depending on the relative magnitudes of λ_a and λ_b, and assuming no daughter nuclei present initially, i.e., $N_b^0 = 0$, several simple conclusions can be drawn from this result.

1. If the half-life of the parent substance is considerably greater than that of the daughter substance, i.e., if $\lambda_b \gg \lambda_a$, we can neglect the ratio λ_a / λ_b as compared to 1 and then write for the solution (1.10) instead:

$$N_b = N_a^0 \frac{\lambda_a / \lambda_b}{1 - \lambda_a / \lambda_b} \exp(-\lambda_a t)[1 - \exp(-\lambda_b t + \lambda_a t)]$$

$$= N_a \frac{\lambda_a}{\lambda_b} [1 - \exp(-\lambda_b t)] \quad (1.11)$$

This shows that, as t increases, the amount of daughter material present approaches an asymptotic value

$$N_b = N_a \frac{\lambda_a}{\lambda_b} \qquad (1.12)$$

This means that after a long enough time-interval has elapsed (in practice, this means after several half-lives of b), the relative proportion of daughter nuclei to parent nuclei present will remain constant.

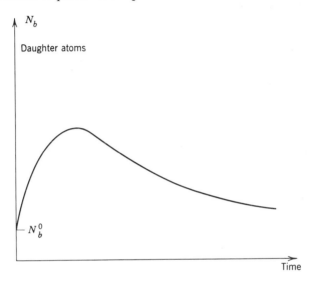

FIG. I.6. The build-up of daughter atoms N_b from parent atoms N_a as a function of time. $N_b{}^0$ is the number of daughter atoms present at time $t = 0$.

It also follows from Eq. 1.12 that $\lambda_b N_b = \lambda_a N_a$, showing that parent and daughter activities are equal. When this stage has been reached, the substance is said to be in a state of **secular equilibrium**.

The accumulation of radon from radium is typical for this case and the growth of Rn^{222} from Ra^{226} is illustrated in Fig. 1.7.

2. If the parent substance is very short-lived as compared to the half-life of the daughter element, i.e., $\lambda_a \gg \lambda_b$, $\lambda_b/\lambda_a \ll 1$, and $\exp(-\lambda_a t) \doteq 0$, the general result of Eq. 1.10 simplifies to:

$$N_b = N_a{}^0 \exp(-\lambda_b t) \qquad (1.13)$$

This means that the $N_a{}^0$ parent nuclei are very rapidly transformed into an equal number of daughter nuclei, which then decay at a rate that is determined by the decay constant λ_b, characteristic of the daughter substance. This case is illustrated in Fig. 1.8 for the case of radium A (Po-218) and radium B (Pb-214). The behavior is very similar to the one described here for parent half-life and daughter half-life more nearly equal but $\lambda_a > \lambda_b$. If the parent half-life is shorter than that of the daughter, a state of equilibrium will not be reached. The parent nuclei will decay more

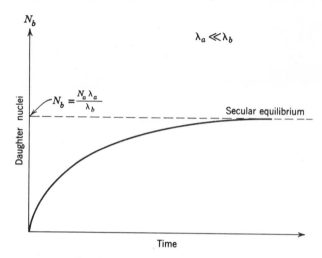

FIG. I.7. Build-up of Rn^{222} from Ra^{226}.

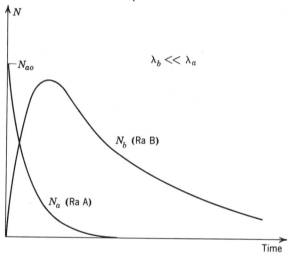

FIG. I.8. Build-up of Ra B from Ra A.

rapidly than the daughter nuclei, with the number of the latter increasing to a maximum and then decaying in accordance with Eq. 1.13.

3. If the parent substance has a half-life comparable to but somewhat larger than that of the daughter substance, i.e., $\lambda_a \lesssim \lambda_b$, the solution 1.10

can be written as

$$N_b = N_a^0 \exp\left(-\lambda_a t\right) \frac{\lambda_a}{\lambda_a - \lambda_b} \left[1 - \exp\left(\lambda_a - \lambda_b\right)t\right]$$

$$= N_a \frac{\lambda_a}{\lambda_a - \lambda_b} \left[1 - \exp\left(\lambda_a - \lambda_b\right)t\right] \tag{1.14}$$

The exponential term decreases with increasing time t, and after a sufficiently long time has elapsed it will become small enough to be negligible.

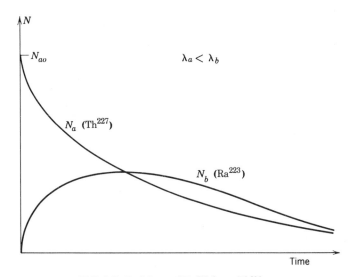

FIG. I.9. Build-up of Ra^{223} from Th^{227}.

When that time span has passed, a state of what is called **transient equilibrium** will have been reached and one can then set

$$N_b = N_a \frac{\lambda_a}{\lambda_b - \lambda_a} = N_a^0 \exp\left(-\lambda_a t\right) \frac{\lambda_a}{\lambda_b - \lambda_a} \tag{1.15}$$

The ratio of number of daughter nuclei to parent nuclei has become constant, and the rate of decay of the daughter nuclei is now determined by the rate of decay of the parent substance. This case is illustrated in Fig. 1.9 for the decay of thorium-227 to radium-223.

Example I.4. Radium-226 decays to radon-222 with a half-life of 1620 years. Radon decays to Po-218 with the considerably shorter half-life of 3.82 days. Starting with an initially pure sample of radium-226, find the number of radon half-lives that have elapsed when the radon reaches 99% of its equilibrium concentration.

By Eq. 1.12

$$N_b(t) = N_a \frac{\lambda_a}{\lambda_b} [1 - \exp(-\lambda_b t)]$$

$$N_b(\infty) = N_a \frac{\lambda_a}{\lambda_b}$$

Therefore

$$\frac{N_b(t)}{N_b(\infty)} = 1 - \exp(-\lambda_b t) = \frac{99}{100}$$

Therefore

$$\exp(-\lambda_b t) = \frac{1}{100}$$

$$t = \frac{1}{\lambda_b} \log 100$$

$$= \frac{T^{1/2}}{\log 2} \log 100$$

The number of half-lives elapsed is, therefore,

$$\frac{t}{T_{1/2}} = \frac{\log 100}{\log 2} = 6.64$$

1.13   Neutron Activation and the Production of Isotopes

An important function of nuclear chain reactors is the production of radioactive isotopes for use in varied fields of research. Many elements, when introduced into a reactor, undergo neutron reactions that lead to the formation of radioactive isotopes. For example,

$$_{79}Au^{197} + {}_0n^1 \longrightarrow ({}_{79}Au^{198})^* \longrightarrow {}_{80}Hg^{198} + \beta^-$$

$$_{15}P^{31} + {}_0n^1 \longrightarrow ({}_{15}P^{32})^* \longrightarrow {}_{16}S^{32} + \beta^-$$

$$_{27}Co^{59} + {}_0n^1 \longrightarrow ({}_{27}Co^{60})^* \dagger \longrightarrow {}_{28}Ni^{60} + \beta^-$$

The induced activity that results from an irradiation process will depend on the rate of production of the radioactive isotope and on its rate of decay. Since the rate of production in the reactor can be taken to remain constant, there will eventually be reached a time after which the rate of decay of the new isotope will become equal to its rate of production. When this state of secular equilibrium has been attained, further irradiation will not increase the activity of the sample.

If R is the constant rate at which the exposed atoms are converted to the radioactive isotope, $N(t)$, the number of radioactive isotopes present at

† Co^{60} also emits γ-rays which are the chief value of this radioisotope in practice. (Compare Problem 7, Chapter 3.)

time t, and λ, the disintegration constant of the radioactive isotope, then the rate of growth or accumulation of these isotopes is

$$\frac{dN}{dt} = R - \lambda N \qquad (1.16)$$

The number of activated atoms will continue to increase until their rate of decay, given by λN, is numerically equal to their rate of activation R. Then

$$R = \lambda N \quad \text{and} \quad \frac{dN}{dt} = 0$$

Once this stage has been reached, the number of activated atoms will not

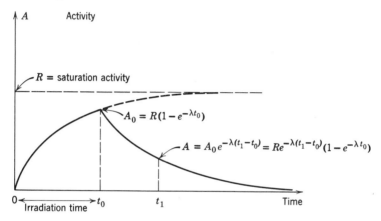

FIG. 1.10. Neutron activation. During the irradiation time the activity increases according to Eq. 1.19. When irradiation is stopped, the activity of the sample decays exponentially according to Eq. 1.5.

change with further irradiation. When the sample is now removed from the reactor, it will have an initial activity A_0 given by

$$A_0 = \lambda N = R \qquad (1.17)$$

which is called the **saturation activity**.

If the sample is removed before equilibrium is reached, the activity at that time, $|dN/dt| = \lambda N$, will be less than R (Fig. 1.10).

The number of activated atoms, N, at any time can be obtained by integrating Eq. 1.16. This gives

$$N = \frac{R}{\lambda} [1 - \exp(-\lambda t)] \qquad (1.18)$$

The activity at time t is, therefore,

$$A = \left|\frac{dN}{dt}\right| = \lambda N = R[1 - \exp(-\lambda t)] \qquad (1.19)$$

After a few half-lives the activity is practically equal to the saturation activity.

This case is very similar to that of a parent of very long half-life, decaying into a daughter of much shorter half-life ($\lambda_a \ll \lambda_b$), which was considered earlier. The constant rate of production of the radioactive daughter isotope corresponds to an infinite half-life for the parent atoms.

Example 1.5. What is the activity of a gold foil that has been irradiated for a period of 5 hr, assuming a constant rate of formation of the radioisotope in the reactor of 10^9 atoms per sec, if its half-life is 2.69 days?

Since
$$\lambda = \frac{\log 2}{T_{\frac{1}{2}}} = \frac{0.693}{2.69 \times 24 \text{ hr}}$$

$$\text{Activity} = \lambda N = R[1 - \exp(-\lambda t)]$$

$$= 10^9\left[1 - \exp\left(\frac{-0.693 \times 5}{2.69 \times 24}\right)\right]$$

$$= 10^9[1 - \exp(-0.0537)]$$

$$= 10^9(1 - 0.948)$$

$$= 5.2 \times 10^7 \text{ dis per sec}$$

$$= \frac{5.2 \times 10^7}{3.7 \times 10^{10}} \text{ curies}$$

$$= 1.4 \text{ millicurie}$$

PROBLEMS

(1) The fraction of thorium atoms that decay each second is 1.58×10^{-18}. After how many years would one-quarter of a given initial amount of this substance have decayed spontaneously?

(2) Using the data of Table 1.1 calculate the disintegration constants of Ra C' (Po^{214}) and of U^{238}.

(3) A short burst of neutrons is allowed to enter one end of a 10 meter long tube and to impinge on a target at the other end. If the total number of neutrons involved is 10^8 and their speed is 2200 meter per sec, calculate the number of protons that are created by the spontaneous decay of neutrons during the transit time of the neutrons passing through the tube. Assume a half-life of 13 min for free neutrons.

(4) Starting with equal amounts of U^{235} and U^{238}, calculate the time that must elapse before the remaining amounts of these isotopes are in a ratio of 140 atoms of U^{238} to 1 atom of U^{235}. Use the data that are cited in Tables 1.1 and 1.2.

(5) Calculate the activity in curies of a sample of Ra F after one year, if the initial amount was 0.5 mg. Refer to Table 1.1.

(6) Calculate the number of grams of material required to produce an activity of 1 millicurie with Rn^{222} and U^{238}. What accounts for this large difference?

(7) Bi^{212} is an α- and β-emitter, with α's emitted in 34% of the disintegrations and β's in 66%. Calculate the initial α- and β-activities for 10^{-6} gram of a freshly prepared sample of Bi^{212}, and the respective activities after 5 hr.

(8) Using the data in Problem 7, calculate separately the disintegration constants λ_α for α-particles and λ_β for β-particles from Bi^{212}. Justify the use of the same λ for both particles in Problem 7. How is that λ related to λ_α and λ_β?

(9) The percentage abundance of U^{234} in natural uranium is 0.0055%. If the half-life of U^{238} is 4.49×10^9 years, calculate the half-life of U^{234}.

(10) How long would a sample of P^{31} have to be irradiated in a nuclear reactor to reach 90% of its saturation activity if the rate of formation of the radioisotope P^{32} in the reactor is 5×10^{10} atoms/sec? (The half-life of P^{32} is 14.5 days.)

BIBLIOGRAPHY

Cork, J. M.: *Radioactivity and Nuclear Physics*, van Nostrand, 1957.

Evans, R. D.: *The Atomic Nucleus*, McGraw-Hill, 1955.

French, A. P.: *Principles of Modern Physics*, Wiley, 1958.

Friedlander, G., and J. W. Kennedy: *Nuclear and Radiochemistry*, Wiley, 1955.

Glasstone, S.: *Sourcebook on Atomic Energy*, van Nostrand, 1958.

Huntley, H. E.: *Nuclear Species*, Macmillan, 1954.

Kaplan, I.: *Nuclear Physics*, Addison-Wesley, 1955.

Lapp, R. E., and H. L. Andrews: *Nuclear Radiation Physics*, Prentice-Hall, 1954.

Moon, P. B.: *Artificial Radioactivity*, Cambridge University Press, 1949.

Perlman, I.: "Alpha Radioactivity and the Stability of Heavy Nuclei," *Nucleonics*, **7**, No. 2 (February 1949).

Pollard, E. C., and W. L. Davidson: *Applied Nuclear Physics*, Wiley, 1951.

Rowlands, S.: "Methods for Measuring Very Long and Very Short Half-Lives," *Nucleonics*, **3**, No. 3 (March 1945).

Rutherford, E. J., J. Chadwick, and C. D. Ellis: *Radiations from Radioactive Substances*, Macmillan, 1951.

chapter 2

Nuclear Forces
and Nuclear Binding

2.1 Introduction

The phenomenological approach of the preceding chapter is supplemented in this chapter by the formulation of some theoretical ideas about the character of intranuclear forces that can lead to an understanding of nuclear properties.

The nature of nuclear forces is expressed in terms of their short-range, saturation, and charge-independent character and the nuclear potential is described for a typical nucleus. The connection between the binding energy, the isotopic mass, and nuclear stability is established, and the consequences of energy and charge conservation during nuclear reactions are applied to the calculation of Q-values. Finally, the semiempirical interpretation of the binding energy curve for the system of nuclei is outlined. All presently known methods of releasing nuclear energy depend upon binding energy changes so that an understanding of the concept of binding energy is a necessary prerequisite for a clear insight into the workings of nuclear energy devices.

2.2 Short Range and Saturation of Nuclear Forces

It is obvious that the forces holding nuclei together must be very strong. This follows from the fact that, although nuclei contain positively charged protons at a mutual separation of less than 10^{-13} cm, yet the strong electrostatic forces of repulsion between them do not bring about the disruption of all nuclei. The characteristic nuclear forces that hold nuclei together must, therefore, be strongly attractive and capable of compensating for the disruptive electric forces in the nuclei. The disruptive effect of the Coulomb forces becomes more and more pronounced, however, as the atomic number Z increases, and is responsible for the lack of stability of the radioactive heavy elements.

It is known from scattering experiments that the nuclear forces come into play only at very short distances from the nucleus, corresponding to the order of magnitude of nuclear dimensions. They decrease very rapidly at distances greater than the nuclear range which is about equal to the nuclear radius.

From Rutherford's experiments on α-particle scattering, on the other hand, we know that the Coulomb law is valid at distances greater than $\sim 2 \times 10^{-12}$ cm, so that the purely nuclear forces must have become negligible at this distance from the nucleus. Because of this, nuclear forces are termed "short-range" forces.

They are also "charge independent," which means that the nuclear attraction between two nucleons is the same whether they be two neutrons, two protons, or a neutron and a proton. There is, however, evidence that the interaction between a neutron and a proton is somewhat stronger than either the neutron-neutron or proton-proton interaction. This circumstance has some bearing on the energy of nuclear binding which will be taken up in more detail later. In the case of two protons there is, of course, also a Coulomb interaction that is superimposed on the purely nuclear attraction between these two nucleons.

An important consequence of the short-range nature of nuclear forces is their **saturation** property. Since the effectiveness of nuclear attraction is restricted to a limited range, nucleons can interact effectively only if they are within this range. Any one nucleon inside a nucleus, therefore, does not interact with all the nucleons of the nucleus, but only with a limited number of adjacent nucleons which are close enough to be within the effective range of the nuclear interaction. This is in sharp contrast with the electrostatic interaction, which is a long-range force that interacts with all the charged particles simultaneously.

The property of saturation and short-range interaction is familiar in the case of liquids, where the molecules show a behavior similar to that of nucleons in that each molecule interacts only with a limited number of adjacent molecules. This analogy in behavior has led to the formulation of a nuclear theory on the basis of a **liquid drop model** of the nucleus, to which we shall return in due course.

2.3 Nuclear Size

It has been found experimentally that the radius R of a nucleus of mass number A is given very satisfactorily by the relation

$$R = r_0 A^{1/3} \qquad (2.1)$$

with $r_0 = 1.3 \times 10^{-13}$ cm.

The precise value of the nuclear radius varies, depending on the type of nuclear interaction used for its determination. Charged particle interactions lead to a value of 1.2×10^{-13} cm for r_0, and a correspondingly smaller "electromagnetic radius," whereas pure nuclear force interactions give the larger value of 1.5×10^{-13} cm for r_0, and therefore a larger "nuclear force radius."

Since the nuclear volume $V = \frac{4}{3}\pi R^3$, therefore, $V \propto A$. This suggests that the average nuclear density is the same for all nuclei.

2.4   Nuclear Potential

Instead of considering the nuclear force (Fig. 2.1) we can plot the nuclear **potential** as a function of the distance between two nucleons or between a nucleon and a nucleus. This is done in Fig. 2.2a for a proton-neutron pair and a proton-proton pair and in Fig. 2.2b for a nucleus and neutron and

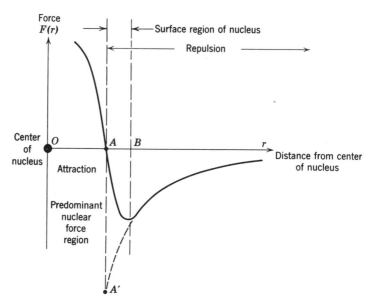

FIG. 2.1. Force of interaction between proton and nucleus. As the proton approaches the nucleus from infinity, it is under the influence of a pure Coulomb repulsive force until it reaches the neighborhood of point B. Here the influence of the attractive nuclear force begins to make itself felt. In the region between B and A the nuclear force increases steadily and is exactly equal to the Coulomb force at point A; it is then equal to $AA' = Ze^2/OA$. For distances smaller than $r = OA$ the nuclear force increases very rapidly and predominates.

nucleus and proton, respectively. They are seen to be very similar, except that the proton-neutron potential has no positive contribution as has the proton-proton potential due to the Coulomb repulsion between the two protons. The potential V at distance r from the center of the nucleus is denoted by $V(r)$, and its general shape for a charge-carrying particle and a nucleus is depicted in Fig. 2.2c.

A proton or other charged particle approaching a nuclear region, represented in Fig. 2.2c by OR_0, will have to pass through a repulsive Coulomb region which is due to the combined proton charges in the nucleus until it reaches the nuclear surface in the vicinity of R_0, where the much larger attractive nuclear potential begins to make its presence felt. Once the proton or charged particle has penetrated beyond this boundary region it is held fast inside the **potential well** of the nucleus.

For an approaching neutron no such **Coulomb barrier** exists. The nuclear attractive potential well, however, is essentially the same in its general characteristics as for the proton. Figure 2.2d illustrates a schematic picture of nucleons inside the potential well of a nucleus.

2.5 Coulomb Barrier Height

A particle of charge ze and energy E, according to classical physics, can approach a nucleus of charge Ze only to a distance r, where the potential energy, as represented by the potential curve of Fig. 2.3a, is equal to the kinetic energy of the incident-charged particle. The distance of closest approach (Fig. 2.3b) as determined by this condition is given by

$$\frac{zeZe}{r} = E \tag{2.2}$$

therefore
$$r = \frac{zZe^2}{E} \tag{2.3}$$

The region between R_0 and r (Fig. 2.3a) is inaccessible to the charged particle as, in this region, the potential energy of the system is greater than the total available energy of the particle.

It can penetrate to the nuclear surface, or to the distance R_0, only if its energy E is at least equal to the barrier height B, which is given approximately by

$$\frac{zZe^2}{R_0} = B \tag{2.4}$$

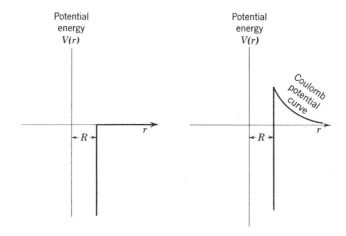

FIG. 2.2a. *Left:* Proton-neutron. This nucleon pair is capable of existing in nature and is known as a deuteron. *Right:* Proton-proton.

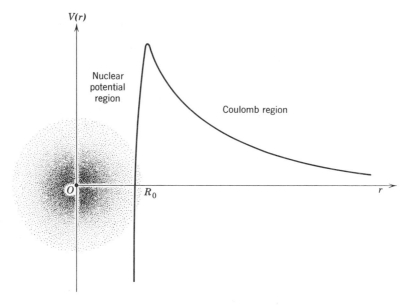

(c). The potential $V(r)$ as it appears to a charged particle approaching a nucleus whose center is at O.

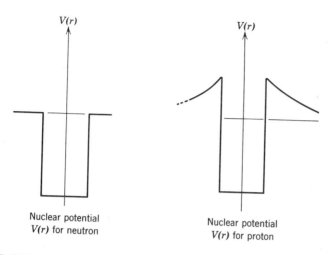

FIG. 2.2b. Nuclear potential well for neutron (*Left*); for proton (*Right*).

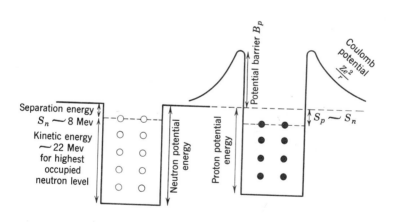

(*d*). *Left:* Nuclear potential as seen by a neutron inside a N¹⁷ nucleus. *Right:* Nuclear potential as seen by a proton from inside the same nucleus. The depth of the potential well is somewhat smaller than for neutrons as there are fewer protons in a typical nucleus than neutrons.

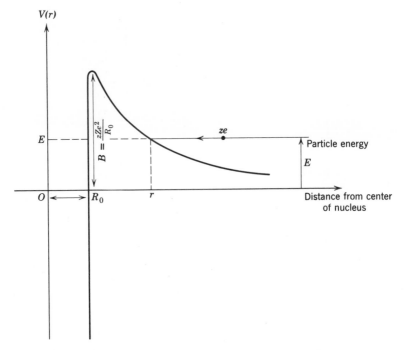

FIG. 2.3a. Potential barrier of a nucleus for a particle of charge ze.

When we use the value for R_0 as given by Eq. 2.1 and $z = 1$ (for a proton), the barrier height becomes

$$B = \frac{(4.8 \times 10^{-10})^2}{1.3 \times 10^{-13}} \frac{Z}{A^{1/3}}$$

$$= 1.1ZA^{-1/3} \text{ Mev} \tag{2.5}$$

Here, we have used the equivalence of 1 Mev $= 1.6 \times 10^{-6}$ erg where 1 electron-volt (ev) is the amount of energy acquired by an electronic charge that has been allowed to be accelerated through a potential drop of 1 volt.

This energy unit is

$$1 \text{ ev} = 4.8 \times 10^{-10} \text{ esu} \times 1 \text{ volt}$$

$$= 4.8 \times 10^{-10} \text{ esu} \times \frac{1}{300} \text{ statvolt}$$

$$= 1.6 \times 10^{-12} \text{ erg,}$$

and therefore

$$1 \text{ Mev} = 1.6 \times 10^{-6} \text{ erg}$$

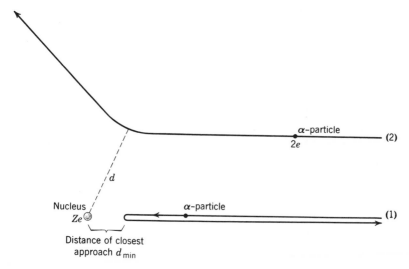

FIG. 2.3b. The scattering of an α-particle by a nucleus. (1) Head-on collision between the α-particle and the nucleus. The α-particle is deflected by an angle of 180° (scattering angle). Its kinetic energy at the point of closest approach, d_{min}, is zero, and the potential energy is equal to the initial α-particle kinetic energy E. $E = (Ze)(2e)/d_{min}$. (2) In this collision only part of the α-particle energy is converted into potential energy $(Ze)(2e)/d$, and the kinetic energy of the α-particle is >0 at distance d.

The barrier heights for some representative nuclei have been evaluated by means of Eq. 2.5 and are given in Table 2.1.

TABLE 2.1

Nuclide	Z	A	B (Mev)
D	1	2	0.7
C	6	12	2.6
S	16	32	5.0
Cu	29	63	8.0
Ag	47	107	10.8
Ba	56	138	11.9
Pt	78	195	13.4
Ra	88	226	15.8
U	92	238	16.3

These barrier heights have been evaluated with respect to a singly charged particle. It should be noted that the barrier height for α-particles is twice the corresponding height for protons because of the double positive charge on α-particles.

An α-particle, once inside the nuclear potential well, should be unable to escape from the nucleus for the same reason that prevents it from entering it, unless its kinetic energy be at least equal to the nuclear barrier height.

The proper nuclear charge, when calculating the barrier height to be overcome by an escaping α-particle, should be that of the residual nucleus, i.e., $Z - 2$.

Example 2.I. To calculate the barrier height for an α-particle inside the $_{88}Ra^{226}$ nucleus.

$$B = \frac{2(Z - 2)e^2}{R_0}$$

$$= \frac{2 \times 86 \times (4.8 \times 10^{-10})^2}{1.3 \times 10^{-13} \times 226^{1/3}} \, erg \times \frac{1}{1.6 \times 10^{-6} \, erg/Mev}$$

$$= 31 \, Mev$$

If the energy of the emitted α-particle is 4.78 Mev, find the closest distance it can approach a gold nucleus.

$$d = \frac{2Ze^2}{E}$$

$$= \frac{2 \times 79 \times (4.8 \times 10^{-10} \, esu)^2}{4.78 \, Mev \times 1.6 \times 10^{-6} \, erg/Mev}$$

$$= 4.75 \times 10^{-12} \, cm$$

The presence of a high potential barrier explains why it is not possible, in general, to achieve nuclear transmutations of heavier elements by means of charged particles, whereas most of the lighter elements ($Z \leqslant 20$) can be transmuted with α-particles obtained from naturally radioactive materials where the bombarding energies do not exceed ~9 Mev. The reason is simply that the potential barrier of the heavier elements is so high that it prevents a close enough approach of charged particles to the nuclear force region of the nucleus, unless relatively high energies are employed which will enable the charged particles to penetrate deeper into the nuclear region.

With neutrons, on the other hand, no intervening potential barrier has to be overcome, and its absence is the reason for the great penetrating power shown by neutrons in collisions with most nuclei.

The only isotope that is known not to react with neutrons of moderate energies is He^4. In order to interact with this very stable nuclear configuration, the neutron must have an extremely high kinetic energy.

2.6   Explanation of α-Particle Emission

The energies of α-particles emitted from radioactive nuclei, in general, are considerably below the barrier height energies just described. On the basis of our classical ideas their abilities, nevertheless, to escape from the nucleus represents therefore a challenging puzzle.

A satisfactory explanation was first given by quantum mechanics in terms of a "tunnel effect," which is a picturesque terminology used to describe a possible escape mechanism. Wave-mechanical calculations show that there always exists a nonzero probability for α-particles to escape from a nucleus, even though their energies of emission are less than the barrier height of the Coulomb potential that hinders their escape.

According to this explanation the α-particle does not have to climb over the barrier in order to escape but, instead, it can leak through the barrier as if passing through a tunnel in the barrier. In the terminology of wave motion, the barrier is not completely opaque but partially transparent and has a small transmissivity.

The escape probability per second which is identical with the previously introduced decay probability λ is a very sensitive function of the α-particle energy E, of the barrier height $B - E$, and the barrier width b. It is given by

$$\lambda = \text{constant} \times \exp\left\{ -\frac{(32\pi^2 m)^{\frac{1}{2}}}{h} \int_{R_0}^{R_0+b} \left[\frac{2(Z-2)e^2}{r} - E \right]^{\frac{1}{2}} dr \right\} \quad (2.6)$$

$$= \text{constant} \times \exp\left(-G\right) \quad (2.7)$$

where G is very well approximated by

$$G = \frac{8\pi^2 Z e^2 (m/2)^{\frac{1}{2}}}{h} E^{-\frac{1}{2}} \quad (2.8)$$

This gives for $\log \lambda$

$$\log \lambda = a - cE^{-\frac{1}{2}} \quad (2.9)$$

which is another form of the empirical Geiger-Nuttall law 1.9, Fig. 1.5.

When we rewrite G in the equivalent but, for our purpose, more perspicuous form, in terms of the barrier height B

$$G = \frac{2\sqrt{2}\pi^2 m^{\frac{1}{2}} R_0}{h} \frac{B}{E^{\frac{1}{2}}} \quad (2.10)$$

we see from Eq. 2.7 that when $B \gg E$ the escape probability is considerably smaller than when B exceeds E only by a small amount. Applying this result to the cases illustrated in Fig. 2.4, it becomes apparent that for *a* the nucleus will have a small decay probability and a large half-life, whereas for *b* the reverse will be true. This leads to the conclusion that radioactive nuclei with large half-lives will emit low-energy α-particles, whereas those with short half-lives will emit high-energy α-particles in accordance with experience and the Geiger-Nuttall law.

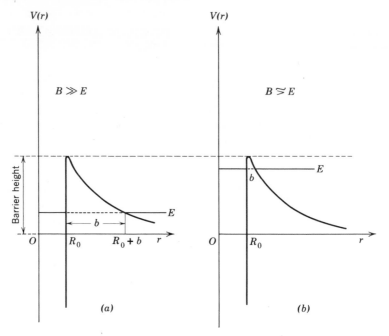

FIG. 2.4. Escape probability of α-particle from a nucleus. (*a*) Small decay probability; long-lived nucleus emits low energy α-particles. (*b*) Large decay probability; short-lived nucleus emits high-energy α-particles.

2.7 Metastable and Bound Energy States

In the two cases of Fig. 2.4 the total energy E of the charged particle inside the nucleus is positive, and no additional energy would be required to remove the particle from the nuclear well. The presence of the potential barrier hinders the immediate emission of the α-particle and its existence is the cause of the nonzero lifetime of the nucleus. Without this barrier the nucleus would not be able to exist at all and would disintegrate immediately. However, its presence cannot prevent the eventual exit of the particle, which is otherwise energetically permissible and possible.

For such positive energies of the α-particle the nucleus is said to be
metastable (Fig. 2.5a).

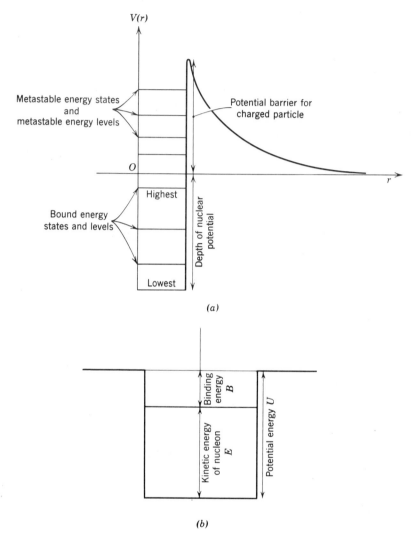

(a)

(b)

FIG. 2.5a. Bound and metastable energy levels. (b) Nucleon energy inside the
nuclear potential well. $|U| = |B| + E$ for nucleon.

If, however, the energy of the particle inside the nuclear well lies below
the zero line (Fig. 2.5a), i.e., $E < 0$, the nucleus is stable with respect to
the emission of this particle. No spontaneous emission of it is possible and,

in order to remove this particle from the nucleus, energy would first have to be supplied to it (Fig. 2.5a).

The particle in this case is said to be bound, and the corresponding energy state is a **bound energy state**. The corresponding energy E is called the **binding energy** of the particle with respect to the residual nucleus.

The smallest energy required to detach a nucleon from the nucleus is also commonly called the **separation energy** S (Fig. 2.2d). For medium heavy nuclei the separation energy for a neutron, S_n, is approximately equal to the separation energy for a proton, S_p. For the lighter elements, both S_n and S_p show considerable fluctuations. For $_4Be^9$, for example, the separation energy for a neutron has the low value of 1.665 Mev, whereas for $_6C^{12}$ it reaches the high value of 19 Mev. In general, S_n for nuclei with an even number of neutrons exceeds by ~ 2 Mev the value of S_n for similar nuclei with an odd number of neutrons.

The binding energy represents the total energy of the particle inside the nucleus and it is made up of its potential energy and its kinetic energy.

$$\text{Binding energy} = \text{potential energy} + \text{kinetic energy}$$

The binding energy (B.E. for short) and the potential energy are usually taken as positive, although, properly, they are negative quantities. Figure 2.5b makes it clear that, numerically,

$$|\text{Potential energy}| = |\text{B.E.}| + \text{kinetic energy}$$

The total binding energy of all the nucleons in the nucleus together with the kinetic energy of all the nucleons add up to the total potential energy of the nucleus.

$$\Sigma\text{B.E.} + \Sigma\text{K.E.} = U(\text{total}) \tag{2.11}$$

The kinetic energy of a nucleon inside a nucleus can be estimated from its de Broglie wavelength λ which must be of the order of the nuclear dimension.* Setting then $\lambda = 2R$, where $2R$ is the nuclear diameter, we have

$$\lambda = 2R = \frac{h}{p}$$

and

$$E = \frac{p^2}{2m}$$

so that

$$E = \frac{h^2}{8mR^2} \tag{2.12}$$

* See Appendix A.

Putting in the appropriate numerical values, we get a representative average value of $\sim$14 Mev for the average kinetic energy of a nucleon. A more refined estimate that takes into consideration the energy distribution of the nucleons inside the nucleus* leads to an expression that is independent of the mass number A of the nucleus in contrast to Eq. 2.12 which depends on A through R.

We shall see later that the average B.E. per nucleon is about 8 Mev, so that we can estimate the nuclear potential per nucleon U

$$|U| = |\text{B.E.}| + \text{K.E.}$$

$$= 8 \text{ Mev} + 14 \text{ Mev}$$

$$= 22 \text{ Mev}$$

The average depth of the nuclear potential is therefore $\sim$22 Mev per nucleon on the basis of this preliminary crude estimate.

Example 2.2. With our present means of measurement, lifetimes of more than $\sim 10^{21}$ sec are unobservable. Accepting this as a limit, estimate a lower limit for the energy of α-particles that can be detected from the radioactive decay of members of the uranium series. The disintegration constant for the 4.195 Mev α-particles from U^{238} is 4.88×10^{-18} sec^{-1}.

From Eqs. 2.7 and 2.8, denoting the constant by c, we get

$$G = \log c - \log \lambda = \frac{8 \times 9.86(4.8 \times 10^{-10})^2(Z - 2)(4 \times 1.66 \times 10^{-24})^{1/2}}{6.63 \times 10^{-27} \times 2^{1/2} \times E^{1/2}}$$

$$= \frac{0.005}{E^{1/2}}(Z - 2)$$

Assuming the same value of $\log c$ for all members of the series its value is found from the given data for U^{238}

$$\log c = \log (4.88 \times 10^{-18}) + \frac{0.45}{(4.195 \times 1.6 \times 10^{-6})^{1/2}}$$

$$= -40 + 173 = 133$$

Hence,

$$\log \lambda = 133 - \frac{0.005(Z - 2)}{E^{1/2}}$$

or,

$$E = \frac{25 \times 10^{-6}(Z - 2)^2}{(\log \lambda - 133)^2}$$

For a half-life of 10^{21} sec, $\log \lambda = -48$, and the limit in the corresponding energy is

$$E = \frac{25 \times 10^{-6}(Z - 2)^2}{(-48 - 133)^2} = \frac{0.76 \times 10^{-9}(Z - 2)^2 \text{ erg}}{1.6 \times 10^{-6} \text{ erg/Mev}}$$

$$= 0.475 \times 10^{-3}(Z - 2)^2 \text{ Mev}$$

* See, e.g., A. P. French, *Principles of Modern Physics*, p. 283, Wiley, 1958.

For α-particles emitted by U^{238} ($Z = 92$), the lowest energy will, therefore, be

$$E = 3.8 \text{ Mev}$$

and for emission from the lightest α-emitter of the series, Po^{210} ($Z = 84$), the lowest energy would be

$$E = 3.2 \text{ Mev}$$

This is in line with the empirical fact that, as a rule, α-particles with energies of less than $\sim$4 Mev are not observed for the natural α-emitters.

Example 2.3. Estimate the average kinetic energy for nucleons in an Al^{27} nucleus.

By Eqs. 2.12 and 2.1

$$E = \frac{(6.63 \times 10^{-27})^2 \text{ erg}}{8(1.67 \times 10^{-24})(1.3 \times 10^{-13})^2 \times 27^{2/3}}$$

$$= \frac{(6.63 \times 10^{-27})^2/(1.6 \times 10^{-6})}{72 \times 1.67 \times 1.69 \times 10^{-50}} \text{ Mev}$$

$$= 13.5 \text{ Mev}$$

2.8 Binding Energy and Isotopic Mass

When two particles approach each other under the influence of an attractive force, their energy decreases, the difference being emitted in the form of radiation. Consequently, when nucleons interact attractively and coalesce to form a nucleus, their energy in this state must be less than what it was when they were separated.

According to the Einstein mass-energy relation (Appendix A) their combined mass in the coalesced state must be less than the sum of their masses before their fusion by an amount corresponding to this loss of energy. We conclude, therefore, that the mass of a nucleus must be smaller than the sum of the masses of its constituents when they are separate. If we denote the loss in mass by Δm, and the energy emitted in the process of combination by ΔE, we can write for the mass defect or mass decrement,

$$\Delta m = \frac{\Delta E}{c^2} \qquad (2.13)$$

ΔE is evidently the binding energy, (B.E.), and, hence,

$$\text{B.E.} = \Delta m c^2 \qquad (2.14)$$

The **total binding energy** of a nucleus is the energy with which all the nucleons are held together in that nucleus. It is also the amount of work or energy required to break up the nucleus and dissociate it into the individual nucleons. This amount of energy is again liberated when Z protons and $A - Z$ neutrons are reassembled to form the nucleus $_Z X^A$.

If M is the **atomic** mass of an isotope $_Z X^A$, i.e., its **isotopic mass**, m_n, m_p,

m_e the masses of neutron, proton, and electron, respectively, and W is the total mass of the separate constituents that make up the isotope, then

$$W = Zm_p + (A - Z)m_n + Zm_e \qquad (2.15)$$

The first term is the combined mass of the nuclear protons, the second, the combined mass of the nuclear neutrons, and the last, the combined mass of the orbital electrons in the neutral atom.

The mass defect D can now be written:

$$D = W - M = \frac{\text{B.E.}}{c^2} \qquad (2.16)$$

Example 2.4. Taking the electronic binding energy for He^4 to be ~60 ev, calculate the error in the total B.E. of this isotope if one neglects this electronic (or atomic) binding energy.

$$
\begin{aligned}
\text{Total B.E. of } He^4 &= 28.28 \text{ Mev} \\
\text{Atomic B.E.} &= 60 \times 10^{-6} \text{ Mev} \\
\text{Error} &= 60 \times 10^{-6}/28.28 \\
&= 0.0002\%
\end{aligned}
$$

This is well below present limits of accuracy, and it is, in general, permissible to neglect atomic binding energies when calculating nuclear B.E.'s.

Example 2.5. Calculate the B.E. for the deuteron $_1H^2$.

The deuteron can be thought to be the result of combining a proton and a neutron.

$$
\begin{aligned}
\text{Mass of proton} &= 1.67243 \times 10^{-24} \text{ gram} \\
\text{Mass of neutron} &= 1.67474 \times 10^{-24} \text{ gram} \\
\hline
\text{Sum of masses} &= 3.34717 \times 10^{-24} \text{ gram} \\
\text{Mass of deuteron} &= 3.34305 \times 10^{-24} \text{ gram} \\
\hline
\text{Mass defect} &= 0.00412 \times 10^{-24} \text{ gram} \\
\text{B.E.} &= 0.00412 \times 10^{-24} \times (3 \times 10^{10})^2 \text{ ergs}
\end{aligned}
$$

$$= \frac{0.00412 \times 10^{-24} \times 9 \times 10^{20}}{1.6 \times 10^{-6}} \text{ Mev}$$

$$= 2.32 \text{ Mev}$$

2.9 The Atomic Mass Unit

The isotopic masses listed in tables are given in terms of atomic mass units, where the **atomic mass unit** is defined as the sixteenth part of the $_8O^{16}$ atom:

$$1 \text{ amu} = \frac{O^{16} \text{ mass}}{16}$$

Since the mass of an O^{16} atom is equal to the atomic weight of O^{16} divided by the Avogadro number N_a

Therefore
$$1 \text{ amu} = \frac{16 \text{ grams/mole}}{6.03 \times 10^{23} \text{ atoms/mole}} \times \frac{1}{16}$$

$$= \frac{1}{6.03 \times 10^{23}} \text{ grams}$$

This shows that the amu is numerically equal to the reciprocal of the Avogadro number N_a.

The energy equivalent of 1 amu is

$$E_0 = 1 \text{ amu} \times c^2 = \frac{9 \times 10^{20}}{6.03 \times 10^{23}} \text{ ergs}$$

$$= \frac{9 \times 10^{20}}{(6.03 \times 10^{23})(1.6 \times 10^{-6})} \text{ Mev}$$

$$= 931.16 \text{ Mev}$$

Accordingly, we have the following energy equivalents:

m_n = neutron mass:	1.008982 amu =	939.53 Mev
m_p = proton mass:	1.007593 amu =	938.23 Mev
m_e = electron mass:	0.000549 amu =	0.511 Mev
H^1-atom mass:	1.008142 amu =	938.74 Mev
$(m_n - H^1)$ mass excess:	0.000840 amu =	0.7822 Mev

2.10 Nuclear Reactions and Q-value

In all nuclear reactions we have strict conservation of (1) the total nuclear charge; (2) the total number of nucleons; and (3) the total energy, (i.e., rest mass + kinetic).

The law of conservation of mass, however, does not hold in nuclear reactions because a conversion of some of the mass into other forms of energy or vice versa generally accompanies these reactions.

The conservation laws can conveniently be stated by referring to the prototype of a nuclear reaction.

$$(Z_1, A_1) + (Z_2, A_2) \rightarrow (Z_3, A_3) + (Z_4, A_4) \tag{2.17}$$

Thus,

1. $Z_1 + Z_2 = Z_3 + Z_4$ charge conservation
2. $A_1 + A_2 = A_3 + A_4$ nucleon conservation   (2.18)
3. $E_1 + E_2 = E_3 + E_4$ energy conservation

To these must be added

4. Conservation of linear momentum.

5. Conservation of angular momentum (spin).

The total energy of a particle is

$$E = m + K \tag{2.19}$$

where m is measured in amu or the equivalent number of Mev. If this is done, we can omit the c^2-factor, since it is already incorporated in the conversion from amu to Mev by using 1 amu = 931.16 Mev.

We have, therefore, from Eqs. 2.18 for the energy conservation

$$(m_1 + K_1) + (m_2 + K_2) = (m_3 + K_3) + (m_4 + K_4) \tag{2.20}$$

Therefore $(m_1 + m_2) - (m_3 + m_4) = (K_3 + K_4) - (K_1 + K_2)$ (2.21)

If we use suffixes i and f to refer to the prereaction and postreaction quantities, respectively, we can write the last equation,

$$\Sigma m_i - \Sigma m_f = -(\Sigma K_i - \Sigma K_f) \tag{2.22}$$

The difference between the initial and final rest mass energies Δm,

where
$$\Delta m = \Sigma m_i - \Sigma m_f \tag{2.23}$$

is called the **reaction energy** or **Q-value** of the reaction.

Hence, if we write

$$\Delta K = \Sigma K_i - \Sigma K_f \tag{2.24}$$

it follows from Eq. 2.22 that

$$\Delta K = -\Delta m \tag{2.25}$$

so that we have finally that

$$Q = \Delta m = -\Delta K \tag{2.26}$$

By transposing some of the terms the reaction Eq. 2.20 can now be obtained as

$$m_1 + m_2 = m_3 + m_4 + Q \tag{2.27}$$

which is the usual way of expressing a nuclear reaction when it is used for numerical calculations.

If $Q > 0$, the reaction is **exoergic**, and the liberated energy will appear in the form of kinetic energy of the reaction products.

If $Q < O$, the reaction is **endoergic**, and it can proceed only if sufficient kinetic energy is contributed by the initial particles. It follows from Eq. 2.25 that during a nuclear reaction some conversion of rest mass energy into an equivalent amount of kinetic energy, for $Q > 0$, takes place, and a similar conversion of kinetic energy into rest mass energy occurs for $Q < 0$, by Eq. 2.26.

2.11 Nuclear Masses and Isotopic Masses

In numerical calculations, it must be remembered that the isotopic masses listed in tables are not those of nuclei but those of the neutral atoms. In order to obtain the corresponding nuclear masses we would have to subtract the mass of the appropriate number of orbital electrons from the listed values.

This procedure, however, is unnecessary in nuclear reaction calculations since the electron masses are exactly balanced in these reactions. The number of electron masses that would have to be added, in order to convert the nuclear masses to atomic masses in Eq. 2.17 are $Z_1 + Z_2$ on the left-hand side and $Z_3 + Z_4$ on the right-hand side of the equation. By the charge-conservation condition 2.18 these additions are equal, so that when we take the mass differences the electron masses would cancel out.

Consider, as an example, the reaction

$$_7N^{14} + {}_2He^4 = {}_8O^{17} + {}_1H^1 + Q$$

Here, the number of orbital electrons involved on the left-hand side is given by the prefixes 7 and 2 and their sum is exactly equal to those on the right-hand side, namely, 8 and 1. The omission or inclusion of 9 electron masses on both sides of the equation does not affect the Q-value of the reaction. This justifies our working with the isotopic masses as listed instead of using nuclear masses which are not so conveniently tabulated.

One exception to this general rule, however, must be mentioned here. It occurs when the reaction involves a positron emission—when the positive charge is not associated with a nucleonic mass.

For example,

$$_8O^{15} = {}_7N^{15} + {}_1e^0 + Q \qquad \text{(nuclear masses)}$$

This equality is correct if we use nuclear masses. If we were to use the atomic masses instead, this would increase the left-hand side by 8 electron masses and that of the right-hand side by only 7. To put matters right, if we want to use isotopic masses instead of the original nuclear masses, we must add an extra electron mass on the right-hand side of the equation. Thus,

$$_8O^{15} = {_7}N^{15} + {_1}e^0 + Q + m_e \qquad \text{(atomic masses)}$$
$$= {_7}N^{15} + 2m_e + Q$$

Example 2.6. Calculate the Q-values for the fusion reactions: (a) $H^2(d, n)He^3$; (b) $H^2(d, p)H^3$; (c) $H^3(d, n)He^4$.

(a) H^2-mass $= 2.014741$ He^3-mass $= 3.016977$

Therefore $\Sigma m_i = 2 \times 2.014741$ $m_n = 1.008987$

               $= 4.029482$ therefore $\Sigma m_f = 4.025964$

therefore $Q = \Sigma m_i - \Sigma m_f = 0.003518 \text{ amu} = 3.27 \text{ Mev}$

(b) $\Sigma m_i = 4.029482$ as (a) H^1-mass $= 1.008145$

                                H^3-mass $= 3.016997$

                       therefore $\Sigma m_f = 4.025142$

therefore $Q = \Sigma m_i - \Sigma m_f = 0.004340 \text{ amu} = 4.03 \text{ Mev}$

(c) H^3-mass $= 3.016997$ He^4-mass $= 4.003879$

           H^2-mass $= 2.014741$ $m_n = 1.008987$

     therefore $\Sigma m_i = 5.031738$ therefore $\Sigma m_f = 5.012866$

therefore $Q = \Sigma m_i - \Sigma m_f = 0.018872 \text{ amu} = 17.5 \text{ Mev}$

Example 2.7. U^{238} emits α-particles of 4.159 Mev energy. Find the Q-value of this nuclear transformation.

In the decay process

$$U^{238} = Th^{234} + He^4 + Q$$

the α-particle will carry off most of the available disintegration energy, although not all of it, since some of it will appear as recoil energy of the Th^{234} nucleus. Q will, therefore, be somewhat greater than the kinetic energy of the α-particle. We apply the conditions of conservation of energy and momentum to the motion of the product nuclei, using the suffix r for the recoil nucleus, Th^{234}.

$$p_\alpha + p_r = 0 \qquad \text{conservation of momentum}$$

By Eq. 2.26, $E_\alpha + E_r = Q$

also $E_r = \dfrac{(p_r)^2}{2m_r}$

Hence

$$E_r = \frac{p_\alpha^2}{2m_\alpha} \times \frac{m_\alpha}{m_r} = E_\alpha \frac{m_\alpha}{m_r}$$

Therefore

$$Q = E_\alpha + E_\alpha \frac{m_\alpha}{m_r} = E_\alpha \left(1 + \frac{m_\alpha}{m_r}\right)$$

$$= 4.159 \left(1 + \frac{4}{234}\right) = 4.267 \text{ Mev}$$

2.12   Threshold Energy for Nuclear Reactions

Substitution of Eqs. 2.26 in 2.24 shows that for endoergic reactions, i.e., for $Q < 0$, $\Sigma K_i = \Sigma K_f + |Q|$. This would seem to indicate that by setting $\Sigma K_f = 0$, we could obtain the minimum amount of kinetic energy that would permit the reaction to proceed. If the bombarding nucleus had an initial kinetic energy $K_i = Q$ and the target nucleus were at rest, just enough energy should be available to provide for the increase in the rest mass of the reaction products, which would then emerge from the reaction with zero kinetic energy.

This reasoning, however, is incomplete, since it omits the fact that linear momentum could not be conserved under the experimental conditions described. If the products of the reaction emerge with zero kinetic energy, their linear momentum must be zero. The linear momentum of the interacting nuclei before the nuclear collision, however, was certainly greater than zero. It is, therefore, clear that the minimum energy E^0 that will make it energetically possible for the reaction to occur must be greater than Q so as to allow the reaction products to emerge with nonzero velocities and a combined linear momentum equal to that of the system before the collision.

The minimum projectile energy that makes it physically possible for a given nuclear reaction to occur is called the **threshold energy** for the reaction.

Let us now find a relation between the threshold energy E^0 and Q. For this purpose we shall first recall a few simple results from elementary mechanics.

Consider a system of two particles of masses m and M moving towards each other in a straight line with velocities v and V, respectively (Fig. 2.6); in the absence of external forces, their combined linear momentum is $mv + MV$. If we describe their motion from the point of view of an observer (i.e., system of coordinates) anchored at their common C.M. (center of mass), their combined linear momentum adds up to zero, by definition of the C.M.

$$mv + MV = 0 \qquad (2.28)$$

If the two masses are perfectly inelastic and collide head-on, their combined kinetic energy is converted into other forms of energy (internal energy), and the two masses will both remain at rest at their common C.M. after the collision, because all available kinetic energy has been converted into internal energy. This is possible without violating the requirement of conservation of linear momentum, since the total linear momentum was zero before the collision and remains so also after it. The amount of kinetic energy converted during the collision is:

$$E = \tfrac{1}{2}mv^2 + \tfrac{1}{2}MV^2 \qquad (2.29)$$

If the two colliding particles are nuclear particles, we conclude that an endoergic nuclear reaction can proceed if $E \geqslant |Q|$, or

$$\tfrac{1}{2}mv^2 + \tfrac{1}{2}MV^2 \geqslant |Q| \qquad (2.30)$$

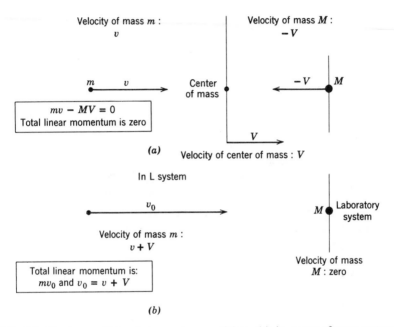

FIG. 2.6. Head-on collision between two particles; (a) in center-of-mass system, (b) in laboratory system.

Next, let us describe the same physical events from the point of view of an observer (i.e., coordinate system), who is attached to the mass M. For him, the velocity of the mass M is zero and the velocity of m is v_0, say, where v_0 is the relative velocity of m with respect to M. The relative velocity, which is the same as the difference of the velocities of m and M, does not depend on the point of view of the observer and, therefore, is the same for an observer situated at the common C.M.

$$v_0 = v - V \qquad (2.31)$$

The coordinate system whose origin is fixed at the common C.M. of the particles is called the **center of mass coordinate system**, whereas the coordinate system whose origin is fixed at the mass M is called the **laboratory system of coordinates**. The name derives from the fact that, in general, the target particle (mass M) is part of a target material which is at rest in the laboratory of the experimenter, upon which the projectile is made to impinge. The distinction between these two systems of co-ordinates is important and will recur in the treatment of neutron motion in reactor assemblies later on.

Expressions for v and V in terms of v_0 and the masses m and M can easily be derived by combining Eqs. 2.28 and 2.31 as follows:

From Eq. 2.28,

$$V = - \frac{m}{M} v$$

and from Eq. 2.31,

$$V = v - v_0$$

Hence,

$$v = \frac{v_0}{1 + m/M} \quad \text{and} \quad V = - \frac{m}{M} \frac{v_0}{1 + m/M} \tag{2.32}$$

Substituting these values for v and V in Eq. 2.30, we get:

$$E = \frac{\frac{1}{2}mv_0^2}{1 + m/M} \geqslant |Q| \tag{2.33}$$

Here, $\frac{1}{2}mv_0^2$ is the kinetic energy of the mass m in the laboratory system, where M is at rest, and it is this energy that is usually referred to when the incident particle energy in a nuclear experiment is specified. Let this energy be denoted by E_0 so that Eq. 2.33 can be stated in this simple form

$$E = \frac{E_0}{1 + m/M} \tag{2.34}$$

This expression relates the combined kinetic energies of the masses in the center-of-mass system, E, to the total kinetic energy in the laboratory system, E_0.

The minimum energy that will allow the nuclear reaction to proceed as obtained from Eq. 2.33 can now be written in terms of E_0.

$$\frac{E_0}{1 + m/M} = |Q| \tag{2.35}$$

so that the minimum energy of the incident particle in the laboratory system, that will make the reaction go, is:

$$E^0 = (E_0)_{min} = |Q|\left(1 + \frac{m}{M}\right) \tag{2.36}$$

Example 2.8. Find the threshold energy for the $N^{14}(n, \alpha)B^{11}$ reaction. If neutrons of 1 Mev energy are used in this transmutation, calculate the maximum energy of the ejected α-particles.

$$\Sigma m_i = \quad 14.007550 \qquad\qquad \Sigma m_f = \quad\ \ 4.003879$$
$$\qquad + 1.008987 \qquad\qquad\qquad\qquad + 11.012811$$

$$\qquad = 15.016537 \qquad\qquad\qquad\quad = 15.016690$$

therefore $\quad Q = \Sigma m_i - \Sigma m_f = -0.000153$ amu $= -0.14$ Mev

Since $Q < 0$, this is an endoergic reaction that cannot proceed unless an amount of energy at least equal to $E^0 = |Q|(1 + m/M)$ is supplied to the system.

The threshold energy is therefore

$$E^0 = 0.14\ (1 + \tfrac{1}{14})$$
$$= 0.15 \text{ Mev}$$

The maximum energy will be carried by those α-particles that are emitted in the forward direction. By Eq. 2.26, $\Sigma K_f = \Sigma K_i + Q = 1$ Mev $- 0.14$ Mev $= 0.86$ Mev. Reverting to the symbol E for the kinetic energy, with suffixes α and B for the products of the reaction,

$$E_\alpha + E_B = 0.86 \text{ Mev} \qquad \text{(energy equation)}$$

$$p_\alpha + p_B = p_n \qquad \text{(conservation of momentum in forward direction)}$$

Since $E_B = \dfrac{p_B{}^2}{2m_B} = \dfrac{(p_n - p_\alpha)^2}{2m_B}$ we can substitute this value for E_B in the energy equation. We first express it in a more convenient form thus:

$$\frac{(p_n - p_\alpha)^2}{2m_B} = \frac{p_n{}^2 + p_\alpha{}^2 - 2p_n p_\alpha}{2m_B} = \frac{p_n{}^2}{2m_n}\frac{m_n}{m_B} + \frac{p_\alpha{}^2}{2m_\alpha}\frac{m_\alpha}{m_B}$$

$$- 2\left(\frac{p_n{}^2}{2m_n}\frac{m_n}{m_B}\frac{p_\alpha{}^2}{2m_\alpha}\frac{m_\alpha}{m_B}\right)^{\frac{1}{2}}$$

$$= \frac{E_n + 4E_\alpha - 4(E_n E_\alpha)^{\frac{1}{2}}}{11} = \frac{1 + 4E_\alpha - 4E_\alpha{}^{\frac{1}{2}}}{11}$$

With this value for E_B, we get

$$E_\alpha + \frac{1 + 4E_\alpha - 4E_\alpha{}^{\frac{1}{2}}}{11} = 0.86$$

which is a quadratic in $E_\alpha{}^{\frac{1}{2}}$.

Brought to the standard form it becomes

$$E_\alpha - \tfrac{4}{15} E_\alpha{}^{\frac{1}{2}} - 0.564 = 0$$

The only real solution of this is

$$E_\alpha{}^{\frac{1}{2}} = 0.90 \qquad \text{therefore} \quad E_\alpha = 0.81 \text{ Mev}$$

2.13 Binding Energy and Nuclear Stability

The B.E. affords a simple and convenient criterion for the stability of a nucleus.

If we compare, for example, the stability of the deuteron with that of the α-particle with respect to the ease of their splitting into nucleonic components, we see that the B.E. of the He⁴ nucleus is 28.28 Mev or $28.28/4 = 7.07$ Mev per nucleon, as compared to the B.E. of the deuteron of 2.2 Mev or $2.2/2 = 1.1$ Mev per nucleon. The He⁴ nucleus is, therefore, considerably more stable than the deuteron.

Although a nucleus may be stable with respect to a complete dissociation into individual nucleons, it may not be stable with respect to another possible mode of splitting up. It is therefore necessary when describing the stability or lack of stability of a nucleus to specify the particular mode of decay to which one is referring.

Consider, for example, the stability of the $_4$Be^8 nucleus which has a lifetime of $\sim 10^{-16}$ sec, and is therefore a highly unstable nucleus. Yet, this nucleus has a B.E. of 56.31 Mev, which is certainly large enough to preclude a spontaneous breaking up into the constituent nucleons. If we compare this B.E. with that of the combined B.E. of two He⁴ nuclei, however, we see that the B.E. of Be⁸ is somewhat smaller than the combined B.E. of two α-particles which is $2 \times 28.28 = 56.56$ Mev.

Hence, the Be⁸ nucleus, although stable with respect to a complete dissociation into nucleons, is unstable with respect to a splitting into two He⁴ nuclei.

The reaction $_4$Be$^8 \longrightarrow {}_2$He$^4 + {}_2$He^4 occurs spontaneously within $\sim 10^{-16}$ sec of the formation of a Be⁸ nucleus, which explains why this nucleus is not found in nature.

It is clear from the preceding discussion, that radioactive decay, by virtue of its spontaneous nature, must be an exoergic process, in the course of which a parent nucleus decays into daughter products whose combined mass is less than that of the parent. The difference in mass is, as we have shown, the Q-value for the decay process.

It follows, therefore, that for an α-process to be possible, we must have:

$$_Z M^A > {}_{Z-2} M^{A-4} + {}_2 He^4$$

so that

$$Q_\alpha = {}_Z M^A - {}_{Z-2} M^{A-4} - {}_2 He^4 \qquad (2.37)$$

Similarly, for a β^--decay to be possible,

$$_Z M^A > {}_{Z+1} M^A + {}_- e \qquad \text{(nuclear masses)}$$

By adding Z electron-masses to both sides, the nuclear masses are changed into isotopic masses and the same condition appears now as

$$_Z M^A > {}_{Z+1} M^A \qquad \text{(atomic masses)}$$

Therefore

$$Q_{\beta^-} = {}_Z M^A - {}_{Z+1} M^A \qquad (2.38)$$

This shows that a β^--decay is energetically possible if the isotopic mass of an atom is greater than that of its isobar with the next higher Z-number.

For a β^+-decay to be energetically possible, we must have,

$$_Z M^A > _{Z-1} M^A + _+e \qquad \text{(nuclear masses)}$$

Again, adding Z electron masses to both sides in order to convert to isotopic masses this condition becomes,

$$_Z M^A > _{Z-1} M^A + 2e \qquad \text{(atomic masses)}$$

Therefore $\qquad Q_{\beta+} = _Z M^A - _{Z-1} M^A - 2m_e \qquad (2.39)$

It follows from this relation that for a β^+-decay to be energetically possible the isotopic mass of the nuclide must exceed that of its isobar of atomic number $Z - 1$ by at least two electron masses, i.e., by at least 1.022 Mev.

For a K-capture to be energetically possible, the condition is,

$$_Z M^A + e > _{Z-1} M^A + E_K \qquad \text{(nuclear masses)}$$

where E_K is the atomic binding energy of the K-electron in the K-shell of the parent atom, which is the energy to be provided in order to detach it from the K-shell of the parent atom.

Adding $Z - 1$ electron masses to both sides of this inequality, we get

$$_Z M^A > _{Z-1} M^A + E_K \qquad \text{(atomic masses)}$$

Therefore $\qquad Q_K = _Z M^A - _{Z-1} M^A - E_K \qquad (2.40)$

This shows that a K-capture is energetically possible if the isotopic mass of an atom exceeds the mass of its isobar of atomic number $Z - 1$ by at least E_K.

Example 2.9. Examine the possibilities of isobaric transitions between the nuclei $_4Be^7$ and $_3Li^7$.

The isotopic masses of these nuclei are

$$_3Li^7 \qquad 7.01822 \text{ amu}$$
$$_4Be^7 \qquad 7.01916 \text{ amu}$$

since $_3Li^7 < _4Be^7$, no β^--decay is possible.

The mass difference for the two nuclei is 0.00094 amu = 0.874 Mev. This is less than the energy equivalent of two electron masses which is 1.022 Mev. Hence, no β^+-decay is possible. The atomic binding energy of the K-electron in the Be^7-atom, however, is considerably less than the available energy difference of 0.874 Mev, so that K-capture is energetically possible.

This transition is known to occur with a half-life of 53 days.

$$_4Be^7 \xrightarrow[\text{53 days}]{K\text{-capture}} _3Li^7$$

2.14   Binding Energy and Q-Value

The Q-value of a reaction can also be obtained in terms of the B.E. of the interacting nuclei. It follows from Eqs. 2.15 and 2.16 that, expressing all masses in energy equivalents, and applying it to the reaction 2.27

$$m_1 = W - \text{(B.E.)}$$
$$= Z_1 m_p + (A_1 - Z_1) m_n + Z_1 m_e - \text{(B.E.)}_1$$
$$m_2 = Z_2 m_p + (A_2 - Z_2) m_n + Z_2 m_e - \text{(B.E.)}_2$$
$$m_3 = Z_3 m_p + (A_3 - Z_3) m_n + Z_3 m_e - \text{(B.E.)}_3$$
$$m_4 = Z_4 m_p + (A_4 - Z_4) m_n + Z_4 m_e - \text{(B.E.)}_4$$

therefore $Q = (m_1 + m_2) - (m_3 + m_4) = [\text{(B.E.)}_3 + \text{(B.E.)}_4] -$
$$[\text{(B.E.)}_1 + \text{(B.E.)}_2] = \Sigma\text{(B.E.)}_f - \Sigma\text{(B.E.)}_i = -\Delta\text{(B.E.)} \quad (2.41)$$

Example 2.10. From the Q-values for the reactions $H^2(d, n)He^3$ and $H^2(d, p)H^3$, as calculated in Example 2.6, find the B.E. of He^3 and H^3, respectively. How can the difference in the B.E. be explained?
For the $H^2(d, n)He^3$ reaction

$$\Sigma B_f = Q + \Sigma B_i$$
$$= 3.27 + 2 \times 2.23 = 7.73 \text{ Mev}$$

For the $H^2(d, p)H^3$ reaction

$$\Sigma B_f = Q + \Sigma B_i$$
$$= 4.03 + 2 \times 2.23 = 8.49 \text{ Mev}$$

The difference in the B.E. is $8.49 - 7.73 = 0.76$ Mev. The smaller B.E. of the He^3 nucleus must be attributed to the Coulomb potential between the two protons in the He^3 nucleus. To decide this point we can calculate the Coulomb energy directly:

$$E_C = \frac{e^2}{R}$$

$$= \frac{(4.8 \times 10^{-10})^2}{1.3 \times 10^{-13} \times 3^{1/3}} \text{ erg}$$

$$= \frac{23 \times 10^{-20}}{1.9 \times 10^{-13} \times 1.6 \times 10^{-6}} \text{ Mev} = 0.77 \text{ Mev}$$

This is in good agreement with the B.E. difference as calculated before.

2.15   Binding Energy of Mirror Nuclei

H^3, He^3 and Li^7, Be^7 are examples of mirror nuclei pairs, so-called because one nucleus of each pair can be transformed into the other by merely interchanging the number of protons and neutrons in the nucleus.

Further examples of mirror nuclei are: (C^{11}, B^{11}), (N^{13}, C^{13}), (O^{15}, N^{15}), (F^{17}, O^{17}), (Si^{29}, P^{29}), (Sc^{41}, Ca^{41}). No mirror nuclei above the mass number 41 have been observed.

The difference in the B.E. of mirror nuclei can be explained as due solely to the difference in their Coulomb energy as was done for the H^3, He^3 pair in the last example.

With the exception of this pair and the Li^7, Be^7 pair (compare Example 2.9), all mirror nuclei of the higher atomic number decay into the image nucleus of lower atomic number by a β^+-decay process.

$$_Z M^A \longrightarrow {}_{Z-1} M^A + {}_+e^0$$

2.16   Binding Energy per Nucleon

The B.E. per nucleon, B.E./A, sometimes called the *binding fraction*, for a given nuclide is obtained by dividing the total B.E. by the number of nucleons contained in that nucleus. With the exception of the very light elements, this quantity varies in a regular manner as shown in Fig. 2.7.

The B.E. per nucleon varies very slowly as we pass from $A = 12$ (carbon) to $A = 238$ (uranium) and it remains within a range of $\sim$7.5 Mev for carbon, its lowest value, and $\sim$8.8 Mev for iron, its highest value. It is larger for the nuclei between $A = 40$ and $A = 100$ than for those outside this interval, which indicates that these intermediate nuclei are more stable than those outside this region, if we apply as our criterion of stability that a greater B.E. is evidence of greater nuclear stability . The most stable nuclide on this basis will be the one for which B.E./A is a maximum. This maximum occurs in the vicinity of $A = 58$.

Those nuclides that are situated in the region of small mass numbers are able to increase the B.E./A ratio by undergoing fusion processes (compare Example 2.6) in which several light nuclei combine to form a heavier nucleus with a higher degree of stability resulting from this transformation.

In contrast with this tendency of the light nuclei, those in the region of large A will show a readiness to move into the region of greater stability in the center of the curve by some process such as the emission of α-particles (natural radioactivity) or by splitting into heavier fragments (fission).

In both the fission and fusion processes the B.E. per nucleon, B.E./A, is reduced (algebraically) and an equivalent amount of energy is liberated, which, in the former case, is utilized in nuclear reactors and, in the latter case, in the H-bomb, if it be permissible to apply the term "utilization" to an, as yet, purely destructive process. Fusion processes are also thought to occur on a large scale on the sun and other similar stars. Fusion reactions could explain the continued production of vast amounts of energy that the sun constantly pours out into space without apparent diminution.*

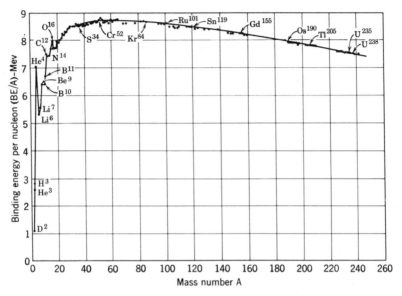

FIG. 2.7. The B.E. per nucleon shown as a function of the mass number.

2.17 Semiempirical Interpretation of the Binding Energy Curve

A fairly satisfactory explanation of the general shape of the B.E. curve can be given in terms of a small number of contributing factors which arise from the general properties of nuclear forces, some of which have already been described.

The dominant feature of the graph (Fig. 2.7) is the essential constancy of the B.E. per nucleon. This behavior is to be expected from and is consistent with the saturation character of the nuclear forces, which gives rise to a potential energy of binding for each nucleon which is due to the limited interaction with only a few adjacent nucleons. This interaction between a nucleon and its immediate neighbors is not influenced by the presence of other more remote nucleons in the nucleus because of the short-range nature of the nuclear interactions.

* For example, Bethe, "Carbon Cycle," *Phys. Rev.*, **55**, 434 (1939), or, E. M. Burbridge et al., "Synthesis of the Elements in Stars," *Rev. Mod. Phys.*, **29**, 547 (1957).

If the binding were the result of a simultaneous interaction between all of the nucleons present, one would expect a binding that increased with increasing the number of nucleons. Thus, the binding of a nucleon in a large nucleus where there are many nucleons present should be far larger than the binding of a nucleon in a light nucleus with only a few nucleons present. This, however, is not the case. The B.E. per nucleon is the same for all nuclei to a first approximation.

For a nucleus of mass number A,

$$\frac{\text{B.E.}}{A} = \text{constant} = a$$

Therefore $\qquad \text{B.E.} = aA$

This is the saturation contribution to the B.E.

This preliminary and still rather crude estimate must be modified by considering several significant and obvious corrections, namely; (1) a surface energy correction; (2) a Coulomb energy correction; (3) an asymmetry correction; and (4) an odd-even ("pairing") correction.

1. The nucleons which are situated at or near the surface of the nucleus will not be bound as tightly as are the nucleons well inside the nucleus, since they are not completely surrounded by other nucleons. This effect is quite analogous to the surface tension in liquids and, for this reason, is sometimes referred to as the surface tension contribution. Owing to the deficiency in binding of the surface nucleons, their contribution to the total B.E. will not be equal to the full saturation binding that had originally been assumed to be the same for all nucleons.

The reduction in the B.E. will be proportional to the number of nucleons that are situated in the nuclear surface region. This number is proportional to the surface area of the nucleus. Since the nuclear radius is proportional to $A^{1/3}$, the surface area is proportional to $A^{2/3}$ and, hence, the B.E. deficiency will also be proportional to $A^{2/3}$.

The correction to be made is therefore a negative term proportional to $A^{2/3}$, i.e.,

$$-bA^{2/3}$$

In a relative sense, the surface tension effect will be most pronounced for light nuclei. For heavier nuclei it becomes less noticeable, since the ratio of surface nucleons to total number of nucleons decreases with increasing A. For this reason, one must expect the B.E. for the light elements to fall well below the saturation value, as is indeed borne out by Fig. 2.7.

2. A second contributory cause for a decrease in the B.E. is to be found in the Coulomb interaction between the intranuclear protons. The electrostatic repulsion between the protons must lead to a decrease in the

B.E. of the nucleus since it opposes and, in a sense, counteracts the nuclear binding. If we assume a uniform distribution of the protons throughout the nucleus, we can set the electrostatic potential energy proportional to Z^2/R, i.e., to $Z^2/A^{1/3}$. The negative contribution to the B.E. due to this factor can then be written as

$$-c\,\frac{Z^2}{A^{1/3}}$$

This term becomes progressively more important as Z increases. We should therefore get a noticeable falling off from the saturation value as we get to the heavier nuclei. This is, in fact, shown clearly by the B.E. graph (Fig. 2.7).

3. The symmetry correction is necessary to take account of the fact that of all possible arrangements of neutrons and protons for a given A, the most stable configuration will be that for which the proton and neutron numbers are equal. Any deviation from this symmetry between protons and neutrons in the nucleus will reduce the stability and, thus, the B.E. of the nucleus. The connection between proton-neutron symmetry and maximum stability is suggested by experimental evidence that indicates a stronger n-p interaction in a nucleus than either the p-p or n-n interaction. The reduction in the B.E. owing to the asymmetry between neutrons and protons is allowed for by including the term

$$-d\,\frac{(N - Z)^2}{A}$$

4. A purely empirical term—the pairing term—for even-even or odd-odd nuclei only is also required further to improve the agreement with the experimental values of nuclear B.E.'s. This term is

$$\pm\,\frac{e}{A^{3/4}} \quad \text{(+ for even-even nuclei,}$$
$$\text{−for odd-odd nuclei)}$$

If we include all contributions that have just been described, the total B.E. for a nucleus (Z, A) appears finally in this form

$$\text{B.E.} = aA - bA^{2/3} - c\,\frac{Z^2}{A^{1/3}} - d\,\frac{(N - Z)^2}{A} \pm \frac{e}{A^{3/4}} \qquad (2.42)$$

Division by the mass number A gives for the B.E. per nucleon

$$\frac{\text{B.E.}}{A} = a - \frac{b}{A^{1/3}} - c\,\frac{Z^2}{A^{4/3}} - d\,\frac{(N - Z)^2}{A^2} \pm \frac{e}{A^{7/4}} \qquad (2.43)$$

The B.E. and the B.E./A are given in Mev for the following numerical values of the constants: $a = 14.0$; $b = 13.0$; $c = 0.585$; $d = 19.3$; $e = 33$. The numerical values of the corrective terms for a few elements are tabulated in Table 2.2, and the result is represented graphically in Fig. 2.8.

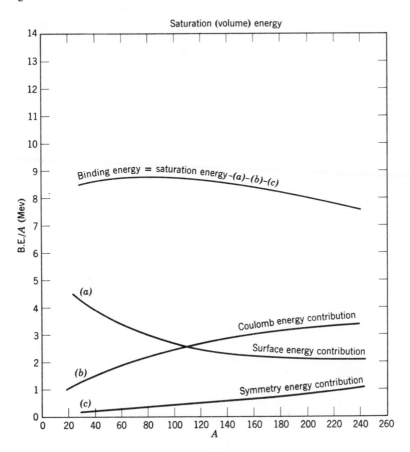

FIG. 2.8. Energy contributions to the B.E. per nucleon curve.

TABLE 2.2

	(a)	(b)	(c)	(d)	B.E. ――― A
Al^{27}	4.33	1.22	0.03	0	8.42 (8.33)†
Cu^{63}	3.26	1.96	0.03	0	8.75 (8.75)
Mo^{98}	2.68	2.28	0.39	−0.03	8.62 (8.63)
Pt^{195}	2.22	3.14	0.77	0	7.87 (7.92)
U^{238}	2.09	3.36	0.99	−0.00	7.56 (7.58)

† The numbers in parentheses are the experimentally found values for the B.E. per nucleon.

PROBLEMS

(1) By means of Eq. 2.1 estimate the density of nuclear matter in a C^{12} nucleus.

(2) Derive expression 2.10 for G starting with Eq. 2.8.

(3) Calculate the barrier height for an α-particle inside a $_{84}Po^{210}$ nucleus, and compare it with the energy of α-particles emitted by this nucleus in spontaneous α-decay.

(4) Calculate the distance of closest approach for a 5.298 Mev α-particle to a Pb^{210} nucleus and express this distance in terms of the nuclear radius of this nucleus.

(5) Calculate the difference in the total binding energy of the two mirror nuclei $_6C^{11}$ and $_5B^{11}$.

(6) Calculate the separation energy for a neutron in $_2He^4$ and in $_8O^{16}$.

(7) $_{84}Po^{212}$ emits α-particles of 8.776 Mev energy. Calculate the disintegration energy that corresponds to it, and compare the α-particle energy inside the Po^{212} nucleus to the barrier height for the α-particle.

(8) Measurements made on the products of the reaction $_3Li^7(d, \alpha)_2He^5$ have led to an isotopic mass of 5.0137 for the hypothetical nuclide $_2He^5$. Show that this nuclear configuration cannot be stable by considering the reaction

$$_2He^5 \longrightarrow {}_2He^4 + n.$$

(9) Examine the stability of the following nuclides, whose isotopic masses are as given:

$$_3Li^5 = 5.0136; \quad _3Li^8 = 8.02502; \quad _5B^8 = 8.0264.$$

(10) The kinetic energy E of two colliding particles in the center of mass system of coordinates is also called the **energy of relative motion**. Show that

(a) $E = \frac{1}{2}\mu v_0^2$, where $\mu = mM/(m + M)$ is the **reduced mass**, and that
(b) $E_0 = \frac{1}{2}\mu v_0^2 + \frac{1}{2}(m + M)V^2$.

What is the physical interpretation of the last term in (b)?

(11) Calculate the Q-value and the threshold energy for the reaction $_9F^{19}(n, p)_8O^{19}$, using the isotopic masses for $F^{19} = 19.0044$ and $O^{19} = 19.0091$.

(12) Calculate the Q-value for the β^+-decay of $_7N^{13}$ and the (maximum) kinetic energy of the emitted positron.

(13) The Coulomb potential energy for a uniform proton distribution in a nucleus is $\frac{3}{5} \times \frac{Z(Z-1)e^2}{R}$. By means of this expression, calculate the difference in the B.E. of two mirror nuclei and compare it with the result obtained by using the semiempirical formula for the B.E.

(14) The isotopic mass of $_{42}Mo^{96}$ is 95.9349. Using the known masses of proton, neutron, and electron, calculate the total B.E. of this isotope. Similarly, find the total B.E.'s for its two isobars, $_{40}Zr^{96}(95.9385)$ and $_{44}Ru^{96}(95.9379)$.

Compare these values for the B.E.'s. with those obtained from the empirical B.E. relation.

(15) Examine the possibilities of isobaric transformations for the isobaric pair Mn^{53}, Cr^{53}, and by means of the binding energy equation 2.42 estimate the β-decay energy for the β-decay of Mn^{53}.

(16) By treating Eq. 2.42 as a quadratic in Z, show that for a constant value of A, the B.E. equation represents (a) a single parabola if A is odd and (b) two identical parabolas separated along the energy axis by an amount equal to twice the pairing term if A is even.

What conclusions can be drawn from this result about the respective β-stability of odd-mass number and even-mass number nuclei?

(17) By differentiating the B.E. equation 2.42 with respect to Z find the value of $Z = Z_0$ which makes the B.E. a maximum, and evaluate Z_0 (to the nearest integer) for $A = 27$.

(18) Calculate the energy liberated when a neutron is added to (a) U^{235}, (b) U^{238}, and (c) Pu^{239}.

BIBLIOGRAPHY

Bethe, H. A., and P. Morrison: *Elementary Nuclear Theory*, Wiley, 1955.

Condon, E. U.: "Fundamentals of Nuclear Physics," *Nucleonics*, 5, No. 9 (September 1947).

Evans, R. D.: *The Atomic Nucleus*, McGraw-Hill, 1955.

Fermi, E.: *Nuclear Physics*, University of Chicago Press, 1950.

French, A. P.: *Principles of Modern Physics*, Wiley, 1958.

Gamov, G., and C. L. Critchfield: *Theory of the Atomic Nucleus and Nuclear Energy Sources*, Clarendon Press, 1949.

Green, A. E. S.: *Nuclear Physics*, McGraw-Hill, 1955.

Green, A. E. S., and N. A. Engler: *Phys. Rev.*, 91, 40 (1953).

Halliday, D.: *Introductory Nuclear Physics*, Wiley, 1955.

Kaplan, I.: *Nuclear Physics*, Addison-Wesley, 1955.

Lapp, R. E., and H. L. Andrews: *Nuclear Radiation Physics*, Prentice-Hall, 1954.

Mansfield, W. K.: *Elementary Nuclear Physics*, Temple Press, 1958.

Perlmann, I., and F. Asaro: "Alpha Radioactivity," *Ann. Rev. Nucl. Sci.*, **4** (1954).

Richtmyer, F. K., E. H. Kennard, and T. Lauritsen: *Introduction to Modern Physics*, McGraw-Hill, 1955.

Semat, H.: *Introduction to Atomic and Nuclear Physics*, Rinehart, 1954.

Strominger, D., J. M. Hollander, and G. T. Seaborg: "Table of Isotopes," *Rev. Mod. Phys.*, **30**, No. 2, Part 2 (April 1958).

chapter 3

The Compound Nucleus and Nuclear Reactions

3.1 Introduction

The theory of nuclear binding presented so far has made use of some of the familiar properties of a liquid drop. The "liquid drop model" of the nucleus is expanded still further in this chapter and is applied to the theory of nuclear reactions which can be explained in terms of the compound nucleus picture. The energy levels of nuclei and the nuclear resonances of the compound nucleus are described, and the relation between level width and half-life is derived.

3.2 The Liquid Drop Model Analogy

The analogy between the behavior of the molecules of a liquid and that of the nucleons inside a nucleus can be extended to lead to a clearer picture of nuclear reactions in general.

We know from the kinetic theory of liquids that the molecules participate in a random thermal motion. The exact counterpart of this behavior is found in the movement of the nucleons inside a nucleus. We have seen that these nucleons have a kinetic energy of about 20 to 25 Mev and their kinetic energy is analogous to the thermal energy of the molecules of a liquid. The principle of equipartition of energy applies within the nucleus and any excess energy contributed by a particle which has just entered the nucleus from the outside is shared by all the nucleons.

The rapid sharing of added energy can readily be understood on the basis of the strong short-range forces that are acting between the nucleons.

They will effect a quick distribution of any excitation energy which has been introduced into the nucleus amongst all the constituents of the nucleus. By way of analogy, this rapid sharing of energy by a large number of nucleons is referred to as "heating of the nucleus."

The sharing of excitation energy is a random process and there is always a definite probability that after some time sufficient energy may be concentrated on a single nucleon, which would then be able to escape from the nucleus. The minimum energy required for this to happen would be equal to the B.E. of this particular nucleon in the parent nucleus, i.e., somewhere between 2 to 8 Mev, depending on the particular nucleus. This process, again in analogy with the corresponding event in liquids, is referred to as "boiling off" of a nucleon.

The liquid drop picture of the nucleus offers a very satisfactory physical description of nuclear properties and it is the basis of a general theory put forward by Bohr to explain some important general features of nuclear reactions. This theory is known as the **compound** or **intermediate nucleus** theory.

An explanation of the fission process in terms of the liquid drop model of the nucleus can be given and is presented in outline in a later chapter.

3.3   Some Features of Nuclear Reactions

When a specific target material is bombarded with a single type of particles, more than just one type of nuclear reaction may be observed to occur. For example, the bombardment of $_{11}Na^{23}$ with α-particles might lead to any one or several of these transformations:

$$_{11}Na^{23} + {}_2He^4 \longrightarrow
\begin{cases}
_{13}Al^{27} + \gamma \\
_{13}Al^{26} + n^1 \\
_{12}Mg^{26} + {}_1H^1 \\
_{12}Mg^{25} + {}_1H^2 \\
_{11}Na^{23} + {}_2He^4
\end{cases}$$

The same end products might also be obtained by bombarding $_{12}Mg^{25}$ with deuterons, or by bombarding $_{12}Mg^{26}$ with protons. We can summarize these facts schematically as is shown on page 67.

This shows that any one of the interactions in the left-hand column might lead to any or all of the reactions appearing in the right-hand column.

Of course, not all the possible transmutations will occur with equal

$$\left.\begin{array}{l} {}_{13}\text{Al}^{27} + \gamma \\[4pt] {}_{12}\text{Mg}^{26} + {}_{1}\text{H}^{1} \\[4pt] {}_{12}\text{Mg}^{25} + {}_{1}\text{H}^{2} \\[4pt] {}_{11}\text{Na}^{23} + {}_{2}\text{He}^{4} \end{array}\right\} \longrightarrow \left\{\begin{array}{l} {}_{13}\text{Al}^{27} + \gamma \\[4pt] {}_{13}\text{Al}^{26} + {}_{0}n^{1} \\[4pt] {}_{12}\text{Mg}^{26} + {}_{1}\text{H}^{1} \\[4pt] {}_{12}\text{Mg}^{25} + {}_{1}\text{H}^{2} \\[4pt] {}_{11}\text{Na}^{23} + {}_{2}\text{He}^{4} \end{array}\right.$$

probability or frequency. The **yield** of the reaction, which is a measure of the number of transmutations that have taken place during the bombardment, will depend on the energy of the bombarding particles. The yield for each possible reaction will show an energy dependence that is characteristic for the particular reaction and that is different for the various possible transformations.

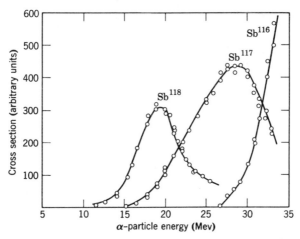

FIG. 3.1. Excitation functions (or yield curves) for the interaction of α-particles with In^{115} leading to the formation of the compound nucleus $_{51}Sb^{119}$. The three curves represent the (a) (α, n); (b) $(\alpha, 2n)$; (c) $(\alpha, 3n)$ reactions: (a) $In^{115}(\alpha, n)Sb^{118}$ (b) $In^{115}(\alpha, 2n)Sb^{117}$ (c) $In^{115}(\alpha, 3n)Sb^{116}$.

The maximum in the cross section of the curves is a consequence of the competition between the different modes of de-excitation of the compound nucleus Sb^{119}. (G. M. Temmer. *Phys. Rev.*, **76**, 424 (1949).)

A particular process often predominates in different energy regions, and it is possible for several nuclear reactions to occur simultaneously at certain suitable energies. In general, as the particle energy is increased, the yield from one process will go through a maximum and then will decrease slowly as another transmutation reaction becomes more prominent (Fig. 3.1).

It follows, therefore, that there must be some competition between the various possible modes of transformations. Increase in one mode must imply a consequent decrease in another or several other modes. Furthermore, each mode of transformation has its characteristic threshold energy, with the yield for the particular mode becoming measurable only when the energy of the bombarding particles exceeds this threshold energy.

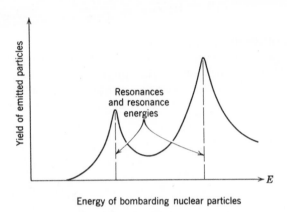

FIG. 3.2. A schematic representation of resonances in a nuclear reaction yield curve.

Another important feature of nuclear reactions is the appearance of distinct peaks or maxima in the yield of the reaction for certain discrete values of the bombarding energy, which is observed when the experiment is repeated over an extended range of projectile energies. This phenomenon is called **resonance**, and the energies at which the various resonances appear are the **resonance energies** (Fig. 3.2).

3.4   The Compound Nucleus

The various experimental results just described can be understood and explained along lines that have been suggested by Bohr. According to these, a nuclear reaction should be looked upon as taking place in two distinct and independent stages: (1) formation of a compound nucleus, and (2) disruption of the compound nucleus.

Consider the target nuclei A being bombarded with a stream of particles a, and this resulting in the production of particles B and b.

$$A + a \longrightarrow B + b$$

The first stage consists in the formation of an intermediate or compound nucleus C through the capture and assimilation of the bombarding particle a by the target nucleus A.

$$A + a \longrightarrow C$$

The second stage, completely independent of the first, is the disintegration of the compound nucleus C into the residual nucleus B and the ejected particle b.

$$C \longrightarrow B + b$$

As the two stages are assumed to be independent of each other, the disintegration of the compound nucleus will be completely independent of the particular reaction mode that may have led to its formation.

The compound nucleus, once having been formed, can decay in several ways. If we look again at the reactions shown diagrammatically at the beginning of section 3.3, we see that we can describe the separate stages (1) and (2) now as

1. Formation of the compound nucleus $_{13}Al^{27*}$

$$
\left.
\begin{aligned}
&_{13}Al^{27} + \gamma \\
&_{12}Mg^{26} + {_1}H^1 \\
&_{12}Mg^{25} + {_1}H^2 \\
&_{11}Na^{23} + {_2}He^4
\end{aligned}
\right\} \longrightarrow {_{13}}Al^{27*}
$$

and

2. Disintegration of the compound nucleus $_{13}Al^{27*}$

$$
_{13}Al^{27*} \longrightarrow
\left\{
\begin{aligned}
&_{13}Al^{27} + \gamma \\
&_{13}Al^{26} + {_0}n^1 \\
&_{12}Mg^{26} + {_1}H^1 \\
&_{12}Mg^{25} + {_1}H^2 \\
&_{11}Na^{23} + {_2}He^4
\end{aligned}
\right.
$$

The asterisk used in the symbol for the compound nucleus is intended to remind us that this nucleus has absorbed more energy than it would normally have. It is, therefore, in an excited state, which accounts for its instability and subsequent decay. The excess energy, or **excitation energy,** is very nearly equal to the sum of the kinetic energy of the incident particle whose absorption brought about the formation of the compound nucleus and its B.E. in the compound nucleus.

Example 3.1. When F^{19} is bombarded with protons a (p, n) reaction with subsequent α-emission occurs.

$$_1H^1 + {_9}F^{19} \longrightarrow {_{10}}Ne^{20*} \longrightarrow {_{10}}Ne^{19} + {_0}n^1$$

One of several resonances for this reaction occurs with a proton energy of 4.99 Mev.

Calculate the excitation energy of the compound nucleus that corresponds to this resonance.

Since we are interested only in the internal energy gain of the compound nucleus the calculation will be simplest if we work in the center-of-mass system. Thus, by Eq. 2.34, the convertible energy of the protons, or the energy of relative motion is

$$E = \frac{E_0}{1 + m/M} = \frac{4.99}{1 + 1/19} = 4.74 \text{ Mev}$$

To this contribution, by virtue of the kinetic energy of the incident proton, must be added the B.E. contribution of the absorbed proton in the compound nucleus. This can be obtained from the isotopic masses

$$_{10}Ne^{20} = 19.998772 \qquad\qquad {_9}F^{19} = 19.004444$$
$$= \Sigma m_f \qquad\qquad\qquad {_1}H^1 = 1.008146$$
$$\overline{\text{therefore } \Sigma m_i = 20.012590}$$

$$\Sigma m_i - \Sigma m_f = 0.013818 \text{ amu} = 12.88 \text{ Mev}$$

The excitation of the compound nucleus therefore is

$$E_{\text{exc}} = 4.74 + 12.88 = 17.62 \text{ Mev}$$

3.5 Energy Levels of Nuclei

The idea of the intermediate compound nucleus was originally put forward in order to explain the phenomenon of resonances in nuclear reactions. Such resonances in the yield curve of a nuclear transmutation will occur whenever the energy of the incident particle together with its B.E. in the compound nucleus is equal to and coincides with an energy level of that nucleus (Fig. 3.3). An energy level that corresponds to an excitation energy greater than the B.E. ($\sim$8 Mev) of the particle in the compound nucleus is a **virtual energy level** and the nucleus is then said to be in a **quasi-stationary state**.

The most stable energy state of the nucleus is the lowest energy level or **ground state**. The energy of the nucleus that corresponds to this state is the B.E. as calculated from the mass defect of the nucleus. For excitation energies less than the B.E., the corresponding energy levels are **bound energy levels** (Fig. 3.5).

A nucleus can exist in a higher bound energy state for a certain length of time, but it will remain in this excited state for only a short period before it returns to its ground state. It has a definite lifetime in the excited state before making a transition back to its ground state. This it can do by emitting the excess energy in the form of a γ-ray.

Evidence for the existence of discrete energy levels in nuclei comes from the emission of discrete energy groups of α-particles and from γ-rays emitted by radioactive substances. In general, these yield information about the low-lying or bound energy levels.

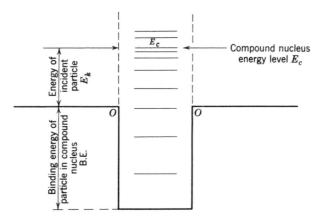

FIG. 3.3. Energy level in compound nucleus E_c is equal to the sum of the kinetic energy of bombarding particle E_k and its B.E. in compound nucleus,
$$E_c = E_k + \text{B.E.}$$

The very rare and exceptionally long-ranged (i.e., high-energy) α-particles that are emitted, for example, by Ra C$'$ and Th C$'$, have been shown to be emitted from the excited energy levels of these nuclei.

Further evidence for the existence of excitation energy levels comes from the appearance of distinct energy groups amongst the product nuclei when monoenergetic particles are used in the bombardment of a given target.

For example, in certain (α, p) reactions, proton groups of different energies are observed, with the energies for the protons of a group being the same for all particles of that group. Discrete energy values are observed amongst the ejected protons, although monoenergetic α-particles are being used in the bombardment of the target.

These experimental results can be understood if one attributes to each energy group a corresponding energy level in the nuclei of their origin. Thus, the largest of the group energies is associated with the formation of the residual nucleus in its lowest or ground state. The smaller energy values of the groups are associated with residual nuclei which have been left in a higher, excited energy state.

Consequently, the energy differences between the various groups can be related to the respective energy level spacings in the residual nucleus. The energy level spacings are in fact equal to the difference in the Q-values for the respective proton groups.

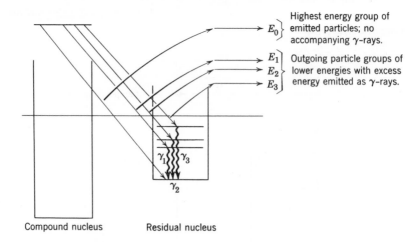

FIG. 3.4. The diagram·illustrates the relation between the energy levels of the residual nucleus and the energies of the observed outgoing particle groups.

This conclusion is supported by the fact that the lower energy groups are accompanied by simultaneous γ-ray emission, whereas the highest energy group is not accompanied by any γ-emission from the residual nucleus (Fig. 3.4).

The experimental evidence here presented can be summed up by saying that (1) the observed energy groups which result from the bombardment of a target with monoenergetic projectiles yield information about the energy levels in the residual or product nucleus, whereas (2) the resonances which appear in the yield curves when the energy of the projectile is varied give us information about the virtual energy levels of the compound nucleus.

The relationship between the various energy levels and energy regions is shown schematically in Fig. 3.5 for a typical nucleus.

In its ground state configuration all levels of the nucleus are occupied by the nucleons up to a definite level. Above this level there exist a series of higher levels which can become occupied when the nucleus is excited by the addition of energy from outside. Above the region of excited energy states is the region of the virtual or quasi-stationary levels which are no longer bound energy states. This region contains those energy levels that can be occupied during a nuclear reaction while the nucleus exists in an inter-mediate state as a compound nucleus. Since each virtual energy level corresponds to one of many possible distributions of the excitation energy amongst the nucleons, the number of virtual levels is very large.

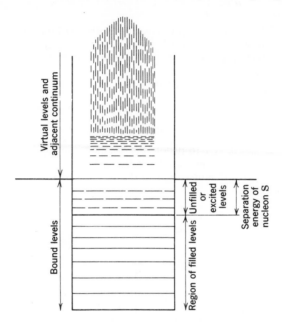

FIG. 3.5. Energy level regions of a nucleus.

The spacings between successive energy levels in the case of intermediate nuclei (A between $\sim$100 and $\sim$150) are of the order of $\sim$1/10 Mev near the ground level and gradually decrease with increasing energy as we move up from the ground state.†

De-excitation of bound energy levels, i.e., return to the ground state from excited bound energy levels, can take place only by emission of γ-rays, whereas de-excitation from a virtual energy level can occur in a variety of ways, either by particle emission or γ-emission. For a very highly excited nucleus even as many as a dozen neutrons can be emitted or "evaporated" from the nucleus.

† As a general rule, the level spacing decreases with increasing atomic mass number of the nuclei, with the exception of the "magic number" nuclei, where the level spacing is very wide and very much like that for the light nuclei.

The radiative capture of slow neutrons is an example of the formation of a compound nucleus with subsequent de-excitation by γ-emission. This **resonance capture** of slow neutrons plays an important part in nuclear reactor processes. It occurs mainly for neutron energies below 1000 ev and the following reaction is a typical example.

$$n^1 + U^{238} \longrightarrow U^{239*} \longrightarrow U^{239} + \gamma$$

Example 3.2. In the $B^{10}(\alpha, p)C^{13}$ reaction with 4.77 Mev α-particles the two most energetic proton groups which were observed to be emitted at an angle of $90°$ with the direction of the incident α-particle beam had energies of 6.84 Mev and 3.98 Mev, respectively.

What information can be gained from these results about the energy levels of the residual C^{13} nucleus?

We first calculate the Q-values for the two proton groups of the given reaction

$$_2He^4 + _5B^{10} \longrightarrow _1H^1 + _6C^{13}$$

If we use suffixes 0, 1, 2 to denote the kinetic energy and momentum of α-particle, proton, and C^{13} nucleus, respectively, we can apply the laws of conservation of energy and momentum to the reaction that is represented by the diagram in Fig. 3.6.

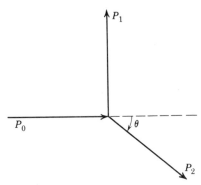

FIG. 3.6.

$$p_0 = p_2 \cos\theta \qquad p_1 = p_2 \sin\theta$$

Therefore
$$p_2{}^2 = p_1{}^2 + p_0{}^2$$

Therefore
$$2m_2E_2 = 2m_1E_1 + 2m_0E_0$$

Therefore
$$E_2 = \frac{m_1}{m_2}E_1 + \frac{m_0}{m_2}E_0$$

$$= \tfrac{1}{13}E_1 + \tfrac{4}{13}E_0$$

Therefore $Q = \Sigma E_f - \Sigma E_i = E_1 + E_2 - E_0 = \tfrac{14}{13}E_1 - \tfrac{9}{13}E_0$

This shows that the Q-value is different for each proton group energy E_1.

The difference in the Q-value for the two proton groups is the excitation energy of the C^{13} nucleus and it represents the energy difference between the ground state and the first excited state of the C^{13} nucleus. Hence

$$Q = (\tfrac{14}{13}E_1 - \tfrac{9}{13}E_0)_{E_1 = 6.84} - (\tfrac{14}{13}E_1 - \tfrac{9}{13}E_0)_{E_1 = 3.98}$$
$$= \tfrac{14}{13}(6.84 - 3.98) = \tfrac{14}{13} \times 2.86 = 3.08 \text{ Mev}$$

Thus, the first excited state of the C^{13} nucleus is 3.08 Mev above the ground state.

3.6   Level Widths and De-excitation

A nucleus left in an excited state is unstable and so will remain in this state for only a finite time interval. The excited nucleus has a definite mean life before it decays by one of the possible modes of de-excitation.

The relation between the probability per second of its de-excitation and the mean lifetime is the same as was found for radioactive decay, namely, the mean lifetime τ is the reciprocal of the decay probability per second

$$\tau = \frac{1}{\lambda} \qquad (3.1)$$

A new quantity, Γ, which is called the **level width** of the excited energy level, is defined in terms of λ by

$$\Gamma = \frac{h}{2\pi} \lambda \qquad (3.2)$$

so that one also has

$$\frac{h}{2\pi\tau} = \Gamma \qquad (3.3)$$

This relationship between the level width Γ and the mean lifetime τ is a method of expressing the Heisenberg uncertainty relationship in a suitable manner so that it can be applied to the de-excitation process.

If we equate the uncertainty in the time-measurement Δt with the mean lifetime of the excited state, we obtain for the uncertainty in the energy of the excited state ΔE,

$$\Delta E = \frac{h}{2\pi \Delta t} = \frac{h}{2\pi\tau} = \Gamma \qquad (3.4)$$

This shows that, what we have called the level width of the excited state, is simply a small spread in the energy of the excited level which appears because of the uncertainty in the exact energy of the level.

Since the level width Γ is proportional to the decay probability and inversely proportional to the mean lifetime τ, it is clear that a long lifetime means a very fine and narrow energy level, whereas a short lifetime will be associated with a broad or diffuse energy level of larger level width (Fig. 3.7).

For each individual mode of decay we can, similarly, define a **partial level width** Γ' in terms of the mean lifetime for each particular mode of de-excitation

$$\Gamma' = \frac{h}{2\pi\tau'} \tag{3.5}$$

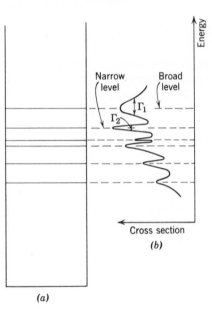

FIG. 3.7. Schematic representation of nuclear energy levels and level widths. Some of the energy levels of the compound nucleus are shown in (*a*) and the corresponding level widths as they might appear from cross-section measurements are shown in (*b*). The difference in level widths reflects the difference in the lifetimes of the nuclear energy levels.

The over-all probability of de-excitation must be equal to the sum of the individual or partial decay probabilities, therefore

$$\lambda = \lambda' + \lambda'' + \lambda''' + \cdots \tag{3.6}$$

Hence

$$\Gamma = \Gamma' + \Gamma'' + \Gamma''' + \cdots \tag{3.7}$$

which shows that the total width Γ is equal to the sum of the partial widths Γ', Γ'', Γ''', ... and is a measure of the average length of time that the nucleus remains in an excited state before decaying.

The total level width Γ can be obtained experimentally. Experimental values of the average lifetime of a representative compound nucleus are found to be $\sim 10^{-14}$ sec.

If this time interval is compared to the **natural nuclear time**, which is the time required for a nuclear projectile to traverse a target nucleus, it is found that the mean life of the compound nucleus is considerably longer than the natural time. To get an estimate, if we take a nuclear diameter of $\sim 10^{-12}$ cm and a velocity of $\sim 10^9$ cm per sec for the absorbed projectile, we obtain a natural nuclear time of $\sim 10^{-12}/10^9$ sec, i.e., $\sim 10^{-21}$ sec. Comparing this time with the experimental value for the mean lifetime we see that it is $\sim 10^{-14}/10^{-21} = 10^7$ times as long as the natural nuclear time.

The lifetime of the compound nucleus is, therefore, long enough to allow numerous collisions between the incident particle and the nucleons inside the nucleus. A kind of statistical equilibrium can readily be established during the lifetime of the compound nucleus so that by the time it has reached the end of its natural life span, it has "forgotten" the mode of its formation and the original cause of its formation.

The breakup occurs when a sufficient amount of energy is again concentrated on one single nuclear subparticle. Each one of the several modes of breakup will happen with a definite probability and these individual probabilities are the same for all modes of formation, leading to the same compound nucleus.

As a rule, emission of radiation in a nuclear interaction is much less likely than the formation of new product nuclei, so that a reaction leading to the emergence of nuclear particles is, on the whole, more probable than a reaction which would result in the emission of a γ-ray. Emission of a γ-ray is, therefore, a less favored nuclear event than the formation of other reaction products in nuclear reactions. In fact, the probability for γ-ray emission becomes exceedingly small whenever the expulsion of a nuclear particle from the compound nucleus becomes energetically possible.

However, when the excitation energy of the compound nucleus is only of about the same order as the separation energy for a nucleon, which is somewhere from ~ 5 Mev to ~ 8 Mev, de-excitation by γ-ray emission becomes the favored mode since only very little kinetic energy would be left available for the emitted nucleon. This circumstance can be used to explain why radiative capture—which is an (n, γ) reaction—is a favored reaction with low-energy neutrons.

Assuming that we have a certain amount of energy available which is to be carried away by the emitted particle in the form of kinetic energy (or radiation), the relative probability of emission from the compound nucleus, or the level-widths, would be greatest for neutron emission, followed by proton emission, then α-particle emission and, last, γ-ray emission.

Example 3.3. The $B^{10}(\alpha, p)C^{13}$ reaction shows among others a resonance for an excitation energy of the compound nucleus of 13.23 Mev. The width of this level, as found experimentally, is 130 kev. Calculate the mean life of the nucleus for this excitation.

The given reaction leads to the formation of the compound nucleus $(N^{14})^*$.

$$_5B^{10} + {}_2He^4 \longrightarrow ({}_7N^{14})^* \longrightarrow {}_6C^{13} + {}_1H^1$$

$$\Gamma = \frac{h}{2\pi} \frac{1}{\tau}$$

therefore $\tau = \dfrac{h}{2\pi} \dfrac{1}{\Gamma} = \dfrac{6.62 \times 10^{-27} \text{ erg sec}}{6.28 \times 130{,}000 \text{ ev} \times 1.6 \times 10^{-12} \text{ erg/ev}} = 5 \times 10^{-21} \text{ sec}$

Example 3.4. The neutron capture of slow neutrons by U^{235} shows a resonance for an energy of excitation of 0.29 ev. The compound nucleus can become de-excited either by a γ-emission or by a fission into larger nuclear fragments. The mean lifetime of the compound nucleus was found to be 4.7×10^{-15} sec and the partial width for γ-emission $\Gamma_\gamma = 34 \times 10^{-3}$ ev.

Calculate the partial fission width Γ_f.

The total width Γ is found from the given lifetime,

$$\Gamma = \frac{h}{2\pi\tau} = \frac{6.62 \times 10^{-27}}{6.28 \times 4.7 \times 10^{-15}} \text{ erg} \times \frac{1}{1.6 \times 10^{-12} \text{ erg/ev}}$$

$$= 140 \times 10^{-3} \text{ ev}$$

Since $\qquad \Gamma = \Gamma_\gamma + \Gamma_f$

therefore $\qquad \Gamma_f = \Gamma - \Gamma_\gamma$

$$= 140 \times 10^{-3} \text{ ev} - 34 \times 10^{-3} \text{ ev}$$

$$= 106 \times 10^{-3} \text{ ev}$$

3.7   Isomers and Isomeric States

The mean lifetime of an excited nuclear energy state before de-excitation by γ-emission is generally $<10^{-13}$ sec, which is well below the present limits of experimental time measurements. There are, however, a number of known cases where a nucleus can exist in an excited state for a length of time which is sufficiently long to be measurable.

Nuclei which can exist in these measurably long states of excitation are called **isomers** and the excited energy states of long enough lifetimes to be measurable are **isomeric states** of the nucleus. Isomeric nuclei are otherwise identical nuclei which differ only in the amount of their excitation.

The existence of isomeric states was first noticed in the case of bromine, where different nuclear reactions were found to lead to the same radioactive isotope Br^{80} with, however, different half-lives. The discrepancy in the half-lives of Br^{80} isotopes was explained as owing to the formation of the isotope in its ground state in one reaction, and its formation in an excited state in the other reaction (Fig. 3.8).

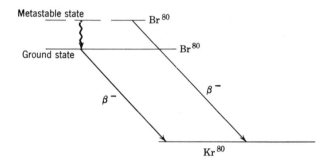

FIG. 3.8. Nuclear isomerism. The nucleus (Br^{80}) can decay directly from metastable state to Kr^{80}, or by preliminary transition from metastable state to ground state with subsequent decay to Kr^{80}.

PROBLEMS

(1) How long will it take a 1 Mev neutron to cross a U^{238} nucleus?

(2) Enumerate the possible modes of decay of the compound nucleus $_{10}Ne^{20}$.

(3) Calculate the kinetic energy in the C.M. and L systems of the α-particles which are formed in the (p, α) reaction of 2 Mev protons with $_3Li^7$.

(4) Show that the excitation energy E_{exc} imparted to a compound nucleus is given by $E_{exc} = (M/M + m)E_0 + $ B.E., where m, E_0 are mass and energy in laboratory system of the incident particle, M the mass of the target nucleus, and B.E. the binding energy of incident particle in the compound nucleus.

(5) Identify the possible residual nuclei for the compound nucleus $Zn^{65}*$. If this compound nucleus is obtained by bombarding Cu^{63} with 6 Mev deuterons, calculate the excitation of the compound nucleus.

(6) In the $Be^9(\alpha, p)B^{12}$ reaction, using 21.7 Mev α-particles, proton groups of 6.96 Mev, 6.08 Mev, and 5.45 Mev were observed at right angles to the incident α-particles. Calculate the Q-values for these groups and the corresponding energy levels. To what nucleus do these energy levels refer?

(7) When Co^{59} is irradiated with neutrons, the radioisotope Co^{60} is produced. This isotope decays by β^--emission of maximum energy 0.31 Mev and two successive γ-rays of energies 1.1715 Mev and 1.3316 Mev. What information about the excited energy levels of a certain nucleus can be derived from these experimental data? Identify the nucleus to which these excited energy levels refer.

(8) The first excited energy level of O^{17} is at 0.87 Mev above ground level. The mean life of this excited state is 2.5×10^{-10} sec. Calculate the width of this energy level.

BIBLIOGRAPHY

Devons, S.: *Excited States of Nuclei*, Cambridge University Press, 1949.

Evans, D. R.: *The Atomic Nucleus*, McGraw-Hill, 1955.

French, A. P.: *Principles of Modern Physics*, Wiley, 1958.

Glasstone, S., and M. C. Edlund: *The Elements of Nuclear Reactor Theory*, van Nostrand, 1952.

Green, A. E. S.: "Nomogram for Estimating Nuclear Reaction Energies," *Nucleonics*, **13**, No. 2 (February 1955).

Green, A. E. S.: *Nuclear Physics*, McGraw-Hill, 1955.

Halliday, D.: *Introductory Nuclear Physics*, Wiley, 1955.

Kaplan, I.: *Nuclear Physics*, Addison-Wesley, 1955.

Mansfield, W. K.: *Elementary Nuclear Physics*, Temple Press, 1958.

Segrè, E. (Ed.): *Experimental Nuclear Physics*, vol. II, part VI, Wiley, 1953.

Semat, H.: *Introduction to Atomic and Nuclear Physics*, Rinehart, 1954.

Weinberg, A. M., and E. P. Wigner: *The Physical Theory of Neutron Chain Reactors*, University of Chicago Press, 1958.

Neutron Reactions

4.1 Introduction

Because of their special importance for reactor physics nuclear reactions initiated by neutrons are more fully described in this chapter. The concept of reaction cross section is introduced and is applied to the calculation of the macroscopic cross section, mean free path, and neutron reaction rates. The energy dependence of the various cross sections is then outlined and the Breit-Wigner formula is explained for simple cases. Finally, the fission cross section is introduced and some general properties of fissionable materials are summarized.

4.2 Slow Neutron Reactions

The most important reactions in reactor physics and in nuclear engineering are nuclear reactions with slow neutrons as these are essential as initiators and perpetuators of nuclear chain reactions in the most common type of reactors. It is, therefore, necessary to gain some understanding of neutron interactions with other nuclei, in particular with fissionable nuclei, and with matter in bulk.

Consider the general type of nuclear reaction

$$a + X \longrightarrow b + Y$$

where the projectiles a are now assumed to be neutrons with kinetic energy of not more than a few Mev.

1. If b is a γ-ray this process is a (n, γ) reaction and it represents the radiative capture of a neutron by the target nucleus with the subsequent emission of a γ-ray and the conversion of the target nucleus X^A into its isotope X^{A+1}.

The (n, γ) reaction is an important factor to be considered in the design of nuclear reactors in that it is a cause of neutron loss to the neutron economy of a reactor and also requires protective measures to shield the experimenter or operator from the injurious effects of the emitted γ-radiation.

A well-known example of a (n, γ) reaction is the radiative capture of a neutron by Cd^{113}.

$$n^1 + Cd^{113} \longrightarrow Cd^{114*} \longrightarrow Cd^{114} + \gamma$$

2. If a and b are identical particles—in the present case neutrons—we have a **scattering process**, which may be either elastic or inelastic. If the target nucleus is raised into an excited state by retaining some of the kinetic energy of the incident neutron, the scattering is inelastic; otherwise, it is elastic.

3. If b is not an elementary particle such as a neutron, proton, deuteron, or α-particle, the result of the reaction will be two nuclei of intermediate mass numbers (assuming of course that X is not an elementary particle).

This type of nuclear reaction is called a **fission process**.

In the case of the readily fissionable isotope U^{235} all of the preceding processes can occur and compete with each other, although the probability for their occurrence is very different. If a sample of that isotope is subjected to a slow neutron bombardment, the relative frequency of occurrence for (1) a fission process, (2) a radiative capture process, and (3) a scattering process is roughly in the proportion of $60:10:1$.

As a rule, several reactions can occur between a neutron and a given nucleus. The probability with which any particular one of the various possible reactions will actually take place depends, however, very strongly on the neutron energy. The probability of a neutron capture as compared to other possible reactions is greatest with slow neutrons, where it is the most common process by far.

The radiative capture of neutrons shows pronounced resonances at certain definite energies, and in the neighborhood of resonances $\Gamma_\gamma \gg \Gamma_n$ for the heavy nuclei. (In a few exceptional cases such as Pd^{108}, Sm^{152}, W^{186} $\Gamma_n \approx \Gamma_\gamma \approx 0.1$ ev, and for Mn and Co, $\Gamma_n \gg \Gamma_\gamma$.)

For the light elements, $\Gamma_n \gg \Gamma_\gamma$, so that neutron scattering is the predominating result in this general energy region. Notable exceptions, however, are the light nuclei He^3, Li^6, Be^7, B^{10}, N^{14}, where the (n, p) or (n, α) reactions have the highest probability by far. Thus,

$$_0n^1 + _2He^3 \longrightarrow _1H^1 + _1H^3 + 0.74 \text{ Mev}$$
$$_0n^1 + _3Li^6 \longrightarrow _1H^3 + _2He^4 + 4.785 \text{ Mev}$$
$$_0n^1 + _4Be^7 \longrightarrow _1H^1 + _3Li^7 + 1.65 \text{ Mev}$$
$$_0n^1 + _5B^{10} \longrightarrow _2He^4 + _3Li^7 + 2.791 \text{ Mev}$$
$$_0n^1 + _7N^{14} \longrightarrow _1H^1 + _6C^{14} + 0.626 \text{ Mev}$$

4.3   Nuclear Reaction Cross Section

The probability of occurrence of a particular nuclear reaction is described by the effective **cross section** for that process. Using this terminology, we can state that for slow neutron reactions with U^{235}, the fission cross section is about six times as great as the radiative capture cross section and about sixty times as great as the scattering cross section. The probability that a given reaction will occur between one neutron and one nucleus is usually called the **microscopic cross section.**

Specifying the cross section is an alternative method of describing the yield of a reaction. Whereas the latter gives the number of nuclear trans-formations that take place per specified number of particles that are shot into a thick target, the effective cross section measures the circular area that a target nucleus must have so that each collision within this area produces a reaction. The reaction will certainly occur if the particle passes through the cross-sectional area; otherwise, no reaction will take place.

We associate a cross section with each particular type of nuclear interaction. Thus, we speak of a **scattering cross section** σ_s when referring to a nuclear scattering process, an **absorption cross section** σ_a when dealing with absorption processes, or a **fission cross section** σ_f when considering nuclear collisions that lead to the fissioning of the target nucleus.

Although the reaction cross section bears no direct or simple relationship to the "geometrical" nuclear cross section πR^2 (R being the nuclear radius), nevertheless, for most nuclear interactions it agrees with it as far as orders of magnitude go, and it generally falls within 10^{-23} and 10^{-27} cm^2.

Nuclear reaction cross sections are measured in units called **barns**, where

$$1 \text{ barn} = 10^{-24} \text{ cm}^2$$

The cross section for a nuclear reaction depends not only on the target nucleus—as one would expect if the cross section were identical with the "geometric" cross section of the target nucleus—but also, and in many cases primarily, on the neutron energy.

4.4   Neutron Cross Sections

If a neutron beam is allowed to pass through a slab of target material, it will emerge with reduced intensity owing to a variety of processes that will have taken place during its passage through the material, such as scattering, absorption with accompanying γ-emission, or absorption leading to subsequent fission. The various possibilities are represented schematically in Fig. 4.1. The attenuation of a neutron beam or its loss in intensity due to the combined effect of all causes is described in terms of the **total cross section** σ_t. It is equal to the sum of the individual cross sections for all processes involved.

$$\sigma_t = \sigma_s + \sigma_a \tag{4.1}$$

In cases where some of the neutron absorptions can lead to a fission reaction, the absorption cross section can be further divided into a fission

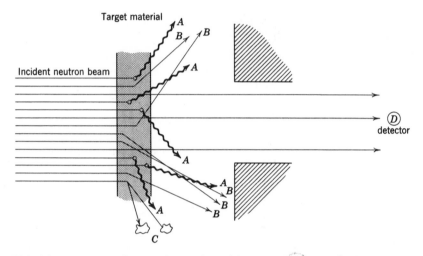

FIG. 4.1. Three types of neutron interactions with matter are illustrated. *A*—represents radiative neutron capture; *B*—represents elastic scattering collision; *C*—represents neutron induced fission process. The attenuated direct neutron beam passes through the material to the detector at *D*.

cross section σ_f, and a nonfission or (radiative) capture cross section σ_c.

$$\sigma_a = \sigma_c + \sigma_f \tag{4.2}$$

The scattering cross section can also be subdivided into an elastic scattering part and an inelastic scattering part. Therefore

$$\sigma_t = \underbrace{\sigma_{el} + \sigma_{inel}}_{\text{(scattering)}} + \underbrace{\sigma_f + \sigma_c}_{\text{(absorption)}} \tag{4.3}$$

4.5   Determination of the Cross Section

We now proceed to find a relation between the cross section and the experimentally available and directly measurable observables, such as the incident beam intensity, and the number of observed interactions or transmutations.

The beam intensity I is measured in terms of the neutron **flux density** (commonly referred to in an abbreviated form as "neutron flux"), i.e., the number of neutrons crossing unit area perpendicular to the beam in 1 sec.

If all the neutrons in the beam move with the same uniform velocity v (Fig. 4.2), then the number of neutrons crossing 1 cm² per sec is equal to the number of neutrons contained in a parallelepiped of base area 1 cm²

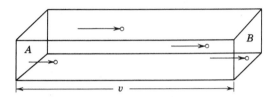

FIG. 4.2. Flux density and neutron density. The number of neutrons crossing surface A per second equals the number of neutrons contained in a parallelepiped of base area 1 cm² and length v cm.

and of length v cm. Neutrons which cross face A at a given instant will have reached face B 1 sec later, where the distance separating A and B is v cm. All neutrons crossing face A during this time interval will be contained within the volume bounded by A and B.

If n is the **neutron density**, i.e., the number of neutrons in 1 cm³ of the volume, then

$$I = n(\text{neutrons/cm}^3)v(\text{cm/sec})$$

$$= nv(\text{neutrons/cm}^2 \text{ sec}) \qquad (4.4)$$

If a homogeneous beam of neutrons is allowed to pass through a thin sheet of target material of area A, thickness t, and having N_0 nuclei per cm³, the effective nuclear target area which is available for nuclear reactions to occur is given by the product of cross section per target nucleus and total number of target nuclei contained in the target sheet.

$$\text{Cross section per nucleus} = \sigma$$
$$\text{Total number of nuclei} = N_0At$$
Therefore $\quad$ Available nuclear target area $= (N_0At)\sigma$

We are assuming that the target is thin enough so that no overlapping of nuclei in successive layers occurs that might cause a screening of some nuclei by those in the preceding layers. Thus, every nucleus presents its entire effective cross section to the incident neutron beam (Fig. 4.3).

The probability or the chance for one incoming neutron to hit a nuclear target area is equal to the ratio of this area to the total area A presented to the incident neutron. Hence

$$\text{Probability of interaction per neutron} = \frac{\text{nuclear target area}}{\text{total target area}}$$

$$= \frac{N_0 A t \sigma}{A} = N_0 t \sigma \qquad (4.5)$$

The number of nuclear reactions per second, r, is obtained from this by

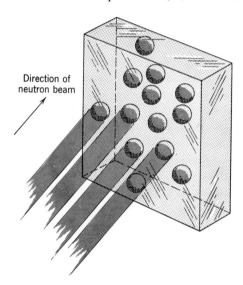

Direction of
neutron beam

FIG. 4.3. Neutrons in the impinging neutron beam have an unobstructed view of all target nuclei, if the target is thin enough so that no nucleus lies in the "shadow" of any other nucleus.

multiplying the probability per neutron (Eq. 4.5) by the total number of neutrons incident on the target per second. This number is given by the product of beam intensity (flux) I and the area of incidence A. Hence

$$\text{Number of incident neutrons per second} = IA \qquad (4.6)$$

The number of reactions per second $=$ (probability of interaction per neutron) $\times$ (number of incident neutrons per second)

$$= (4.5) \times (4.6)$$

Therefore $\qquad\qquad r = (N_0 t \sigma)(IA) = (N_0 \sigma)IV \qquad (4.7)$

where V is the volume of the target, At. Hence

$$\sigma = \frac{r}{N_0 I A t} = \frac{r}{N_0 I V} \tag{4.8}$$

Expression 4.7 for the reaction rate contains the product of σ, the cross section per nucleus or the microscopic cross section, and N_0 the number of nuclei per cm³. This product is called the **macroscopic cross section** and is denoted by Σ.

$$\Sigma = N_0 \sigma \tag{4.9}$$

From expression 4.7 we get for the interaction rate (i.e., number of interactions per second) per unit volume, r_V

$$r_V = \frac{r}{At} = \Sigma I \tag{4.10}$$

showing that the interaction rate per unit volume is equal to the macroscopic cross section multiplied by the flux density. It also follows from 4.10 that

$$\Sigma = \frac{r_V}{I} \tag{4.11}$$

showing that the macroscopic cross section can also be interpreted as the rate of interactions per unit volume per unit neutron flux.

Very often the target material is specified by its areal nuclear density n_A, where

$$n_A = \frac{\text{total number of target nuclei}}{\text{total target area}}$$

$$= \frac{N_0 A t}{A} = N_0 t \tag{4.12}$$

The connection between the volume density N_0 and the areal density is expressed by 4.12. (The term "density" used here refers to "number of nuclei per unit volume" and not to their mass per unit volume.)

The cross section as given by expression 4.8 can now also be written in this form

$$\sigma = \frac{r/A}{n_A I} = \frac{r_A}{n_A I} \tag{4.13}$$

where $r_A = r/A$ is the rate of nuclear reactions per unit target area. Expression 4.13 corresponds to 4.11 and they both give the nuclear cross section as the **reaction rate per nuclear density per neutron flux**, if we match the reaction rate per unit area with the corresponding areal density, and the reaction rate per unit volume with the corresponding volume density of target nuclei.

If the density and the atomic weight of the target material are known, the volume density of the nuclei in the target, N_0, can be derived in terms of the density ρ, the atomic weight M, and the Avogadro number N. The mass per atom can be obtained either as the ratio of ρ/N_0 or the ratio of M/N. Hence $\rho/N_0 = M/N$ and

$$N_0 = \frac{\rho}{M} N \tag{4.14}$$

Example 4.1. A thin sheet of Co^{59}, 0.03 cm thick, is irradiated with a neutron beam of flux density 10^{12} neutrons per cm^2 sec for a period of 2 hr. If the cross section for neutron capture by Co^{59} is 30 barns, how many nuclei of the isotope Co^{60} will have been produced at the end of the irradiation period per cm^2 and what will be the initial β^- activity of the sample? The half-life of Co^{60} is 5.2 years, and the density of Co^{59} is 8.9 grams per cm^3.

$$r_A = n_A I \sigma \quad \text{by (4.13)}$$
$$= N_0 t I \sigma \quad \text{by (4.12)}$$
$$= N\left(\frac{\rho}{M}\right) t I \sigma \quad \text{by (4.14)}$$
$$= 6.03 \times 10^{23} \left(\frac{8.9}{59}\right) \times 0.03 \times 10^{12} \times 30 \times 10^{-24}$$
$$= 8.19 \times 10^{10} \text{ reactions/cm}^2 \text{ sec}$$

The number of transmutations during a period of 2 hr is, therefore,

$$R = 8.19 \times 10^{10} \times 2 \times 3600 = 59 \times 10^{13} \text{ reactions/cm}^2$$

The number of Co^{60} nuclei produced is equal to the number of neutron captures, as the fraction of Co^{60} that decay during the irradiation process is negligible because of their long half-life compared to the length of the irradiation period.
    The initial activity per cm^2

$$= \lambda \times 59 \times 10^{13}$$
$$= \frac{0.693 \times 59 \times 10^{13}}{5.2 \times 3.15 \times 10^7} \text{ decays/sec}$$
$$= 2.5 \times 10^6 \text{ decays/sec}$$
$$= \frac{2.5 \times 10^6}{3.7 \times 10^{10}} \text{ curies} = 67 \text{ microcuries}$$

4.6 Attenuation of Neutrons

We have seen that a neutron beam when passing through matter suffers a reduction in intensity through collision processes with the nuclei of the intervening matter, which lead either to scattering or absorption of the neutrons (Fig. 4.1). The emerging beam will be attenuated or weakened by an amount which can be readily calculated.

In order to do this, let us start with a homogeneous neutron beam that passes through a slab of material of 1 cm² cross-sectional area (Fig. 4.4). If the incident flux is I_0 and the flux after penetrating a distance x is I. it will become $I - dI$ after a further penetration of distance dx. The change in the flux, $-dI$, between the penetration distances x and $x + dx$

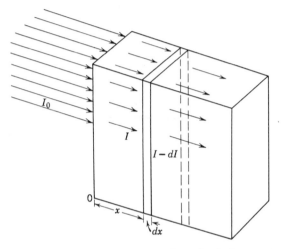

FIG. 4.4. The neutron beam I_0 is reduced to intensity I after penetrating a thickness x in the material. A further penetration of distance dx causes a further change in the beam intensity of amount $-dI$.

is caused by the various collision events that have taken place within this distance. We can, therefore, equate $-dI$ and the number of collisions that have occurred within dx.† By Eq. 4.7 the number of collisions in the volume $V = A\,dx$ is

$$r = \sigma N_0 I A\, dx$$
$$= \sigma N_0 I\, dx \qquad \text{since } A = 1 \text{ cm}^2$$

Therefore
$$-dI = \sigma N_0 I\, dx$$

or
$$-\frac{dI}{I} = \sigma N_0\, dx = \Sigma\, dx \qquad (4.15)$$

By integrating both sides of the last equation between the limits $x = 0$

† Strictly speaking, this conclusion is only true for absorption collisions, since for scattering collisions the neutrons are not entirely removed from the beam but may be scattered in such a way as to reappear in the beam unless special experimental arrangements are employed. (See page 345.)

and $x = x$ we find the intensity of the neutron beam after penetrating a distance x in the target material.

$$-\int_{I_0}^{I} \frac{dI}{I} = \Sigma \int_{0}^{x} dx$$

Therefore $\qquad\qquad -\log \frac{I}{I_0} = \Sigma x \qquad\qquad (4.15a)$

and $\qquad\qquad I = I_0 \exp(-\Sigma x) \qquad\qquad (4.16)$

This result shows that Σ corresponds to a linear absorption coefficient and has the dimensions of a reciprocal length. Penetration through a distance equal to $1/\Sigma$ reduces the beam intensity by a factor of e.

Example 4.2. The absorption cross section of Cd^{113} for certain neutrons is 20,800 barns. Taking the density of this material to be 8.67 grams/cm³, calculate the macroscopic cross section and the thickness of Cd^{113} required to reduce the intensity of the neutron beam to 1 % of its original value.

$$\Sigma = N_0 \sigma = \frac{\rho}{M} N\sigma \qquad \text{by Eq. 4.14}$$

$$= \frac{8.67}{113} \times 6.03 \times 10^{23} \times 20800 \times 10^{-24} \text{ cm}^{-1}$$

$$= 962 \text{ cm}^{-1}$$

$$\Sigma x = \log \frac{I_0}{I} \qquad \text{by Eq. 4.15}a$$

$$= \log 100 = (\log_{10} 100) \log 10 = 2 \times 2.30 = 4.60$$

Therefore $\qquad\qquad x = \frac{4.60}{962} = 0.0048 \text{ cm}$

4.7 Macroscopic Cross Section and Mean Free Path

The penetration distance $\lambda = 1/\Sigma$ can also be defined as the path length over which the neutrons can travel without suffering a collision with a target nucleus with a probability of $1/e$. The distance λ is called the **mean free path** because it is also the average or mean distance that a neutron can travel in the material without making a collision. We can prove this by evaluating the average path length for the neutrons according to the standard method of finding an average quantity.

We recall that the beam intensity is proportional to the neutron density (Eq. 4.4), so that Eq. 4.16 can also be written as

$$n = n_0 \exp(-\Sigma x) \qquad\qquad (4.17)$$

which gives the number of neutrons per cm³ that can penetrate to a distance x without making a nuclear collision of any kind (Fig. 4.4). Upon penetrating a further distance dx, of the n remaining neutrons, a number dn will undergo a collision and drop out where dn is obtained by differentiating Eq. 4.17 and is

$$dn = -n_0 \Sigma \exp(-\Sigma x) \qquad (4.18)$$

The combined path length of the group of neutrons that travel a distance x and then suffer a collision within the short distance between x and $x + dx$ is, therefore, $x \, dn$.

If we consider the neutron beam to consist of a collection of many similar groups of neutrons that stick together for a distance x and then drop out together, we can find the total combined path length for all the neutrons in the beam by integrating $x \, dn$ over all possible values of x from 0 to ∞. Therefore

$$\text{Total combined path length} = \int_0^\infty x \, dn$$

The average path length is obtained from the total path length by dividing it by the total number of neutrons, n_0. Hence

$$\text{Average path length} = \frac{\displaystyle\int_0^\infty x \, dn}{n_0} = \bar{x} \qquad (4.19)$$

Therefore $\qquad \bar{x} = \displaystyle\int_0^\infty -\Sigma x \exp(-\Sigma x) \, dx \qquad$ by Eq. 4,18

$$= \frac{1}{\Sigma} = \lambda \qquad (4.20)$$

It can be shown that this result applies not only to a uniform neutron beam but that it is quite general. The average path length between successive collisions for neutrons moving in a medium of macroscopic cross section Σ is equal to $1/\Sigma$.

No distinction was made in our derivation between a scattering collision and an absorption collision as they both contribute to the attenuation of the neutron flux. The macroscopic cross section to which we have referred is therefore the total macroscopic cross section. It follows from Eq. 4.1 that

$$\Sigma_t = N_0 \sigma_t = N_0 \sigma_s + N_0 \sigma_a$$

$$= \Sigma_s + \Sigma_a \qquad (4.21)$$

In analogy with Eq. 4.20 we can define a mean free path for scattering collisions only, and one for absorption collisions only.

$$\lambda_s = \frac{1}{\Sigma_s} \quad \text{and} \quad \lambda_a = \frac{1}{\Sigma_a} \tag{4.22}$$

It follows from Eq. 4.21 that

$$\lambda_t = \frac{1}{\Sigma_t} = \frac{1}{\Sigma_s + \Sigma_a}$$

$$= \frac{1}{1/\lambda_s + 1/\lambda_a} = \frac{\lambda_a \lambda_s}{\lambda_a + \lambda_s} \tag{4.23}$$

Clearly, λ_t is smaller than either λ_s or λ_a as one would expect it to be. Since the total cross section includes more collision possibilities than either the scattering cross section or the absorption cross section separately, the chances of evading a particular type of collision are greater than the chance of evading all types of collisions. A smaller chance of evading any collision means also a smaller mean free path.

Example 4.3. Calculate and compare the collision and absorption mean free paths for neutrons in graphite, using these values: $\sigma_s = 4.8$ barns; $\sigma_a = 3.2 \times 10^{-3}$ barns; density $\rho = 2.25$ grams/cm^3.

$$\lambda_s = \frac{1}{\Sigma_s} = \frac{1}{N_0 \sigma_s} = \frac{1}{(N\rho/M)\sigma_s}$$

$$= \frac{12}{6.03 \times 10^{23} \times 2.25 \times 4.8 \times 10^{-24}} \text{ cm}$$

$$= 1.88 \text{ cm}$$

$$\lambda_a = \lambda_s \times \frac{\sigma_s}{\sigma_a} = \frac{1.88 \times 4.8}{3.2 \times 10^{-3}} \text{ cm}$$

$$= 2820 \text{ cm}$$

The absorption mean free path is seen to be considerably greater than the scattering mean free path, so that, on the average, a neutron can travel over 1500 times as far before being absorbed than it can travel before making a scattering collision in graphite.

This result has important implications for the usefulness of graphite in nuclear reactor design.

Example 4.4. Calculate the macroscopic scattering cross section for neutrons of a certain energy in H_2O, assuming the following values for the microscopic scattering cross sections of H and O, respectively.

$$\sigma_O = 4.2 \text{ barns}$$

$$\sigma_H = 38.0 \text{ barns}$$

The macroscopic cross section for a compound or a mixture of several components is equal to the sum of the individual macroscopic cross sections

$$\Sigma = \Sigma_1 + \Sigma_2 + \Sigma_3 + \cdots \qquad (4.24)$$

Therefore

$$\Sigma = \Sigma_H + \Sigma_O$$

$$= N_H \sigma_H + N_O \sigma_O$$

The number of water molecules per cm^3 is

$$N_0 = \frac{6.03 \times 10^{23}}{18} = 0.0335 \times 10^{24}$$

The number of O nuclei per cm^3 is equal to this number, whereas the number of H nuclei is twice this number.

$$N_{0(O)} = 0.0335 \times 10^{24}; \quad N_{0(H)} = 0.067 \times 10^{24}$$

Hence

$$\Sigma_{H_2O} = 0.067 \times 10^{24} \times 38 \times 10^{-24} + 0.0335 \times 10^{24} \times 4.2 \times 10^{-24}$$

$$= 2.54 + 0.14$$

$$= 2.68 \ cm^{-1}$$

4.8 Neutron Flux and Reaction Rate

It is convenient and physically reasonable, when working with large numbers of neutrons, to consider them as constituents of a neutron gas and to describe their movements and random motion in a manner analogous to and familiar to us from the molecular theory of gases. If the neutrons that make up such a gas move with a speed v, which we shall assume at present to be the same for all the neutrons, and have a mean free path λ, the time interval t between two successive collisions for a given neutron, will be

$$t = \frac{\lambda}{v} \qquad (4.25)$$

The reciprocal of this, v/λ, will give the number of collisions per second made by a neutron. For an assembly of n neutrons per cm^3, the total number of collisions made each second is then

Number of collisions/cm^3 sec = (number of collisions per neutron/sec) × (number of neutrons/cm^3)

that is,

$$r_V = \frac{v}{\lambda} n \qquad (4.26)$$

This is the same result as was found for a beam of neutrons with all neutrons traveling in a given direction (Eq. 4.10). It is shown here to be valid also for an assembly of neutrons with the neutrons traveling in different and arbitrary directions.

If we interpret v as the distance traveled by a neutron in 1 sec, then the product nv represents the total distance traveled in 1 sec by all the neutrons which are contained in 1 cm³. By dividing the total distance by the average distance between successive collisions, we arrive at the number of collisions per second per cm³, i.e., r_V, confirming Eq. 4.26.

The product nv is called the neutron **flux** (i.e., flux density) and commonly denoted by ϕ.

$$\phi = nv \qquad (4.27)$$

In terms of the neutron flux ϕ, the reaction rate/cm³ can now be written

$$r_V = \phi\Sigma \qquad (4.28)$$

The reaction rate for a medium of volume V cm³, is, therefore,

$$R = r_V V = \phi V \Sigma \qquad (4.28a)$$

Previously, we had defined the flux density as the number of neutrons falling on unit area each second. That definition is satisfactory and equivalent to the new definition for a parallel beam of neutrons, all traveling in the same direction. It is, however, not general enough to be applicable to an assembly of neutrons that move in all directions at random like the molecules of a gas. The neutrons in a nuclear reactor are more realistically described in terms of the random motion of gas molecules than as a parallel beam of particles incident on a plane surface. The reaction rate should depend only on the product nv, i.e., the flux ϕ of the neutrons and not on the direction of approach of the neutrons. The number of neutrons falling on 1 cm² per sec would, however, be less for random motion of the neutrons than if they were all moving in a direction perpendicular to that area, so that the number of reactions would also be correspondingly smaller.

As with gas molecules, the neutrons in a reactor do not all have the same speed, but instead manifest a considerable spread in the range of their velocities. It is therefore necessary and desirable to generalize the definition of the neutron flux (Eq. 4.27). This can be done by defining a flux element $d\phi$ for a small range of neutron velocities between v and $v + dv$, so that $n(v)\, dv$ is the number of neutrons per cm³ having velocities within this range (Fig. 4.5).

$$d\phi = n(v)v\, dv$$

Therefore
$$\phi = \int_0^\infty n(v)v\, dv \qquad (4.29)$$

Alternately, we can divide the neutrons into groups of small energy ranges, denoting the number of neutrons with energies between E and $E + dE$ by $n(E) \, dE$. In terms of this decomposition the neutron flux can be defined as

$$\phi = \int_0^\infty n(E)v \, dE \qquad (4.30)$$

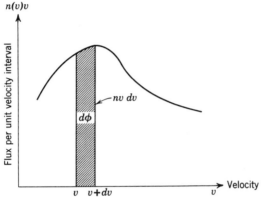

FIG. 4.5. The shaded area represents the flux of neutrons with velocities lying between v and $v + dv$.

A third method of defining the flux which we shall find useful later on is the following:

$$\phi = \int_0^\infty \phi(E) \, dE \qquad (4.31)$$

where $\phi(E) \, dE$ is the flux in the small energy range between E and $E + dE$ (Fig. 4.6).

Example 4.5. A typical natural uranium reactor assembly contains about 50,000 kg of natural uranium of which 0.7% is the readily fissionable isotope U^{235}. Assuming an average neutron flux of 10^{12} neutrons/cm²/sec and a fission cross section of $\sigma_f = 580$ barns for the readily fissionable isotope U^{235}, estimate the fraction of this isotope "burnt up" by fission in one year, assuming the reactor to be in continuous operation and neglecting other U^{235} consuming reactions.

The number of U^{235} nuclei used up in one year is given by the number of U^{235} nuclei that undergo fission reactions during that time. Hence

$$\text{Number of fission reactions/year} = (\text{number of fission reactions/sec})$$
$$\times \, 3.15 \times 10^7 \text{ sec/year}$$
$$= V\Sigma_f\phi \times 3.15 \times 10^7$$
$$= VN_0\sigma_f\phi \times 3.15 \times 10^7$$

Hence, the fractional burn-up is this number, divided by the original number N_0V. Therefore

$$\text{Fractional burn-up} = 3.15 \times 10^7 \times \sigma_f \times \phi$$
$$= 3.15 \times 10^7 \times 580 \times 10^{-24} \times 10^{12}$$
$$= 1.83 \times 10^{-2}$$

Therefore, the annual burn-up through fission is somewhat less than 2%.

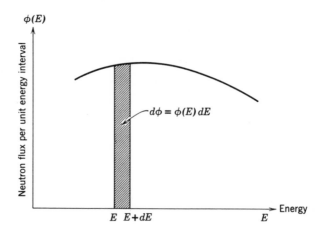

FIG. 4.6. The shaded area represents the flux of neutrons with energies lying between E and $E + dE$.

4.9 Energy Dependence of Neutron Cross Sections

In our preliminary discussion of neutron reactions it was noted briefly that the neutron cross sections depend not only on the nature of the target nucleus but also on the energy of the interacting neutron. It is convenient to classify neutrons that are involved in nuclear reactions according to the general behavior of the various cross sections and to divide the neutron energies into several regions to take account of these general trends. It will be sufficient for our purposes to distinguish four principal regions.

1. A high-energy region which comprises neutron energies between ∼10 Mev to ∼0.1 Mev. Neutrons within this range will be called **fast neutrons**.
2. An intermediate energy region for energies between ∼0.1 Mev and ∼1000 ev. Neutrons with energies in this range will be termed **intermediate neutrons**.

3. A region for energies between ~1000 ev and ~1 ev. Neutrons with energies lying in this range will be called **epithermal neutrons**.

4. A region for energies of ~1 ev and less. Neutrons with energies in this region will be referred to as **thermal neutrons** or **slow neutrons**.

Using this classification, we can survey the neutron cross sections in the given order.

1. FAST NEUTRONS. The most probable interaction between neutrons and nuclei in this region is the (n, n) reaction, i.e., scattering, so that the absorption cross section will be very much smaller than the scattering cross section, $\sigma_a \ll \sigma_s$. The total cross section σ_t is almost entirely due to scattering and it approaches a value of

$$\sigma_t \doteq \sigma_s \doteq 2\pi R^2 \qquad (4.32)$$

For medium and heavy nuclei, σ_t can be expressed fairly well by

$$\sigma_t = 0.125 A^{\frac{2}{3}} \qquad (4.33)$$

2. INTERMEDIATE NEUTRONS. In this region the (n, n) process is still the most favored reaction for intermediate and heavy nuclei, with scattering making the chief contribution to the total cross section. $\sigma_t \doteq \sigma_s$ is of the order of 1 barn, whereas the cross section σ_c for the (n, γ) or radiative capture process is of the order of 1 millibarn.

For light nuclei ($A < 25$) this region contains well separated and distinct resonances, whereas for the medium and heavy nuclei the resonances overlap and appear smoothed out. The nature of these resonances is described in more detail in what follows.

3. EPITHERMAL NEUTRONS. In this energy region which is also known as the resonance region, the neutron cross sections of most elements show many distinct and high maxima in the total cross section. The peaks in the nuclear cross section point out the existence of resonance levels in the compound nucleus of the kind discussed in an earlier chapter, and they are, therefore, generally known as **resonances**. They appear to be superimposed on a background that varies as $E^{-\frac{1}{2}}$ (or $1/v$). The number of absorption peaks and their mutual separations vary considerably for different nuclei, and the general appearance of the energy-dependence of σ_t for a typical nucleus is shown in Fig. 4.7.

The maxima are resonances in the capture cross section σ_c that are superimposed on a background, which is practically entirely a scattering cross section. The scattering cross section for energies lying between the individual resonance energies is of the order of a barn, with the capture cross section σ_c of the order of a millibarn.

The total background cross section σ_t between resonances is given by

$$\sigma_t = 4\pi R^2 \tag{4.34}$$

which is twice that of the corresponding cross section for fast neutrons (Eq. 4.32).

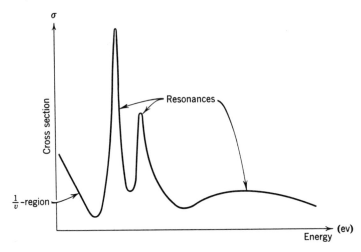

FIG. 4.7. Variation of neutron cross section with energy for a typical nucleus.

The energy dependence of σ_c in the resonance region is given by the Breit-Wigner formula.

$$\sigma_c = \frac{\lambda^2}{4\pi} \frac{\Gamma_n \Gamma_\gamma}{(E - E_0)^2 + (\Gamma/2)^2} \tag{4.35}$$

Equation 4.35 is the so-called single-level formula which holds for resonances that are well separated and do not overlap, so that the collision reaction which is responsible for this maximum can be ascribed to a single resonance level of the compound nucleus.

In this formula, λ is the de Broglie wavelength of the incident neutron, $\lambda = h/mv$, and Γ is the width of the resonance line at half the maximum value of the cross section (Fig. 4.8). Γ_n and Γ_γ are the partial level widths for the (n, n) and (n, γ) reactions, respectively, and each is a measure of the probability for the corresponding reaction to take place (compare Eqs. 3.2 and 3.7). Since these two processes are the only modes of decay of the compound nucleus in this energy region that need be considered, we must have, by Eq. 3.7, that

$$\Gamma_n + \Gamma_\gamma = \Gamma \tag{4.36}$$

so that the probability for the (n, n) reaction is Γ_n/Γ and that for the (n, γ) reaction, Γ_γ/Γ.

In most cases, when E is small, the probability for the (n, γ) process is much higher than for the (n, n) process (see section 4.2), so that $\Gamma_\gamma \gg \Gamma_n$ and, consequently, $\Gamma \doteq \Gamma_\gamma$. For most nuclei Γ_γ is $\sim$0.1 ev, whereas Γ_n is usually two or three orders of magnitude smaller.

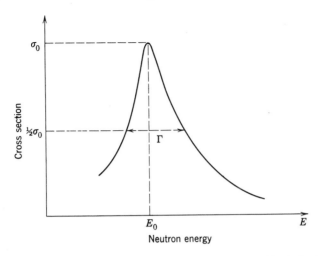

FIG. 4.8. The width of a resonance is expressed in terms of its half-width Γ.

The Breit-Wigner formula can also be written in the form

$$\sigma_c = \sigma_0 \left(\frac{E_0}{E}\right)^{1/2} \frac{1}{1 + \dfrac{(E - E_0)^2}{(\Gamma/2)^2}} \tag{4.37}$$

where σ_0 is the maximum value of the resonance capture cross section for $E = E_0$.

A well-known example of a neutron absorption resonance is that of cadmium with a maximum value of 7200 barns for a neutron energy of 0.18 ev (Fig. 4.9).

For the case of a broad resonance, i.e., when $\Gamma \gg E - E_0$, Eq. 4.37 simplifies to

$$\sigma_c = \sigma_0 \left(\frac{E_0}{E}\right)^{1/2}$$

$$= \frac{\text{constant}}{v} \tag{4.38}$$

This is the well-known $1/v$ dependence of the capture cross section for slow neutrons, which is exhibited clearly in the (n, α) cross section with boron, (Fig. 4.10), for example.

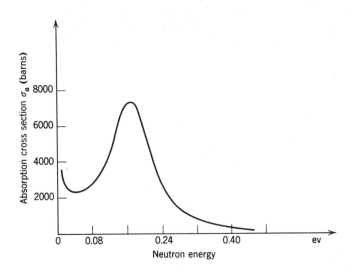

FIG. 4.9. The slow neutron cross section of cadmium, showing a strong resonance peak at 0.18 ev, with a maximum of about 7200 barns.

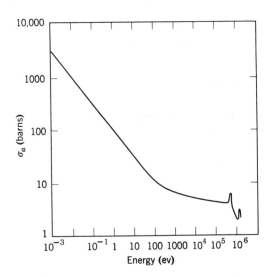

FIG. 4.10. Neutron absorption cross section of boron. The cross section varies as $1/v$ for neutron energies below 100 ev. For energies between 100 ev and 0.1 Mev it remains fairly constant and has several resonances between 0.5 and 5 Mev.

For light nuclei the resonances are very broad and widely separated from each other, so that the condition $\Gamma \gg E - E_0$ is well satisfied and the $1/v$ dependence is quite generally obeyed.

4. THERMAL NEUTRONS. In the thermal energy region the scattering cross section σ_s rises steadily as we go from the lighter to the heavier elements from about 1 barn to a value below 10 barns. The capture cross section σ_c follows the $1/v$ law, and the Breit-Wigner formula may be applied to the (n, γ) cross section, even though there are no resonances present in the thermal energy region. For E_0 we use the value of the nearest resonance in the low-energy region.

A schematic representation of the variation of neutron cross section with energy for a typical nucleus is given in Fig. 4.7, and the thermal neutron absorption cross sections for some representative nuclides are listed according to orders of magnitude in Table 4.1.

Example 4.6. Assuming a resonance cross section of 55,000 barns for Cd^{113} at a resonance energy of 0.176 ev, estimate the relative probability of a neutron emission as compared to a resonance capture if the total width is 0.113 ev and $\Gamma_\gamma \gg \Gamma_n$.

Setting $E = E_0$ in Eq. 4.35, we get

$$\sigma_0 = \frac{\lambda^2}{\pi} \frac{\Gamma_n \Gamma_\gamma}{\Gamma^2} = \frac{\lambda^2 \Gamma_n}{\pi \Gamma_\gamma} \quad \text{since} \quad \Gamma_\gamma \doteq \Gamma$$

With $\lambda = h/mv = h/(2mE)^{1/2}$, this gives for σ_0

$$\sigma_0 = \frac{h^2}{2\pi mE} \frac{\Gamma_n}{\Gamma_\gamma}$$

Therefore

$$\frac{\Gamma_n}{\Gamma_\gamma} = \frac{2\pi mE\sigma_0}{h^2} = \frac{6.28 \times 1.67 \times 10^{-24} \times 0.176 \times 1.6 \times 10^{-12} \times 55,000 \times 10^{-24}}{(6.63 \times 10^{-27})^2}$$

$$= 3.7 \times 10^{-3}$$

The probability for a radiative capture is, therefore, nearly 300 times as great as the probability for neutron scattering.

Example 4.7. The cross section for the (n, α) reaction with boron follows the $1/v$ law. If the cross section for 50 ev neutrons is 16.8 barns, calculate the cross section for 0.025 ev neutrons.

Using Eq. 4.38, we get

$$\sigma = \sigma_0 \left(\frac{E_0}{E}\right)^{1/2}$$

$$= 16.8 \left(\frac{50}{1/40}\right)^{1/2}$$

$$= 336 \times 5^{1/2} = 753 \text{ barns}$$

TABLE 4.1   Thermal Neutron Absorption Cross Sections of Some Nuclides (in barns)

Nuclide	σ_a	Nuclide	σ_a	Nuclide	σ_a
He^4	0	N^{14}	1.75 (n, p)	Li^6	945 (n, α)
H^2	0.00046	K^{39}	1.94	V^{50}	<450
S^{32}	0.002 (n, α)	K^{41}	1.24	Kr^{83}	220
		Ti^{48}	8.3	Rh^{103}	156
Be^9	0.010	Fe^{56}	2.7	Te^{123}	410
Mg^{24}	<0.044	Ni^{58}	4.4	Xe^{131}	120
Mg^{26}	<0.120	Zr^{91}	1.58	Nd^{143}	324
Si^{28}	<0.110	Mo^{96}	1.2	Eu^{153}	450
Zr^{90}	<0.170	I^{127}	7.0	Hf^{177}	380
Zr^{94}	<0.140	W^{184}	2.0		
Pb^{206}	0.025	Pt^{194}	<2.1	He^3	5500 (n, p)
Pb^{208}	<0.030	Pt^{198}	4.0	B^{10}	3813 (n, α)
Bi^{209}	0.034			Eu^{151}	7700
		Mn^{55}	13.2	Eu^{152}	<7000
H^1	0.332	Ni^{62}	15	Eu^{154}	<1900
Na^{23}	0.505	Mo^{95}	13.9	Hg^{196}	<4100
Mg^{25}	<0.370	Ag^{107}	31	Hg^{199}	<3300
Al^{27}	0.230	Ag^{109}	87		
Si^{29}	<0.370	W^{186}	35	Be^7	~54,000 (n, p)
P^{31}	0.200	Pt^{195}	27	Cd^{113}	20,000
Ca^{40}	0.220	Au^{197}	98.8	Xe^{135}	2,720,000
Cr^{52}	0.760			Sm^{149}	40,800
Ge^{74}	0.620			Sm^{151}	~10,000
Se^{80}	0.610			Eu^{155}	14,000
Pb^{207}	0.700			Gd^{155}	~66,000
				Gd^{157}	240,000

4.10   The Fission Cross Section

Some of the very heavy elements undergo fission as a result of neutron capture and this is the basic phenomenon that has made possible the large-scale applications of nuclear energy.

The naturally occurring fissionable nuclides are primarily: U^{235}, U^{238}, and Th^{232}. The U^{235} isotope can be fissioned with thermal neutrons as well as with fast neutrons, whereas U^{238} and Th^{232} can only be fissioned with neutrons that exceed a threshold energy of about 1 Mev.

The other fissionable uranium isotope U^{233} and also Pu^{239} can be produced artificially by neutron bombardment of Th^{232} and U^{238}, respectively, and both are fissionable by thermal as well as fast neutrons. The fission cross sections of these nuclides are shown in Figs. 4.11, 4.12, and 4.13 and the total neutron cross sections of U^{238} and Th^{232} in Fig. 4.14.

In the case of fissionable materials, we must be careful to distinguish between the terms "absorption" and "capture" cross section which, in the case of nonfissionable materials, can be used interchangeably. For fissionable substances, the absorption cross section σ_a is the sum of the capture cross section σ_c and the fission cross section σ_f.

$$\sigma_a = \sigma_c + \sigma_f \qquad (4.39)$$

The capture cross section refers to the radiative capture cross section only.

The various thermal neutron cross sections for some reactor fuel materials are listed in Table 4.2.

All cross sections are in barns and refer to a neutron energy of 0.0253 ev.

TABLE 4.2†

	σ_c	σ_f	σ_s
U^{233}	57	523	
U^{235}	101	582	10.0
U^{238}	2.73	0	8.3
U (natural)	3.50	4.18	8.3
Pu^{239}	286	742	11.0

† D. J. Hughes and R. B. Schwartz, BNL–325, *Neutron Cross Sections*, 2nd ed., supplement 1.

Example 4.8. Calculate the thermal fission cross section for an enriched uranium mixture which contains 5% of U^{235} atoms.

The fission cross section for the mixture is given by the weighted average

$$\sigma_f = \frac{N_{0(238)}\sigma_{f(238)} + N_{0(235)}\sigma_{f(235)}}{N_{0(238)} + N_{0(235)}}$$

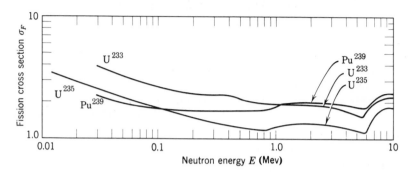

FIG. 4.11. Neutron fission cross sections of U²³³, U²³⁵, Pu²³⁹ for high-energy neutrons.

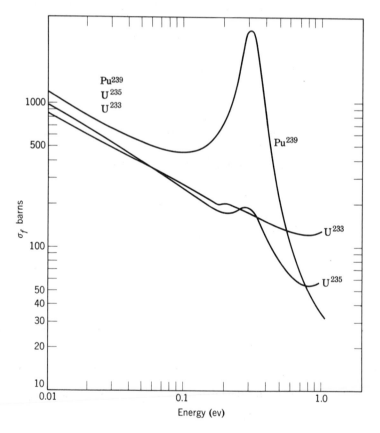

FIG. 4.12. Low-energy neutron fission cross sections of U²³³, U²³⁵, Pu²³⁹.

and referring to the tabulated values, this becomes

$$\sigma_f = \frac{\sigma_{f(235)}}{1 + \dfrac{N_{0(238)}}{N_{0(235)}}} = \frac{582}{1 + \dfrac{95}{5}} = 29.1 \text{ barns}$$

This same result could also have been obtained by means of Eq. 4.24 directly by calculating the macroscopic cross section for the mixture first, and then dividing by the number of nuclei per cm^3.

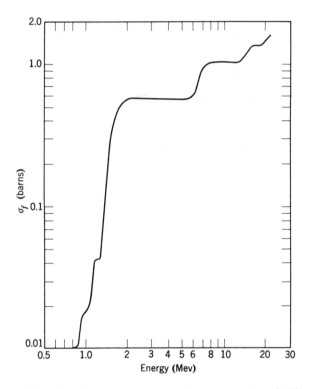

FIG. 4.13. High-energy neutron fission cross section of U^{238}.

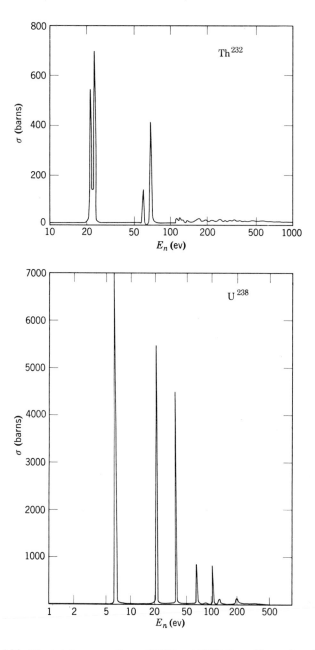

FIG. 4.14. The total cross sections of U^{238} and Th^{232} for epithermal neutrons.

PROBLEMS

(1) An indium foil of 2 cm^2 cross section and 10^{-3} cm thickness is exposed to a broad beam of neutrons of uniform energy. If the neutron flux is 5×10^9 neutrons/cm^2 sec and the microscopic absorption cross section for these neutrons is 190 barns, calculate the number of neutron captures that will occur during a 3 min exposure of the foil.

(2) Calculate the macroscopic scattering cross section of N^{14} at STP if the microscopic scattering cross section is 10 barns.

(3) Calculate the mean free path for scattering collisions in air at STP for thermal neutrons, assuming air to be composed of 79% of nitrogen and 21% of oxygen (by mass). Refer to the tables of constants in the Appendix for the necessary information.

(4) A nuclear reactor has an initial fuel inventory of 2500 grams of U^{235}. If the average thermal neutron flux in the reactor is 4×10^{12} neutrons/cm^2 sec, find how long it will take for 5 grams of U^{235} to be "burnt up." Consider also burn-up through radiative capture.

(5) Calculate the geometrical cross section of a uranium nucleus in barns and compare it with the neutron absorption cross sections for the two isotopes U^{235} and U^{238}.

(6) A gold foil (Au^{197}) of 1.5 cm^2 area and 300 mg/cm^2 areal density is irradiated with a neutron flux of 10^{12} neutrons/cm^2 sec for 1 hr. Subsequent measurements indicate that, in all, 49×10^{13} Au^{197} nuclei have been transmuted. Calculate the neutron absorption cross section of this nuclide.

(7) Calculate the neutron density for a neutron flux of 10^{14} neutrons/cm^2 sec. What would be the gas pressure of an ideal gas with the same density of gas molecules? (Assume a neutron energy of 0.025 ev).

(8) Prove that $\lambda = 1/\Sigma$ by carrying out the integration in Eq. 4.19.

(9) Prove Eq. 4.24 and derive an expression for $\bar{\sigma}$.

(10) A certain type of concrete used in reactor shielding consists of the following materials of given weight percentages (as well as a small amount of Mg, C, and Co): H—1%; O—53%; Si—34%; Al—3.5%; Fe—1.5%; Ca—4.4%; Na—1.6%; K—1.3%.
Look up the thermal absorption cross sections and calculate the macroscopic cross section of this material which has a density of 2.3 gram/cm^3.

(11) The thermal neutron mean free path in a certain material is 47.8 cm. Calculate the thickness of material required to reduce to one-tenth the intensity of a beam of thermal neutrons passing through it.

(12) Derive Eq. 4.37 from 4.35 by making use of the fact that Γ_n is proportional to the neutron velocity v, whereas Γ_γ is nearly independent of v for slow neutrons, and further show that the $1/v$ law follows from this if $\Gamma \gg E - E_0$.

(13) The elastic scattering cross section for slow neutrons is given by the Breit-Wigner formula with Γ_γ replaced by Γ_n. Show that this expression leads

to an elastic scattering cross section which is independent of the neutron energy. Make any reasonable assumption that may be necessary.

(14) Neglecting the scattering cross section and using the values for the thermal neutron cross sections for U^{235}, calculate Γ_γ/Γ and Γ_f/Γ.

(15) Natural silver, which consists of the isotopes Ag^{107} and Ag^{109} in roughly equal proportions, has pronounced resonances between 1 ev and 100 ev. The resonance at 16.60 ev (belonging to the Ag^{107} isotope) has a capture level width $\Gamma_\gamma = 0.170$ ev and a neutron scattering level width $\Gamma_n = 0.0048$ ev. Calculate the maximum absorption cross section for this resonance energy.

BIBLIOGRAPHY

Curtiss, L. F.: *Introduction to Neutron Physics*, van Nostrand, 1958.

Evans, R. D.: *The Atomic Nucleus*, McGraw-Hill, 1955.

Glasstone, S., and M. C. Edlund: *The Elements of Nuclear Reactor Theory*, van Nostrand, 1952.

Hughes, D. J.: *Pile Neutron Physics*, Addison-Wesley, 1955.

Hughes, D. J.: *Neutron Cross Sections*, Pergamon Press, 1957.

Kaplan, I.: *Nuclear Physics*, Addison-Wesley, 1955.

Lapp, R. E., and H. L. Andrews: *Nuclear Radiation Physics*, Prentice-Hall, 1954.

Segrè, E. (Ed.): *Experimental Nuclear Physics*, vol. II, part VII, Wiley, 1953.

Weinberg, A. M., and E. P. Wigner: *The Physical Theory of Neutron Chain Reactors*, University of Chicago Press, 1958.

U.S. Atomic Energy Commission: "Reactor Handbook," *Physics*, AECD-3645.

chapter 5

Nuclear Fission

5.1 Introduction

Although nuclear fission has been observed to occur with many of the heavy nuclides when they are bombarded with neutrons, protons, deuterons, α-particles, and even electrons and γ-rays, the only type of nuclear fission that, so far, has acquired practical importance is neutron fission of uranium and plutonium. Neutron fission is the topic of this chapter, where are summarized some of the fundamental aspects of nuclear fission as they have emerged from a large amount of experimental research by scientists of many nations.

The chapter concludes with an abbreviated exposition of a possible fission mechanism in terms of the liquid drop model of the nucleus.

5.2. Fissionable Materials

The primary feature that has made nuclear fission such an outstanding reaction is the production of more than one neutron per fission on the average when a neutron interacts with certain heavy nuclei, and this net gain in free neutrons makes a nuclear chain reaction possible.

The only naturally occurring nuclide that can be fissioned with thermal neutrons is U^{235}, which constitutes 0.71% of naturally occurring uranium. The only other nuclides that can undergo fission with thermal neutrons are U^{233} and Pu^{239}. These do not occur naturally but can be produced by allowing neutrons to interact with Th^{232} (which is even more abundant in the earth's crust than uranium) and with U^{238}, respectively. Because of their convertability into the nuclear fuels U^{233} and Pu^{239}, the two substances Th^{232} and U^{238} are called **fertile materials**. The nuclear reactions which convert these fertile materials into fissionable materials are called **breeding reactions**. They are neutron capture processes with subsequent β^--decay.

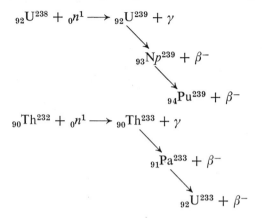

$$_{92}U^{238} + {}_0n^1 \longrightarrow {}_{92}U^{239} + \gamma$$
$$_{93}Np^{239} + \beta^-$$
$$_{94}Pu^{239} + \beta^-$$
$$_{90}Th^{232} + {}_0n^1 \longrightarrow {}_{90}Th^{233} + \gamma$$
$$_{91}Pa^{233} + \beta^-$$
$$_{92}U^{233} + \beta^-$$

In addition to U^{233}, U^{235}, and Pu^{239} which can undergo fission with both thermal and fast neutrons, there are a number of heavy nuclei which can be fissioned with fast neutrons only. The most important of these is U^{238} which has a fission threshold† of ~ 1 Mev. No such threshold requirements exist for the thermal neutron nuclear fuels, and it is of interest to note that they are all odd mass number fuels (with an even number of protons and an odd number of neutrons).

5.3   Yields and Mass Distribution of Fission Products

The fission process for U^{235} can be said to represent a type of nuclear reaction where the neutron and the U^{235} nucleus combine to form the intermediate or compound nucleus U^{236}, which then breaks into two nuclei P_1 and P_2 of intermediate mass numbers with the simultaneous emission of one to several neutrons. The number of emitted neutrons is indicated by ν_0 in the equation of the fission reaction.

$$_0n^1 + {}_{92}U^{235} \longrightarrow {}_{92}U^{236*} \longrightarrow P_1^{A_1} + P_2^{A_2} + \nu_0\, {}_0n^1$$

ν_0 is always an integral number. The probability of a particular value of ν_0 neutrons to be emitted in a thermal fission of a U^{235} nucleus (for different integral values of ν_0) is shown in Table 5.1.

The average number of neutrons emitted per fission which is universally denoted by ν is an important quantity in nuclear reactor physics. Its value

† This is not a sharp threshold in the usual sense, but an energy where the fission yield has fallen below measurable amounts (Fig. 4.13).

TABLE 5.1†

Number of Fission Neutrons Emitted	Number of Cases for Which This Number Occurs per 1000 Fissions
ν_0	n_{ν_0}
0	27
1	158
2	339
3	302
4	130
5	34

† Adapted from B. C. Diven et al., *Phys. Rev.* **101**, No. 3, 1012 (1956).

for U^{235} can be obtained from Table 5.1 by the standard relation for the average, $\nu = \Sigma(\nu_0 n_{\nu_0})/\Sigma n_{\nu_0}$. For U^{235} this is equal to 2.43. The most recent values of ν for different nuclear fuels are cited in Table 5.2 page 118.

Fission into more than two intermediate mass fragments is extremely rare. The fission fragments P_1 and P_2 can be almost any one of the nuclides in the center third of the periodic table. The abundance or frequency with which the various nuclides appear among the fission fragments varies, however, within very wide limits. This is shown by the fission yield curve for U^{235} (Fig. 5.1), where the fission yield percentage is plotted against the mass number of the fission fragment. Since two nuclear fragments are emitted per fission in practically all cases, we customarily set the total fission yield equal to 200%.

Altogether about 300 nuclides, both stable and radioactive, are known to occur after uranium fissioning, and about 180 different β^--emitters have been identified among the products that result from uranium fissioning.

The most outstanding feature of the yield curve is the twin peaks in the mass distribution, with a maximum yield shown for mass numbers near 95 and 140, and the comparative rarity of symmetric fission (i.e., two primary product nuclei of equal mass numbers). The mass ratio of 3/2 occurs in a little over 6% of all fissions, compared to 0.01% for symmetric fission. This asymmetry of fission, which is characteristic of thermal neutron fission, is also shown with U^{233} and with Pu^{239} and their yield curves are very similar to that for U^{235} (Fig. 5.1).

For fast neutrons symmetric fission becomes increasingly more probable with increasing neutron energy, and for high-energy neutrons only a single peak appears. Thus, symmetric fission is the most likely event for high-energy neutron fission. As can be seen from Fig. 5.1 the probability of

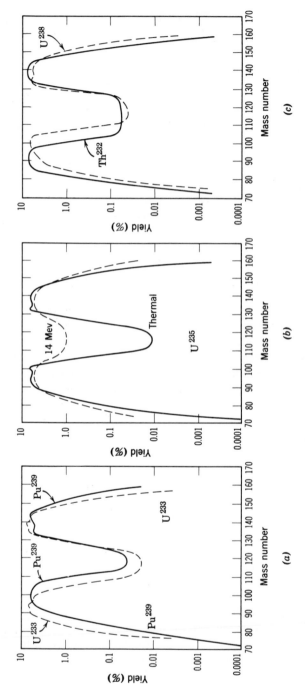

FIG. 5.1. Fission yields from U^{233}, U^{235}, U^{238}, and Pu^{239}. (a) Thermal neutron fission yields from U^{233}, Pu^{239}. (b) Fission yields from U^{235} with thermal neutrons and with 14 Mev neutrons. (c) Fast neutron fission yields from U^{238} and Th^{232}. (After S. Katcoff, "Fission Product Yields from U, Th, and Pu," *Nucleonics*, **16**, No. 4, 78 (1958)).

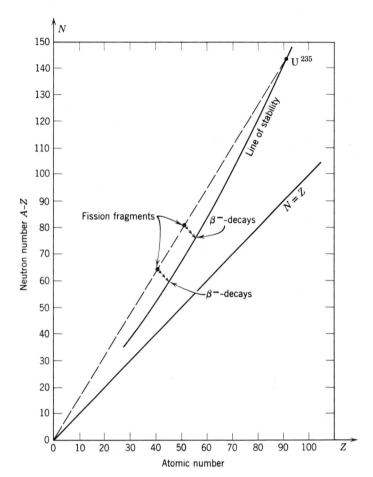

FIG. 5.2. Fission fragments with excessive neutron proton ratios move into the region of stability by series of successive β^--emissions.

symmetric fission for U^{235} with 14 Mev neutrons is greater than the probability of symmetric fission with thermal neutrons by a factor of 100.

A comparison of the U^{235} and Pu^{239} fission yield curves further shows that the distribution of the heavier products are practically the same, whereas the portions of the curves for the lighter fission fragment yields are displaced by four mass units with respect to each other.

All fission fragments are inherently unstable because of their excessive neutron/proton ratio. Thus, according to the general principles of nuclear stability which were described earlier, they should give rise to short radioactive series with emission of β^- and γ-radiation. This is in fact what happens. On the average, three β^--emissions are required for a fragment to regain a place in the region of nuclear stability. One can understand this more clearly by referring to the nuclear stability curve, a portion of which is shown in Fig. 5.2.

To simplify matters and without affecting the basic reasoning, we have assumed here that the fission products initially have the same neutron/proton ratio as the original prefission nucleus. We can then represent the unstable fission products as situated on the straight line between the origin and the point representing the U^{235} nucleus.

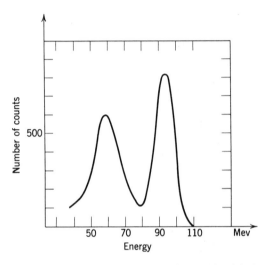

FIG. 5.3. Energy distribution of fission fragments from U^{235} with thermal neutrons.

5.4 Energy Distribution of Fission Fragments

If we can assume the nucleus which is being fissioned to have been initially at rest, and the mass of the neutrons to be negligible as compared to the masses of the other fission components, the two fission fragments P_1 and P_2 (assuming only two) must fly apart with numerically equal but opposite momenta

$$m_1 v_1 = m_2 v_2 \qquad (5.1)$$

and the ratio of their energies must be

$$\frac{E_1}{E_2} = \frac{\tfrac{1}{2} m_1 v_1^2}{\tfrac{1}{2} m_2 v_2^2}$$

$$= \frac{v_1}{v_2} = \frac{m_2}{m_1} \qquad \text{by Eq. 5.1} \qquad (5.2)$$

An experimental determination of the product energies leads, therefore, to information about the mass ratio of the fission fragments. As a result of such measurements on the fission fragment energies, clear evidence for the asymmetry of the fission process has been obtained, as is shown by Fig. 5.3 where the relative yield is indicated as a function of the fragment energy. Peaks are seen to occur for thermal neutron fission of U^{235} at energies of $\sim$60 Mev and $\sim$95 Mev, which agree closely with the ratio of $\sim$3/2 as obtained from Fig. 5.1.

5.5 Energy Release from Fission

We can get a good estimate of the average amount of energy released per fission by referring to the B.E. curve, part of which is reproduced in Fig. 5.4a.

We have seen that when a U^{235} nucleus breaks up during a fission process, the two resultant fragments will most likely lie in the neighborhood of $A = 95$ and $A = 140$. A close average value for the B.E. per nucleon in the region of $A = 95$ and $A = 140$ is seen to be 8.5 Mev as compared to the B.E. per nucleon for U^{235} of 7.6 Mev. The B.E. per nucleon differs, therefore, by 0.9 Mev between the U^{235} and the favored fission fragments region. The total B.E. difference for the 236 nucleons that participate in the fission reaction amounts therefore to $236 \times 0.9 = 210$ Mev.

A similar estimate is also obtained if we compare the isotopic masses of the interacting neutron and the U^{235} nucleus with those of the resultant fission products.

Let us assume, for example, that the compound nucleus U^{236*} splits into two neutrons and Mo^{98} and Xe^{136} as end products of this fission chain.

$$_{40}Zr^{98} \longrightarrow {_{41}}Cb^{98} \longrightarrow {_{42}}Mo^{98}$$

$$_{0}n^1 + {_{92}}U^{235} \longrightarrow {_{92}}U^{236*} \Big\langle$$

$$_{52}Te^{136} \longrightarrow {_{53}}I^{136} \longrightarrow {_{54}}Xe^{136} + {_{0}}n^1 + {_{0}}n^1$$

The combined isotopic masses before and after fission are:

$$U^{235} = 235.124 \text{ amu} \qquad Mo^{98} = 97.936 \text{ amu}$$
$$n^1 = 1.009 \text{ amu} \qquad Xe^{136} = 135.951 \text{ amu}$$
$$\overline{\Sigma m_i = 236.133 \text{ amu}} \qquad 2n^1 = 2.018 \text{ amu}$$
$$\overline{\Sigma m_f = 235.905 \text{ amu}}$$

Therefore $\Sigma m_i - \Sigma m_f = 0.228$ amu $= 210$ Mev

To this should be added the energy represented by the several β^--emissions which raises the last figure by a few Mev to $\sim$215 Mev. This estimate agrees very well with that obtained from the B.E. curve. A convenient value to use in numerical calculations is 200 Mev per fission which is closer to the experimentally determined value.

The total amount of energy released by the fissioning of a U^{235} nucleus is distributed over the fission products roughly as follows:

Kinetic energy of fission fragments	168 Mev
Kinetic energy of fission neutrons	5 Mev
Energy associated with β^--decays	16 Mev
Energy emitted as γ-rays	10 Mev
Total energy per fission	199 Mev

Figure 5.4b shows the relation between the B.E. of a U^{238} nucleus and the B.E. of two primary fission fragments and the amount of energy released during the fission process.

Example 5.1. Calculate the fission rate for U^{235} required to produce 1 watt and the amount of energy that is released in the complete fissioning of 1 kg of U^{235}.

$$\text{The required fission rate} = \frac{1 \text{ watt}}{200 \text{ mev/fission}}$$

$$= \frac{10^7 \text{ erg/sec}}{200 \times 1.6 \times 10^{-6} \text{ erg/fission}}$$

$$= 3.1 \times 10^{10} \text{ fission/sec}$$

The number of nuclei per kilogram is

$$\frac{1000 \text{ grams}}{235 \text{ grams}} \times 6.03 \times 10^{23}$$

On fissioning this number of nuclei, the energy release will be

$$= \frac{1000}{235} \times 6.03 \times 10^{23} \times 200 \text{ Mev}$$

$$= 5.13 \times 10^{26} \text{ Mev}$$

$$= 5.13 \times 10^{26} \times 1.6 \times 10^{-6} \text{ erg}$$

$$= 8.2 \times 10^{13} \text{ joules} \doteq 2 \times 10^{10} \text{ kcal}$$

If this amount of U^{235} were fissioned per year, it would be equal to a power output of 8.2 $\times$ 10^{13} joules/3.15 $\times$ 10^7 sec = 2.6 megawatts.

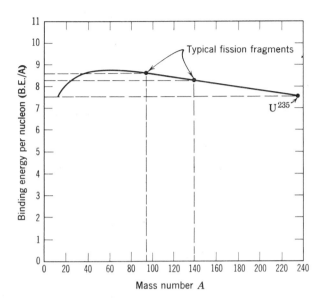

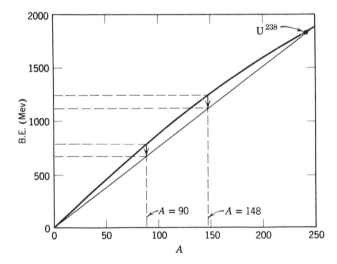

FIG. 5.4. (*a*) The amount of energy released upon the fissioning of a U^{235} nucleus can be obtained from the B.E./A-curve by comparing the B.E. of the fission fragments with that of U^{235}. (*b*) Total Binding Energy shown as a function of A. The amount of energy released in the fissioning of a U^{238} nucleus into a nucleus of mass number 148 and one of mass number 90 is indicated by the vertical separation between the straight line and the curved line in the diagram.

5.6   Neutron Yield and Neutron Production Ratio

An accurate knowledge of the average number of neutrons emitted per fission, v, is of great importance to the nuclear engineer or scientist and the most recent published values of this constant are cited in Table 5.2.

We must be careful to distinguish between the **number of neutrons released per fission**, v, and the **number of fission neutrons released per absorption**, η.† Since not all thermal neutrons that are absorbed cause a nuclear fission, η is smaller than v, in the same ratio as is the fission cross section σ_f to the absorption cross section σ_a. Hence

$$\eta = v \frac{\sigma_f}{\sigma_a} = v \frac{\sigma_f}{\sigma_f + \sigma_c} = \frac{v}{1 + \alpha} \tag{5.3}$$

where $\alpha = \sigma_c / \sigma_f$.

The values of η for thermal neutrons are listed in Table 5.2.

TABLE 5.2‡

	v	η	v/η
U^{233}	2.50	$v \times (523/580) = 2.29$	1.099
U^{235}	2.43	$v \times (582/683) = 2.07$	1.179
U (natural)	2.47	$v \times (4.18/7.68) = 1.34$	1.85
Pu^{239}	2.89	$v \times (742/1028) = 2.08$	1.38

‡ D. J. Hughes and R. B. Schwartz, BNL-325, *Neutron Cross Sections*, 2nd ed., supplement 1.

5.7   Prompt and Delayed Neutrons

Except for a very small fraction, all fission neutrons are emitted virtually instantaneously; the time delay, if any, certainly being less than 10^{-12} sec. These neutrons are called **prompt neutrons**. In terms of the compound nucleus picture, they are neutrons which are "boiled off" from the highly excited compound nucleus. In the case of U^{235} about 0.64% of all fission neutrons are, however, emitted with a time lag of several seconds to more than a minute after the fission. These are called **delayed neutrons**. They arise from the radioactive decay of a fission product nucleus. When the excitation energy of the daughter nucleus after a β^--emission is greater than the neutron separation energy S_n, the subsequent de-excitation occurs in the form of a neutron emission with a half-life practically identical with that of the preceding β^--decay. This process is shown schematically in Fig. 5.5.

Six distinct groups of delayed neutrons have been identified, each group with its own characteristic half-life and decay rate. They all obey the

† Some authors call η the **regeneration factor**.

exponential law of radioactive decay and are very important because of the decisive part they play in the control of nuclear reactors. Although they are only a minute fraction of the total neutron yield, yet their influence on the time dependent behavior of thermal reactors is pronounced so that they furnish a ready means of control which is discussed in more detail when that topic is covered in a later chapter. To avoid confusion, it should

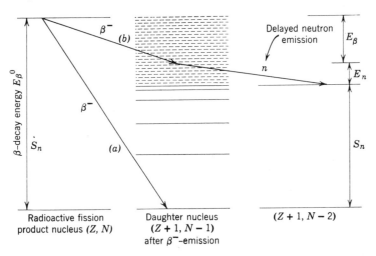

FIG. 5.5. Delayed neutron emission scheme. Two possible β^--decays are indicated: (a) If the energy of the emitted β^--particle is equal to the maximum possible β^--energy E_β^0, the daughter nucleus is left in its ground state. (b) If the β^--particle is emitted with energy E_β less than $E_\beta^0 - S_n$ the daughter nucleus is left in an excited state with excitation energy $E = E_\beta^0 - E_\beta$ which is greater than S_n. It then emits a neutron of energy E_n where $E_n = E - S_n = E_\beta^0 - E_\beta - S_n$ and transforms into the nucleus $(Z + 1, N - 2)$.

perhaps be pointed out that the decay rate and half-life associated with each group of delayed neutrons refers to properties of parent nuclei that undergo radioactive decay in the course of which the delayed neutrons are emitted and not to the half-lives of the neutrons themselves.

5.8   Energy Distribution of Fission Neutrons

The energy distribution for the neutrons resulting from the fission of U^{235} can be represented analytically (to within $\sim 15\%$) by the expression

$$n(E)\,dE = \text{constant} \times \exp(-E) \sinh(2E)^{1/2}\,dE \qquad (5.4)$$

where $n(E)\,dE$ is the number of neutrons emitted with energies lying between E and $E + dE$.

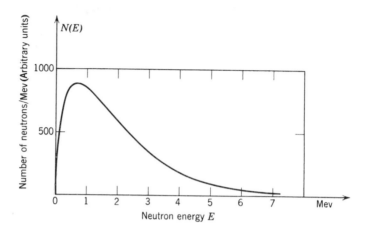

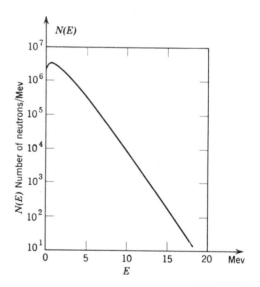

FIG. 5.6. (*a*) Energy distribution of neutrons from U²³⁵ fission. (*b*) Energy distribution of neutrons from U²³⁵ fission with $N(E)$ plotted on a logarithmic scale to show the relative minor contribution of the high-energy neutrons to the fission spectrum.

Expression 5.4 is in agreement with observation for fission energies up to ~17 Mev. The average energy of this distribution is 2 Mev and the most probable energy is ~0.75 Mev. It is shown in Fig. 5.6.

Alternative empirical expressions that have been proposed to represent the fission neutron spectrum are

$$n(E) \, dE = 0.775E^{\frac{1}{2}} \exp(-0.775E) \, dE† \tag{5.4a}$$

and

$$n(E) \, dE = 0.453 \exp\left(\frac{-E}{0.965}\right) \sinh(2.29E)^{\frac{1}{2}} \, dE‡ \tag{5.4b}$$

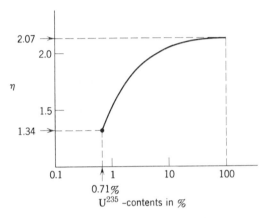

FIG. 5.7. Increase of η with U^{235} enrichment in uranium. The most rapid increase in the value of η is seen to occur for an enrichment of a few per cent. Enrichment above ~10% yields only a relatively slight gain in η.

Example 5.2. Calculate the average number of fission neutrons per neutron absorbed in a uranium mixture which contains the U^{235} and U^{238} isotopes in a 1:10 ratio.

We use Eq. 5.3 where the cross sections are now those for the mixture which have to be evaluated first.

$$\sigma_a = \frac{N_0(235)\sigma_a(235) + N_0(238)\sigma_a(238)}{N_0(235) + N_0(238)}$$

$$= \frac{\sigma_a(235) + \dfrac{N_0(238)}{N_0(235)}\sigma_a(238)}{1 + \dfrac{N_0(238)}{N_0(235)}}$$

$$= \frac{683 + 10 \times 2.73}{1 + 10} = 64.6 \text{ barns}$$

† R. B. Leachman, Geneva Conf. Rep., 1955, vol. 2, 193.
‡ L. Cranberg et al., *Phys. Rev.*, **103**, No. 3, 662, 1956.

Similarly,

$$\sigma_f = \frac{\sigma_f(235)}{1 + \dfrac{N_0(238)}{N_0(235)}} = \frac{582}{11} = 53 \text{ barns}$$

Hence,

$$\eta = 2.43 \times \frac{53}{64.6} = 2.0$$

This result shows that by enriching the natural uranium, i.e., increasing the U^{235} content above its natural abundance of 0.71%, a considerable gain in the value of η can be achieved, (Fig. 5.7.)

5.9 Nuclear Fission and the Liquid Drop Model

A reasonably clear picture of the fission mechanism can be gained by means of the liquid drop model of the nucleus. This model is capable of explaining some of the chief features of nuclear fission and it is in fair agreement with a number of experimental results.

According to this theory, when the nucleus is in equilibrium it assumes a spherical shape, which corresponds to its most stable configuration. As long as the nucleus is left undisturbed, it remains in this state and shape under the joint action of (1) the cohesive short-range nuclear forces which act throughout the nuclear volume and along the surface of the nucleus, and (2) the electrostatic forces of repulsion between the protons of the nucleus which tend to push them apart and to disrupt the nucleus.

It is interesting on the basis of this model to calculate the energy E_f which is released by a nucleus of mass number A and atomic number Z when, upon fission, it divides into two lighter nuclei. Let us assume symmetrical fission in order to simplify the numerical work, and as the energy released will differ only slightly for other less convenient ratios, the result will not be affected significantly by this convenient assumption. According to Eq. 2.41 E_f, which is the Q-value for the fission reaction, is given by

$$E_f = B_A - 2B_{A/2} \tag{5.5}$$

An expression for the B.E. was derived in Chapter 2 in the form of 2.42 which, for fissionable† (odd-even) nuclei, simplifies to

$$B_A = aA - bA^{\frac{2}{3}} - c\frac{Z^2}{A^{\frac{1}{3}}} - d\frac{(N-Z)^2}{A} \tag{5.6}$$

    (volume   (surface   (Coulomb   (symmetry
    energy)   energy)   energy)   energy)

† From now on we shall use the term "fissionable" to describe nuclei that can be fissioned by thermal neutrons (e.g., U^{235}) and "nonfissionable" those that cannot (e.g., U^{238}).

Substitution of Eq. 5.6 in 5.5 leads to the result

$$E_f = b\left[A^{\frac{2}{3}} - 2\left(\frac{A}{2}\right)^{\frac{2}{3}}\right] + c\left[\frac{Z^2}{A^{\frac{1}{3}}} - 2\frac{(Z/2)^2}{(A/2)^{\frac{1}{3}}}\right]$$

$$= -3.42A^{\frac{2}{3}} + 0.22\frac{Z^2}{A^{\frac{1}{3}}} \tag{5.7}$$

if one uses the numerical values for $b = 13.0$ and $c = 0.585$, where E_f is now given in Mev.

It is clear from the disappearance of the volume energy part from Eq. 5.7 that this has not changed as a result of the splitting process as the difference is zero. A similar conclusion holds for the symmetry term of the B.E. The only surviving portions are the change in the surface energy and that in the Coulomb energy which appear with opposite signs. This shows that the splitting of a nucleus affects these two contributions in opposing ways so that the change in the surface energy and that in the Coulomb energy tend to cancel one another partially. This is reasonable and to be expected, since the division of the nucleus increases the separation between proton groups, thus reducing their Coulomb potential energy, while, at the same time, it increases the total nuclear surface which must cause an increase in the surface energy.

Thus, the contribution to E_f made by the Coulomb part of the B.E. is positive, or exoergic, since it is made at the expense of a reduced Coulomb potential for the two fragments which are now at a greater mutual separation than before the fission, whereas the surface energy term contribution is negative, or endoergic, because the potential surface energy has increased by the division of one nuclear drop into two.

Since spontaneous fission is energetically possible only if $E_f \geqslant 0$, it follows from Eq. 5.7 that this condition is fulfilled if

$$-3.42A^{\frac{2}{3}} + 0.22\frac{Z^2}{A^{\frac{1}{3}}} \geqslant 0$$

or

$$\frac{Z^2}{A} \geqslant 15 \tag{5.8}$$

This condition is satisfied for nuclides with mass numbers greater than ~85.†

---

† The spontaneous fission of certain heavy nuclei has been found to offer a possible explanation for the energies produced in the outbursts of supernovae. (A. G. W. Cameron, "Nuclear Astrophysics," *Ann. Rev. Nucl. Sci.*, **8**, 1958.)

Example 5.3. Calculate the contributions of the surface and Coulomb energies, respectively, to the energy release when a U^{236*} compound nucleus undergoes symmetric fission.

By Eq. 5.7

$$E_f = 236^{2/3}\left(-3.42 + 0.22\frac{92^2}{236}\right)$$

$$= -130 + 300 = 170 \text{ Mev}$$

This result agrees well with the measured kinetic energy of the fission fragments. The explanation for the discrepancy between this amount of energy release and the accepted value of 200 Mev per fission is to be found in the fact that the fission fragments assumed in this example are not stable nuclei in their ground state but, because of their neutron excess, must be in an excited energy state. This excitation energy is released with the ejection of the two or three neutrons and the several β^--transformations that accompany the process of stabilization of the fission fragments as well as some γ-ray energy.

5.10   Spontaneous Fission and Potential Barrier

A comparison between the energy of the initial spherical drop and the final spherical drop fragments led to the criterion of stability 5.8. The obvious question now arises that if the spontaneous breakup of nuclei above $A \doteq 85$ is energetically possible, why does it not always take place? The answer to this can be given by referring to the now familiar "Coulomb barrier." The existence of this barrier prevents the immediate breaking apart of these nuclei, in complete analogy to the function of a similar Coulomb barrier with respect to the emission of α-particles which was treated in an earlier chapter.

If we denote the height of the Coulomb barrier by E_b, we can say that the nucleus will certainly be unstable and break apart immediately upon its formation if $E_f > E_b$; so that no nuclei will be able to survive for any length of time if this condition is fulfilled (Fig. 5.8).

To get an approximate idea of the value of E_b for symmetric fission—for which E_f was previously calculated—we shall for the moment assume that the barrier height corresponds to the Coulomb potential between the two symmetric fragments when they are just in contact with each other (Fig. 5.9d). This is only approximately true as will become apparent in the course of a somewhat more refined examination of this process later, but it is sufficient for our present purpose. We have, therefore,

$$E_b = \frac{(Z/2)^2 e^2}{2R} = \frac{Z^2 e^2}{8r_0(A/2)^{1/3}}$$

$$= 0.15\frac{Z^2}{A^{1/3}} \text{ Mev} \qquad (5.9)$$

Combining 5.9 with 5.7, the condition for stability becomes

$$E_b - E_f = 0.15\frac{Z^2}{A^{1/3}} + 3.42A^{2/3} - 0.22\frac{Z^2}{A^{1/3}} \geqslant 0$$

or

$$\frac{Z^2}{A} \leqslant 49 \qquad\qquad (5.10)$$

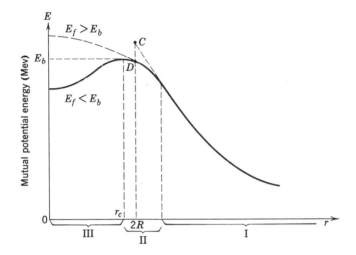

FIG. 5.8. The potential energy of two symmetric fission fragments is plotted as function of the separation of their centers.

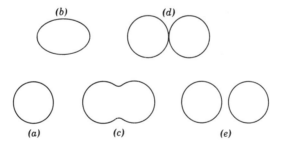

FIG. 5.9. Schematic picture of a fission process.

We can conclude from this that nuclei for which this parametric condition of stability is not fulfilled cannot exist because immediately after their formation the slightest disturbance would be sufficient to trigger the disruption of the nucleus.

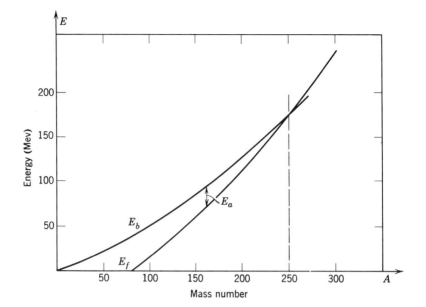

FIG. 5.10. E_f and E_b shown as functions of the mass number A.

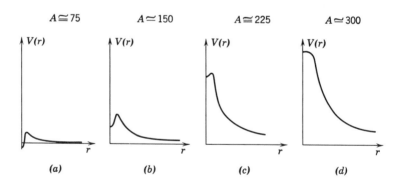

FIG. 5.11. Nuclear potential energy as a function of the separation between two hypothetical fission fragments during a fission process for nuclei of atomic mass numbers. (a) $A \simeq 75$, (b) $A \simeq 150$ (c) $A \simeq 225$, (d) $A \simeq 300$.

(a) Spontaneous fission is energetically impossible.

(b) Spontaneous fission is energetically possible but highly improbable.

(c) Spontaneous fission is energetically possible with measurable probability.

(d) Spontaneous fission is energetically possible and will occur immediately upon hypothetical formation of such a nucleus since no potential barrier exists to prevent it or to delay it.

Nuclei for which E_b exceeds E_f by a few Mev will be stable against spontaneous fission (Fig. 5.8), although there is always the possibility of a disruption occurring through an effect described as "tunneling," as in the case with α-particles. The rate of fissioning for such nuclei will be very small, as for instance with U^{238} which has a half-life for spontaneous fissioning of about 3×10^{23} sec. As we saw with α-decay and so also with fissioning, the half-life of a nucleus with respect to a spontaneous decay depends on the general shape of the Coulomb barrier, its height and width, as well as on the mass of the escaping particle. All these factors will influence the rate of spontaneous fission, which in turn determines whether or not the process is observable for a particular nuclide.

In Fig. 5.10 the relationship between E_f and E_b and their general behavior is shown as a function of the mass number A. E_f and E_b have been computed for symmetric fission and the graph shows that for $A \simeq 250$, E_b becomes equal to E_f, so that we do not expect nuclei with $A > 250$ to be found in nature. The graph also shows that fission begins to become exoergic, i.e., $E_f > 0$, in the neighborhood of $A \simeq 85$, in agreement with the result expressed by 5.8. The fission possibilities for four different atomic mass numbers are illustrated in Fig. 5.11.

Example 5.4. U^{235} has a half-life of $\sim 3 \times 10^{17}$ years for spontaneous fission. Estimate the rate of spontaneous fissioning for 1 gram of U^{235}.

$$\frac{dN}{dt} = \lambda N = \frac{\log 2}{T_{1/2}} N$$

with
$$N = \frac{6.03 \times 10^{23}}{235}$$

Therefore
$$\frac{dN}{dt} = \frac{0.693 \times (6.03 \times 10^{23}/235)}{3 \times 10^{17} \text{ years} \times 3.15 \times 10^7 \text{ sec/year}}$$

$$= 2 \times 10^{-4} \text{ sec}^{-1}$$
$$= 0.7 \text{ hour}^{-1}$$

The spontaneous fission rate of U^{235} is somewhat less than one fission per hour per gram.

5.11 Deformation of the Liquid Drop

A more reliable estimate for the critical value of Z^2/A can be obtained by investigating the possible distortions and oscillations of a liquid drop type nuclear model. Such a nuclear drop can be disrupted by causing it to vibrate with a large enough amplitude. The energy required to initiate these vibrations is supplied by the absorbed neutron.

The introduction of excitation energy into the nuclear system profoundly disturbs the equilibrium of the nucleus which prevailed for as long as the nucleus retained its spherical shape. Once the spherical shape of the nucleus becomes sufficiently distorted by oscillations set up in the drop by the incoming neutron, the equilibrium that existed in the undisturbed nucleus will have been irrevocably destroyed because a considerable deviation from the original spherical shape causes a redistribution of the electric charges which persist in their tendency to move apart as far as possible; thus the nucleus is eventually split in two. At first, for small distortions of the nuclear drop, the surface energy increase is more rapid than the electrostatic energy decrease, so that the drop tends to return to its status *quo ante*. But once a critical point of distortion has been passed, this relationship is reversed for increasing distortion. The total energy of the nucleus will then continue to decrease with increasing deformation, and this will finally lead to an irreversible breakup of the nuclear drop.

When the distortion produced is not pronounced enough to get the nucleus beyond the critical point and thus lead to fissioning, the nucleus can return to the spherical shape and re-emit the excitation energy in the form of a γ-ray. When this happens, we have a radiative capture process which, as we know from the respective cross sections, occurs in about 15% of all neutron captures by U^{235}.

We can visualize this nuclear behavior more clearly and also fill in some pertinent details by plotting the mutual potential energy of the two symmetrical fission fragments against the separation of their centers (Figs. 5.8 and 5.9).

In region I the fragments are completely separated and their mutual potential energy E is simply the Coulomb energy E_c. When $r = 2R$, R being the radius of each spherical fragment, the two fragments just touch one another and E at that point, (point D on the curve), is less than the corresponding Coulomb potential by an amount DC, which is equal to the potential of the surface forces which are just beginning to come into play at this point.

As we pass through region II we reach the critical distance r_c, where the potential curve has a maximum value E_b. This hump represents the barrier against spontaneous splitting, and the magnitude of this potential energy barrier as seen from the inside of the nucleus is given by the energy difference $E_b - E_f$. The presence of this barrier is the reason why fission does not take place spontaneously in all cases where $E_f > 0$ and when it would be energetically possible. An additional amount of energy $E_a = E_b - E_f$, the **activation energy**, is required by the nuclear system before the potential barrier can be surmounted and fission can take place.

In region III, the fragments have coalesced and the short-range nuclear forces have become predominant.

In Fig. 5.9 are shown the approximate deformations of the liquid drop that correspond to the different regions of the potential curve of Fig. 5.8: (*a*) corresponds to the undisturbed spherical drop and to point 0 on the potential graph with a nuclear potential energy E_f. (*b*) corresponds to the region $0 < r < r_c$, where small deformations are reversible and do not lead to a fissioning of the nuclear drop. (*c*) corresponds to the critical deformation. (*d*) corresponds to a stage where fission has already occurred with the fragments just separating. (*e*) complete separation has taken place.

Bohr and Wheeler have made detailed calculations about the behavior of a nuclear drop under small deformations. They found that for a small deformation the net change in the potential energy ΔE was given by an expression proportional to

$$1 - 0.022 \frac{Z^2}{A} \tag{5.11}$$

As long as ΔE was positive the nucleus would return to its equilibrium position and spherical shape upon removal of the cause of the distortion (region III). For $\Delta E < 0$, the nucleus will not return to its original shape since to do so would mean to increase its potential energy; thus such a nucleus is not stable and will break apart.

Using this criterion and setting $\Delta E = 0$, we can determine a nucleus (A, Z) which would just be unstable with respect to any small deformation. Thus

$$1 - 0.022 \frac{Z^2}{A} = 0 \tag{5.12}$$

or

$$\frac{Z^2}{A} = 45 \tag{5.13}$$

as compared to our previous cruder estimate of 49.

For the heaviest natural element, uranium, $Z^2/A = 36$, which is well below the limiting value 45, so that all naturally occurring nuclides are stable with respect to small deformations.

For deformations that exceed the critical limit the total energy declines and the nucleus continues to break apart. The critical energy that will cause such a breakup, the **activation energy**, E_a, can be calculated on the basis of the Bohr-Wheeler theory, and it is given by the expression,

$$E_a = E_b - E_f$$
$$= A^{2/3} \times 0.89 \left(1 - 0.022 \frac{Z^2}{A}\right) \tag{5.14}$$

If this is compared with the excitation energy E_e provided by a thermal neutron when it is absorbed by a particular nucleus, it becomes possible to predict whether that nucleus is fissionable with thermal neutrons or not. The excitation energy E_e that is contributed to the resultant compound nucleus by the capture of a neutron is equal to the B.E. of the neutron in the compound nucleus and can be calculated by the B.E. relation 2.41.

$$E_e = B_{(A,Z)} - B_{(A+1,Z)} \qquad (5.15)$$

The values of E_e and E_a are tabulated in Table 5.3 for some nuclei.

TABLE 5.3

(From CRP-642-A, 1956)

Compound Nucleus	Excitation Energy, E_e(Mev)	Activation Energy, E_a(Mev)	$E_e - E_a$ (Mev)
U^{234}	6.6	4.6	2.0
U^{236}	6.6	5.5	1.1
U^{239}	5.9	6.5	−0.6
Th^{233}	5.1	6.5	−1.4
Pa^{232}	5.4	5.0	0.4
Np^{238}	5.0	4.2	0.8
Pu^{240}	6.4	4.0	2.4

This shows that for U^{235}, thermal neutrons provide an excitation energy that is greater than the activation energy and can, therefore, produce fission. In the case of U^{238}, however, the added excitation energy is 0.6 Mev below the required activation energy so that no fission is possible with thermal neutrons. If the neutrons have a kinetic energy of ~ 0.6 Mev fission becomes possible, since this energy is added to the excitation energy contributed by the neutron to the U^{238} nucleus. Fast fission should, therefore, be possible with U^{238} on the basis of this theory. The experimental threshold energy for fast fission of U^{238} is 1.1 Mev, as compared to the predicted value of 0.6 Mev.

The reason for the difference in the excitation energy for U^{236} and U^{239} lies in the "pairing term" which appears in the B.E. relation 2.42 and which takes into account the empirical fact that even-even nuclei are more stable than even-odd nuclei.

The liquid drop model has been applied successfully to a number of problems connected with nuclear fission and has been able to explain some of the main features of this process. Among its shortcomings is its failure to explain the observed nonsymmetry of the masses of the fission fragments. This fact does not agree with the prediction of this theory, according to which symmetric fission should be the most favored division, although some progress has lately been made in this respect.

Example 5.5. By means of the B.E. equation compare the excitation energies for U^{236*} and U^{239*} and calculate their difference. For U^{236}

$$E_e = (B.E.)_{236} - (B.E.)_{235}$$

$$= a(236 - 235) - b[236^{2/3} - 235^{2/3}]$$

$$- c\left[\frac{92^2}{236^{1/3}} - \frac{92^2}{235^{1/3}}\right] - d\left[\frac{52^2}{236} - \frac{51^2}{235}\right]$$

$$+ e\left[\frac{1}{236^{3/4}} - 0\right]$$

$$= a - b \times 0.1 + c \times 2.2 - d \times 0.4 + \frac{e}{60.2}$$

$$= 6.8 \ Mev$$

For U^{239}:

$$E_e = (B.E.)_{239} - (B.E.)_{238}$$

$$= a(239 - 238) - b[239^{2/3} - 238^{2/3}]$$

$$- c\left[\frac{92^2}{239^{1/3}} - \frac{92^2}{238^{1/3}}\right] - d\left[\frac{55^2}{239} - \frac{54^2}{238}\right]$$

$$+ e\left[0 - \frac{1}{238^{3/4}}\right]$$

$$= a - b \times 0.1 + c \times 2.19 - d \times 0.39 - \frac{e}{60.4}$$

$$= 5.9 \ Mev$$

We notice that the a, b, c, and d terms in the excitation energies differ only slightly for the two nuclei. However, the e term (which is the "pairing energy" term) appears with opposite signs in the two results. We can, therefore, conclude that the excitation energy difference is chiefly attributable to this property, which means that the excitation energy for the even-mass-number nucleus is greater than that for the odd-mass-number nucleus by about twice the pairing energy. Since the pairing energy term here is about 0.55 Mev, the excitation energy difference would be about 1.1 Mev. This conclusion agrees reasonably well with our numerical result for the two nuclei U^{236} and U^{239}.

PROBLEMS

(1) The ratio of capture cross section to fission cross section, σ_c/σ_f, is commonly denoted by the letter α. Using the data in Table 5.2 calculate α for U^{235}, U^{233}, U_{nat}, and Pu^{239}.

(2) Calculate the **regeneration factor** η for 93% enriched uranium.

(3) The fuel in a certain reactor consists of enriched uranium containing 2400 grams of U^{235}. If the fuel occupies a volume of 0.28 cubic meter and the

reactor is run at a steady power level of 1000 kw calculate (a) the power density, i.e., the power per unit volume, and (b) the specific power, i.e., the power per unit mass of U^{235}.

(4) About 7% of the total heat generated in nuclear fission is produced by the radioactive decay of the fission products. When a reactor is shut down, heat will continue to be produced by this fission product decay. According to Way and Wigner, the power output after reactor shut down can be estimated by means of the expression $5.9 \times 10^{-3}P_0[t^{-0.2} - (T_0 + t)^{-0.2}]$, where P_0 is the operating power of the reactor (in watts) before shutdown, T_0 the duration of steady power operation before shutdown (in hours), and t, the time (in hours) since shutdown.

By means of the Way-Wigner expression, calculate the power output 10 days after shutdown of a reactor that has been operating for 250 days before shutdown at a steady power level of 200 megawatts.

(5) How much U^{235} is consumed by a reactor during one year's operation at a constant power output of 1000 kw?

(6) What is the power output of a reactor which burns up 5 grams of U^{235} per day?

(7) Find the most probable energy for the fission neutron energy distribution 5.4 and calculate the average energy for this distribution.

(8) Calculate the energy released in the fissioning of Pu^{239} by thermal neutrons, assuming that the fission fragments are Mo^{96}, Ce^{142}, and two neutrons. (Isotopic masses: Mo^{96}—95.9355, Ce^{142}—141.9537.)

(9) Calculate the activation energy for Pu^{240} and for Pu^{241}.

(10) Estimate the amount of energy released if a U^{235} nucleus were fissioned into three fragments of mass number $A = 78$ and two neutrons, assuming a thermal neutron to initiate the reaction.

(11) Find an expression for the energy released when a nucleus is split into two fragments of mass ratio 3 : 2, and evaluate this energy for the U^{236} compound nucleus.

By neglecting the "symmetry" and "pairing" terms obtain the condition for spontaneous fission for this ratio and compare it with the condition for symmetric fission.

BIBLIOGRAPHY

Binford, F. T.: "How to Integrate the U^{235} Fission Neutron Spectrum, *Nucleonics*, **15**, No. 2 (February 1957).

Bradley, J. E. S.: *Physics of Nuclear Fission*, Pergamon Press, 1958.

Cranberg, L. et al.: "Fission Neutron Spectrum of U^{235}," *Phys. Rev.*, **103**, 662, 1956.

Diven, B. C. et al.: "Capture to Fission Ratios for Fast Neutrons in U^{235}," *Phys. Rev.*, **109**, 144 (1958).

Evans, R. D.: *The Atomic Nucleus*, McGraw-Hill, 1955.

Geneva Conference on the Peaceful Uses of Atomic Energy—1955:

    P/592—Leachman, R. B.: "Determination of Fission Quantities of Importance to Reactors," vol. 2, 193.

    P/593—Wheeler, J. A.: "Fission Physics and Nuclear Theory," vol. 2, 155.

    P/836—Huizenga, J. R.: "The Nuclear Fission Process," vol. 2, 208.

Glasstone, S., and M. C. Edlund: *The Elements of Nuclear Reactor Theory*, van Nostrand, 1952.

Halliday, D.: *Introductory Nuclear Physics*, Wiley, 1955.

Hill, D. L., and J. A. Wheeler: "Nuclear Constitution and the Interpretation of Fission Phenomena, *Phys. Rev.*, **89,** 1102 (1953).

Huizenga, J. R.: "Spontaneous Fission Systematics," *Phys. Rev.*, **94,** 158 (1954).

Kaplan, I.: *Nuclear Physics*, Addison-Wesley, 1955.

Katcoff, S.: "Fission Product Yields from U, Th, and Pu," *Nucleonics*, **16,** No. 4 (April 1958).

Leachman, R. B.: "Velocities of Fragments from Fission of U^{233}, U^{235} and Pu^{239}," *Phys. Rev.*, **87,** 444 (1952).

Meem, J. L.: "Energy Released per Fission in the BSR," *Nucleonics*, **12,** No. 5 (May 1954).

Murray, R. L. et al.: "Fission Spectrum Formula in Reactor Calculations," *Nucleonics*, **12,** No. 9 (September 1954).

Pollard, E. C., and W. L. Davidson: *Applied Nuclear Physics*, Wiley, 1951.

Present, R. D.: "The Liquid Drop Model for Nuclear Fission," *Nucleonics*, **3,** No. 3 (March 1945).

Seaborg, G. T.: "Activation Energy for Fission," *Phys. Rev.*, **88,** 1429 (1952).

Segrè, E. (ed.): *Experimental Nuclear Physics*, vol. II, Wiley, 1953.

Wahl, J. S.: "Energy Distributions of Fragments from Fission of U^{235}, U^{238} and Pu^{239} by Fast Neutrons," *Phys. Rev.*, **95,** 126 (1954).

Watt, B. E.: "Spectrum of Neutrons from Fissions Induced by Thermal Neutrons," AECD-3073 (1951); *Phys. Rev.*, **87,** 1037 (1952).

Weinberg, A. M., and E. P. Wigner: *The Physical Theory of Neutron Chain Reactors*, University of Chicago Press, 1958.

Whitehouse, W. J.: "Nuclear Fission," *Prog. Nucl. Phys.*, vol. 2 (1952).

chapter 6

Thermal Neutrons

6.1 Introduction

The nuclear reactor is the most copious source of supply of **thermal neutrons**, which are neutrons that are in thermal equilibrium with their immediate surroundings. They derive from the fast fission neutrons in the reactor which are made to dissipate their high initial energy through numerous collisions with the other materials that are incorporated in a common type of reactor for just this purpose.

One of the reasons for wanting to reduce the neutron energies from fission energies to thermal energies is the very considerable increase in the fission cross section for thermal neutrons as compared to that for the nonfission capture cross sections, which implies a corresponding increase in the probability of fission reactions taking place.

A reactor which is so designed that almost all neutron fissions occur with neutrons of thermal energies is called a **thermal reactor** and this type represents the main object of interest to us in this book.

The large number of neutrons present in a nuclear reactor make it necessary, if one wants to get some understanding of the physical processes involved, to employ a statistical approach very similar to that of the kinetic theory of gases. This chapter begins, therefore, with a short review of some of the principles of kinetic theory, which can be usefully applied to the neutrons in a reactor. It then treats the collisions of neutrons with nuclei in detail sufficient for a satisfactory picture of the process of **moderation** to emerge from the mathematical background.

6.2 Energy Distribution of Thermal Neutrons

The neutrons in a nuclear reactor are not of uniform energy but are distributed over an energy range that extends from very slow to very fast neutrons of some 17 Mev (Fig. 6.1).

Fast neutrons are continually being produced by the nuclear fissions that occur in the reactor, and slow neutrons are steadily being removed by absorption processes that lead primarily to fissioning and the creation of new fast neutrons. To compensate for the steady loss of slow neutrons through absorption and other losses the fast neutrons must be slowed down rapidly and efficiently so as to replenish the supply of slow neutrons. This process is called **moderation** or **thermalization.**

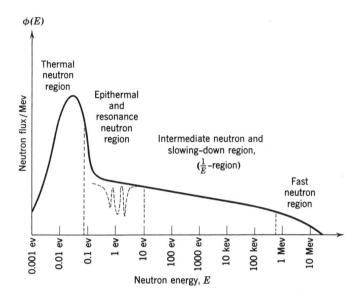

FIG. 6.1. Hypothetical neutron flux distribution in a thermal reactor.

The rapid transformation of fast neutrons to slow neutrons is achieved by a moderating material or **moderator** that is incorporated in the reactor. Its presence effects a slowing down of the fast fission neutrons by elastic collisions between the moderator nuclei and the neutrons until the average kinetic energy of the neutrons corresponds to that of the moderator nuclei.

The choice of a suitable moderator material is determined by the consideration that its scattering cross section should be much larger than its absorption cross section in order to allow the colliding neutrons to reach thermal energies rapidly and to decrease the chance of their being absorbed nonproductively.

When a kind of thermal equilibrium has been established between the neutrons and the host material, the neutrons are said to have been thermalized and their energy distribution will be approximately Maxwellian, corresponding to the temperature of the surrounding medium.

We shall examine the process of moderation in more detail later, and for the time being can picture it qualitatively as shown in Fig. 6.2.

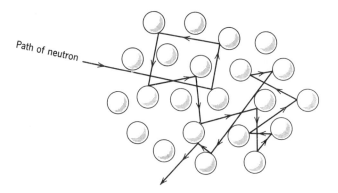

FIG. 6.2. Moderation of neutrons by elastic collisions with moderator nuclei.

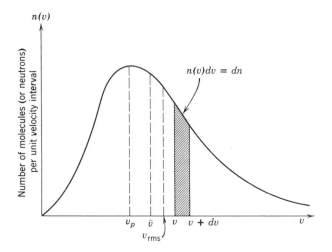

FIG. 6.3. Velocity distribution of molecules (or neutrons) according to the Maxwell-Boltzmann distribution law.

For neutrons in thermal equilibrium with the moderator the **velocity distribution** will be given by the Maxwell-Boltzmann expression

$$dn = n(v)\, dv = \frac{4\pi n_0}{(2\pi kT/m)^{3/2}}\, v^2 \exp\left(-\frac{\frac{1}{2}mv^2}{kT}\right) dv \qquad (6.1)$$

where n_0 is the number of neutrons per cm³, m is the neutron mass, T the temperature, and k the Boltzmann constant. The number of neutrons whose velocities lie between v and $v + dv$ is given by $dn = n(v)\,dv$. This distribution is shown in Fig. 6.3.

The **energy distribution** of the neutrons can be written in the form

$$dn = n(E)\,dE = \frac{2\pi n_0}{(\pi kT)^{3/2}}\,E^{1/2}\exp\left(\frac{-E}{kT}\right)\,dE \qquad (6.2)$$

This distribution is shown in Fig. 6.4.

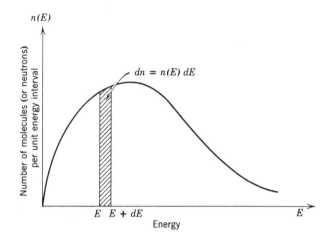

FIG. 6.4. Maxwell-Boltzmann energy distribution.

The distribution functions $n(v)$ and $n(E)$ are "density" functions; that means that they give the number of neutrons per unit velocity interval and per unit energy interval, respectively.

$$n(v) = \frac{dn}{dv} \quad \text{and} \quad n(E) = \frac{dn}{dE} \qquad (6.3)$$

The number of neutrons that are found within a small velocity or energy interval are given by Eqs. 6.1 and 6.2, respectively, as represented by the small shaded areas in Figs. 6.3 and 6.4.

The velocity distribution function 6.1 has a maximum for a value of the velocity, v_p, which is called the **most probable velocity**. By differentiating 6.1 and setting this equal to zero, the most probable velocity is found to be

$$v_p = \left(\frac{2kT}{m}\right)^{1/2} \qquad (6.4)$$

The energy E_p that corresponds to this velocity is given by

$$E_p = \tfrac{1}{2}mv_p^2 = kT \tag{6.5}$$

This relation is also used to associate a temperature with the kinetic energy of neutrons. The **neutron temperature** corresponding to a neutron energy E_{kin} is defined as

$$T = \frac{E_{\text{kin}}}{k} = \frac{\tfrac{1}{2}mv_p^2}{k} \tag{6.6}$$

The energy distribution 6.2 leads to a **most probable energy** E_0 which can be found by differentiating Eq. 6.2 and equating this to zero. This leads to a value for E_0

$$E_0 = \tfrac{1}{2}kT \tag{6.7}$$

Thus, the most probable energy E_0 is not equal to E_p, the energy which corresponds to the most probable velocity, but rather

$$E_p = 2E_0 \tag{6.8}$$

The **average energy** $\bar{E}$ is given by kinetic theory as

$$\bar{E} = \tfrac{1}{2}m\overline{v^2} = \tfrac{3}{2}kT \tag{6.9}$$

Therefore $\qquad\qquad (\overline{v^2})^{1/2} = v_{\text{rms}} = \left(\dfrac{3kT}{m}\right)^{1/2} \tag{6.10}$

In combination with Eq. 6.4 this leads to

$$v_{\text{rms}} = (\tfrac{3}{2})^{1/2} v_p \tag{6.11}$$

The average velocity $\bar{v}$ is related to v_p by

$$\bar{v} = \left(\frac{2}{\pi}\right)^{1/2} v_p \tag{6.12}$$

These relations are summarized here for reference.

$$v_p = \left(\frac{2kT}{m}\right)^{1/2} \qquad E_p = kT$$

$$\bar{v} = \left(\frac{8kT}{\pi m}\right)^{1/2} \qquad E_0 = \tfrac{1}{2}kT$$

$$v_{\text{rms}} = \left(\frac{3kT}{m}\right)^{1/2} \qquad \bar{E} = \tfrac{3}{2}kT$$

The energy distribution of neutrons in a reactor is not exactly Maxwellian insofar as it corresponds to a temperature which is slightly higher than that of the moderator material. This is so because there is a steady influx of high-energy neutrons from the fissioning that is taking place in the reactor and, at the same time, a steady absorption of the low-energy neutrons by the fissionable material or fuel. This has the effect of raising the high-energy end of the Maxwell distribution and depressing the low-energy portion of the distribution. The actual neutron distribution will, therefore, correspond to an effective temperature that is somewhat higher than that of the actual reactor material (Fig. 6.5).

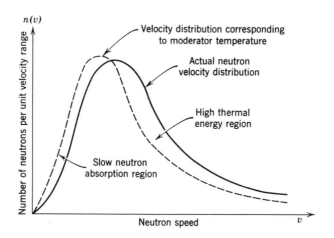

FIG. 6.5. Moderator temperature and "effective neutron temperature."

Because of the displacement of the neutron spectrum toward higher energies that goes hand in hand with the rise in the effective neutron temperature, this effect is known as **spectrum** or **thermal hardening**.

The elevation of the "neutron temperature" T_n above that of the moderator temperature T can be calculated by the relation

$$\Delta T = T_n - T = 0.89 \; TA\left(\frac{\Sigma_a}{\Sigma_s}\right) \tag{6.13}$$

where A is the atomic mass number of the moderator atoms and Σ_a, Σ_s their cross sections at temperature T. This expression is valid for $A < 25$ and $A(\Sigma_a/\Sigma_s) < 0.5$.†

---

† For heavy moderator atoms the numerical factor of 0.89 is to be replaced by the value 0.6. R. R. Coveyou, R. R. Bate, and R. K. Osborne, *Journ. Nucl. Energy*, **2**, 153 (1956); E. R. Cohen, Geneva Conference Report, 412, 5 (1955); R. W. Deutsch, *Nucleonics*, 47, **15**, No. 1 (1957). Argonne National Laboratory, *Reactor Physics Constants*, ANL-5800, p. 108.

Example 6.1. Calculate the most probable velocity and the energy corresponding to it for a neutron distribution in thermal equilibrium at 25° C.
The absolute temperature is $T = 298°$ K; hence

$$v_p = \left(\frac{2kT}{m}\right)^{1/2} = \left(\frac{2 \times 1.38 \times 10^{-16} \times 298}{1.675 \times 10^{-24}}\right)^{1/2} \text{cm/sec}$$

$$= 2220 \text{ meters/sec}$$

$$E_p = kT = \frac{1.38 \times 10^{-16} \times 298 \text{ ergs}}{1.6 \times 10^{-12} \text{ erg/ev}} = 0.0257 \text{ ev}$$

6.3　Effective Cross Section for Thermal Neutrons

We have seen that the absorption cross sections for slow neutrons are strongly dependent on the neutron energies. In many cases this dependence follows the "$1/v$ law," the (n, α) reaction with boron being a classical example of this behavior. In other cases the $1/v$ law is not strictly observed but must be corrected by a "not $1/v$" or f-factor which can be as high as 1.5 for samarium and as low as 0.85 for gadolinium. The "not $1/v$" correction factors for some nuclides are listed in Table 6.1 and the published cross sections are to be multiplied by the values in Table 6.1. (The "not $1/v$" factors show a temperature dependence which must be considered for more refined calculations.)

TABLE 6.1

Cd^{113}	Xe^{135}	Sm	Eu	Gd	Hg	U(nat.)	U^{233}	U^{235}	Pu^{239}
1.3	1.16	1.5	0.95	0.85	0.95	0.99	0.996	0.974	1.073

With a thermal neutron distribution where one has a spread of neutron speeds over a wide range of values and a corresponding spread in the numerical values of the absorption cross section, one employs an **effective cross section**, which is defined as that value of the cross section that results when the total number of absorptions per second per unit volume is averaged over the neutron flux. This is given by dividing 4.28 by 4.29, where ϕ is first expressed by 4.29; hence

$$\bar{\sigma} = \frac{\displaystyle\int_0^\infty n(v)v\sigma(v)\,dv}{\displaystyle\int_0^\infty n(v)v\,dv} \tag{6.14}$$

If the neutron absorber obeys the $1/v$ law, then $v\sigma(v) = \text{constant} = c_0$ and 6.13 simplifies to

$$\bar{\sigma} = c_0 \frac{\displaystyle\int_0^\infty n(v)\, dv}{\displaystyle\int_0^\infty n(v)v\, dv} \tag{6.14a}$$

Using the fact that the average speed $\bar{v}$ is defined by

$$\bar{v} = \frac{\displaystyle\int_0^\infty n(v)v\, dv}{\displaystyle\int_0^\infty n(v)\, dv} \tag{6.15}$$

and substituting this in 6.14 we get finally

$$\bar{\sigma} = \frac{c_0}{\bar{v}} \tag{6.16}$$

This shows that the effective cross section is equal to the cross section for neutrons with speeds equal to the average speed for the thermal neutron distribution. The constant c_0 is conventionally taken with reference to the most probable velocity v_p for the thermal neutrons, so that

$$c_0 = v_p \sigma_p \tag{6.17}$$

with σ_p being the cross section for neutrons of speed v_p.

Therefore
$$\bar{\sigma} = \left(\frac{v_p}{\bar{v}}\right)\sigma_p = \frac{\pi^{1/2}}{2}\sigma_p \tag{6.18}$$

The effective cross section is smaller than the cross section corresponding to the most probable velocity by a factor of $\pi^{1/2}/2 = 0.886$ since the average speed for the Maxwell-Boltzmann distribution is greater than the most probable speed by this same factor.

The thermal neutron cross sections as commonly tabulated are usually referred to a speed of 2200 meters/sec which is the most probable speed of a Maxwellian neutron distribution at $293.6°$ K and corresponds to a neutron energy of 0.0253 ev.

The effective neutron cross section to be used in reactor calculations[†] for a neutron distribution at a temperature T, other than the reference temperature, is obtained from the tabulated value by first multiplying it by

† In this connection see Hughes, *Pile Neutron Research*, Addison-Wesley, Chapter 7.1, p. 181, for some pertinent remarks about the use of thermal neutron cross sections.

$\pi^{\frac{1}{2}}/2$ (according to Eq. 6.18), then multiplying it by $(293.6/T)^{\frac{1}{2}}$ (according to Eq. 6.4) and, finally, multiplying it by the "not $1/v$" factor. Thus,

$$\sigma = \frac{\pi^{\frac{1}{2}}}{2} \left(\frac{293.6}{T} \right)^{\frac{1}{2}} (\text{"not } 1/v\text{" factor}) \sigma^0_{p(2200)} \qquad (6.18a)$$

The procedure to be followed is illustrated in the following example.

Example 6.2. Calculate the effective cross section of U^{235} for neutrons thermalized at 360° K.

The value of σ^0_p for a temperature of 293.6° K as obtained from Table 4.2 is $\sigma^0_p = 683$ barns. The cross section for a temperature of 360° K, assuming $1/v$-dependence, is

$$\sigma_p = \sigma^0_p \left(\frac{v^0_p}{v_p} \right) = \sigma^0_p \left(\frac{T_0}{T} \right)^{\frac{1}{2}} \qquad \text{by 6.4}$$

This must be corrected for "not $1/v$" dependence by the factor of 0.974 for U^{235}. Hence,

$$\sigma_p = 0.974 \times \sigma^0_p \left(\frac{T^0}{T} \right)^{\frac{1}{2}} = 0.974 \left(\frac{293.6}{360} \right)^{\frac{1}{2}} \times 683 = 601 \text{ barns}$$

Therefore

$$\bar{\sigma} = 0.886 \times \sigma_p = 0.886 \times 601 = 532 \text{ barns}$$

6.4 The Slowing Down of Reactor Neutrons

The rapid slowing down and thermalization of the fast fission neutrons are an important phase in the design and operation of a nuclear reactor of a type most commonly used at present. This is necessary in order to reduce neutron loss due to nonfission and resonance absorption and to increase the fissioning rate.

Since neutrons are not electrically charged they cannot lose energy by ionization but only through interaction with nuclei. For all practical purposes, the most important contribution to slowing down of neutrons in a nuclear reactor are elastic collisions with the moderator nuclei, whereby a neutron transfers a portion of its kinetic energy to its collision partner.

In order to get an indication of the amount of energy lost by a neutron in an elastic collision with a moderator nucleus, let us investigate such a collision process in more detail and recapitulate some of the results of section 2.12.

A collision between the two particles can be described either in a system of coordinates in which the target nucleus (moderator nucleus) is initially (i.e., before the collision) at rest, or in a coordinate system in which the center of mass of the colliding particles is at rest initially and throughout the collision. We shall call the first system, the L system and the latter, the C.M. system (Fig. 6.6).

The total linear momentum of the colliding particles is zero in the C.M. system by definition of the C.M. of two particles, and for this reason this system is often more convenient for purposes of calculation. The L system,

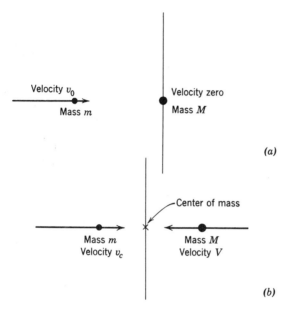

FIG. 6.6. (a) Laboratory system and (b) center-of-mass system of coordinates.

on the other hand, is the frame of reference in which all experimental measurements are made. It is therefore important to establish relations that will permit us to relate the motion of a particle in one system to its motion in the other system.

It is clear from Fig. 6.6 that the velocity of the target nucleus in the C.M. system is equal and opposite to the velocity of the C.M., and the system attached to it, in the L system. If the velocity of the C.M. in the L system be $\mathbf{V}$, the velocity of a particle in the L system be $\mathbf{v}_0$, and the velocity of the same particle in the C.M. system be $\mathbf{v}_c$, the three velocities are related by Fig. 6.7.

$$\mathbf{v}_0 = \mathbf{v}_c + \mathbf{V} \tag{6.19}$$

Applying the condition that the total linear momentum of the colliding particles must be zero in the C.M. system, we have,

$$m v_c - M V = 0 \tag{6.20}$$

where m = neutron mass, M = moderator nucleus mass, and $-V$ is the velocity of M.

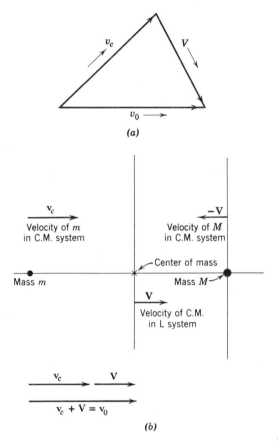

FIG. 6.7. Relation between particle velocities in the L and C.M. systems. (a) General case. (b) Particular case under consideration.

Combining Eqs. 6.19 and 6.20, we find for V and v_c

$$V = \frac{m}{m + M} v_0 \qquad v_c = \frac{M}{m + M} v_0 \tag{6.21}$$

When we apply the principle of conservation of energy, it follows that after the collision the speeds of the colliding particles are not changed in the C.M. system. They must also be collinear to give zero linear momentum, so that the net result of the collision in the C.M. system is a rotation of the particle system by an angle ϕ (Fig. 6.8).

Figure 6.9 pictures the collision of a neutron of mass m with a moderator nucleus of mass M in the two systems, with v_1 denoting the velocity of m after the collision and v_2 that of M after the collision in the L system.

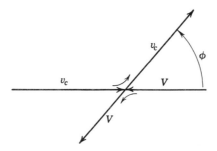

FIG. 6.8. Collision in C.M. system. The particles remain collinear after the collision with their original speeds unchanged. The net result of an elastic collision in the C.M. system is a rotation of the particle system by an angle of ϕ, which is the scattering angle in the C.M. system.

These velocities, shown in the figure by broken lines, have been obtained from the corresponding velocities in the C.M. system by means of Eq. 6.19.

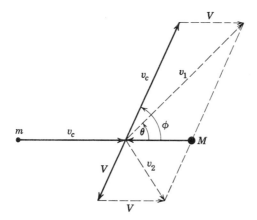

FIG. 6.9. Neutron-moderator collision as it appears in the C.M. and L systems, respectively. The broken lines represent the velocities of the collision partners after collision in the L system, and θ is the scattering angle of the neutron in the L system.

The following geometrical relations can be read off the figure: ϕ = scattering angle in C.M. system; and θ = scattering angle in L system

$$v_1{}^2 = V^2 + v_c{}^2 + 2Vv_c \cos \phi \qquad (6.22)$$

$$\frac{v_1}{v_c} = \frac{\sin \phi}{\sin \theta} \qquad (6.23)$$

By introducing the mass number A of the moderator nucleus, and the mass number 1 of the neutron we can write, with only a negligible error,

$$\frac{m}{M} = \frac{1}{A} \tag{6.24}$$

and using this ratio in 6.21 we have instead

$$V = v_0 \frac{1}{1 + A} \qquad v_c = v_0 \frac{A}{1 + A} \tag{6.25}$$

If E_0 is the neutron energy in the L system before the collision and E_1 the neutron energy in the same system after the collision, we can, by combining Eqs. 6.22 and 6.25, establish the following relation between E_0 and E_1.

$$\frac{E_1}{E_0} = \frac{v_1^2}{v_2^2} = \frac{1 + A^2 + 2A \cos \phi}{(1 + A)^2} \tag{6.26}$$

For a grazing collision $\phi = 0$ and Eq. 6.26 reduces to $E_1 = E_0$, which means that no energy is transferred from the neutron to the moderator nucleus. For a head-on collision $\phi = \pi$ and Eq. 6.26 reduces to

$$\frac{E_1}{E_0} = \left(\frac{A - 1}{A + 1}\right)^2 \qquad \text{(for } \phi = \pi\text{)} \tag{6.27}$$

This type of collision causes the maximum energy transfer from neutron to moderator nucleus, and thus the largest possible energy loss for the neutron in a single collision.

If we set

$$\left(\frac{A - 1}{A + 1}\right)^2 \equiv \alpha \tag{6.28}$$

we can write for the maximum energy loss possible

$$(\Delta E)_{\text{max}} = (E_0 - E_1)_{\text{max}} = E_0 \left(1 - \frac{E_1}{E_0}\right)_{\text{max}}$$

$$= E_0(1 - \alpha) \tag{6.29}$$

The maximum **fractional** energy loss $(\Delta E / E_0)_{\text{max}}$ is then

$$\left(\frac{\Delta E}{E_0}\right)_{\text{max}} = 1 - \alpha \tag{6.30}$$

For all intermediate angles of scattering $0 < \phi < \pi$, the fractional energy loss lies between 0 and $1 - \alpha$.

Therefore $\qquad 0 < \dfrac{\Delta E}{E_0} < 1 - \alpha \qquad$ for $0 < \phi < \pi$

Equation 6.26 can be expressed in terms of α in the following convenient form.

$$\frac{E_1}{E_0} = \frac{1 + \alpha}{2} + \frac{1 - \alpha}{2} \cos \phi \qquad (6.31)$$

The maximum fractional energy loss depends through α on the atomic mass number of the moderator nucleus A. By expanding α we get from 6.30

$$\left(\frac{\Delta E}{E_0}\right)_{max} = 1 - \alpha$$

$$= \frac{4}{A} - \frac{8}{A^2} + \frac{12}{A^3} - \frac{16}{A^4} + \frac{20}{A^5} - \cdots$$

$$= \left(\frac{4}{A}\right)\left(1 - \frac{2}{A} + \frac{3}{A^2} - \cdots\right) \qquad (6.32)$$

This shows that the maximum fractional energy loss is greater the smaller the mass of the moderator nucleus, so that we expect light nuclei to be more effective moderators than heavy nuclei.

Example 6.3. Calculate the maximum fractional energy loss for neutrons in collisions with Be^9 nuclei and compare this with that for collisions with U^{238} nuclei.

$$\text{For } Be^9 \qquad \left(\frac{\Delta E}{E_0}\right)_{max} = 1 - (A - 1)^2/(A + 1)^2$$

$$= 1 - (8/10)^2 = 0.36 \quad \text{or} \quad 36\%$$

$$\text{For } U^{238} \qquad 1 - \left(\frac{237}{239}\right)^2 = 0.02 \quad \text{or} \quad 2\%$$

Example 6.4. Calculate the fractional energy loss of a neutron being scattered through an angle of 60° in the C.M. system in collision with a C^{12} nucleus.

By 6.31, $\quad \dfrac{E_1}{E_0} = \dfrac{1 + (11/13)^2}{2} + \dfrac{1 - (11/13)^2}{2} \cos 60° = 0.928$

Therefore $\quad \dfrac{\Delta E}{E_0} = 1 - \dfrac{E_1}{E_0} = 0.072 \quad \text{or} \quad 7.2\%$

6.5   Scattering Angles in L System and C.M. System

The neutron energy after scattering, E_1, is given by Eq. 6.31, which relates this energy as measured in the L system to the scattering angle ϕ in the C.M. system. This may seem inconsistent at first sight, but it is very convenient in this form because, as we shall see presently, the angular dependence of the scattering in the C.M. system is very simple.

A relation between the scattering angle ϕ and the scattering angle θ as measured in the L system can be established by combining Eqs. 6.23 and 6.26. Thus

$$\frac{\sin^2 \theta}{\sin^2 \phi} = \frac{v_c^2}{v_1^2} = \frac{v_0^2}{v_1^2}\left(\frac{A}{1+A}\right)^2 \qquad \text{by 6.25}$$

$$= \frac{E_0}{E_1}\left(\frac{A}{1+A}\right)^2 = \frac{A^2}{1 + A^2 + 2A \cos \phi} \qquad \text{by 6.26}$$

Therefore $\qquad \sin^2 \theta = \dfrac{A^2 \sin^2 \phi}{1 + A^2 + 2A \cos \phi}$

Therefore $\qquad \cos^2 \theta = 1 - \sin^2 \theta$

$$= 1 - \frac{A^2 \sin^2 \phi}{1 + A^2 + 2A \cos \phi}$$

$$= \frac{(1 + A \cos \phi)^2}{1 + A^2 + 2A \cos \phi}$$

Therefore $\qquad \cos \theta = \dfrac{1 + A \cos \phi}{(1 + A^2 + 2A \cos \phi)^{1/2}}$ $\qquad$ (6.33)

6.6 Angular and Energy Distribution

We must now make the transition from the single neutron collision of the previous section to an examination of the average behavior of neutrons as they make numerous scattering collisions with the moderator nuclei. In order to be able to do this, we must know the distribution function for the neutron scattering, which conveys the necessary information about the comparative frequency of scattering in a given direction as compared to other directions. To get a reliable average value of a property, we must include the proper weighting factor corresponding to the frequency of its occurrence. The distribution function provides this appropriate weighting factor, and our first task will be to derive this function for the scattered neutrons.

The basic experimental fact to be considered, in this connection, is that for neutrons with energies not exceeding ~ 10 Mev the scattering is isotropic in the C.M. system.† This means that all directions in space are

---

† This is strictly true only for hydrogen. For a nucleus of mass number A the scattering becomes nonisotropic at somewhat lower energies. The approximate upper limit for isotropic scattering for moderator nuclei of mass number A is given by $10A^{-2/3}$ Mev. Nevertheless, the isotropy assumption is generally made (see Glasstone and

equally probable and no favored directions for scattering can be distinguished. In other words, the probability of a neutron being scattered into a given space element, $d\omega$, does not depend on its location in space or on its shape but only on its size.

The size of the space element $d\omega$ subtended by an area dS at the center of scattering O is found by projecting dS onto a spherical surface of unit radius surrounding the center O (Fig. 6.10). The probability of a particle

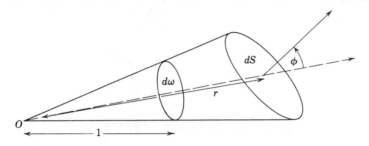

FIG. 6.10. Space angle $d\omega$ subtended by dS at 0.

being scattered in such a way that it passes through dS is then equal to the fraction of the projected area onto the unit sphere as compared to the total surface area of this sphere.

If ϕ is the angle between the radius vector from O to dS and the normal to dS, and r the distance of dS from O, the projection of dS onto the unit sphere is then $d\omega$, as given by

$$d\omega = \frac{dS \cos \phi}{r^2} \tag{6.34}$$

Let dW denote the probability of scattering into the space element $d\omega$, then by the preceding argument

$$dW = \frac{d\omega}{4\pi} \tag{6.35}$$

It follows, therefore, that if we write $P(\omega) = dW/d\omega$,

$$P(\omega) = \frac{dW}{d\omega} = \frac{1}{4\pi} \tag{6.36}$$

Edlund, *The Elements of Nuclear Reactor Theory*, p. 142, van Nostrand) and leads to satisfactory results for commonly used moderators. (For a derivation that is not restricted to isotropic scattering, see Weinberg and Wigner, *op. cit.* and references cited there.)

For inelastic collisions the scattering in the C.M. system deviates considerably from spherical symmetry even at low neutron energies but this type of scattering is not significant in our case.

Here, $P(\omega)$ represents the probability per unit space angle and is the desired distribution function. It might be helpful to compare the distribution function 6.36 with the distribution functions 6.3 in order to appreciate the formal analogy that exists between them.

To find the probability of a neutron being scattered through an angle lying between ϕ and $\phi + d\phi$ we must evaluate the corresponding space angle $d\omega_\phi$. For this purpose we describe a unit sphere about the scattering center O (Fig. 6.11), and calculate the shaded area dS. This element of

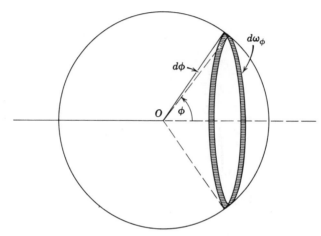

FIG. 6.11. Neutrons scattered through an angle lying between ϕ and $\phi + d\phi$ pass through area shown shaded in the figure, which is the element of space angle $d\omega_\phi$.

area is a portion of the spherical surface that contains all directions in space, making an angle between ϕ and $\phi + d\phi$ with the direction of incidence of the neutron. The area of this annular ring can be read off the figure and is

$$d\omega_\phi = 2\pi \sin \phi \, d\phi \qquad (6.37)$$

Hence,

$$dW = \frac{d\omega}{4\pi}$$

$$= \frac{2\pi \sin \phi \, d\phi}{4\pi} = -\tfrac{1}{2}d(\cos \phi) \qquad (6.38)$$

It should be pointed out here that this result is not inconsistent with our previous conclusion that all angles in space are equally probable; the presence of the factor $\sin \phi$ is merely a consequence of the fact that $d\omega_\phi$ increases like $\sin \phi$ as the scattering angle ϕ increases. In 6.38, $P(\omega)$ is constant, but $d\omega$ increases and, hence, also dW.

We see then that dW is proportional to $d(\cos \phi)$, which means that all values of $\cos \phi$ are equally probable. Since, by 6.31 the neutron energy after scattering is proportional to $\cos \phi$, we are led to the important conclusion that **all permissible values of the energy after a collision are equally probable** (Fig. 6.12).

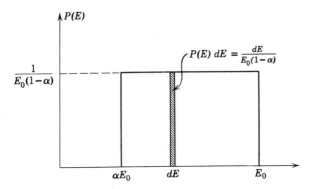

FIG. 6.12. Probability distribution of neutron energies after neutron moderator collision.

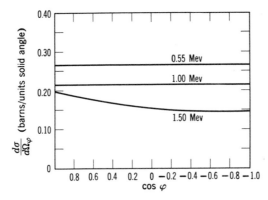

FIG. 6.13. Differential elastic cross section for neutron scattering by carbon nuclei. The scattering is seen to be isotropic for neutron energies of 1 Mev and slightly higher. For an energy of 1.5 Mev a slight preference for forward scattering is evident. (After Willard, H. B., Bair, J. K., Kingston, J. D., *Phys. Rev.*, **98**, 669 (1955).)

This conclusion has been reached on the basis of our empirical knowledge of isotropic scattering in the C.M. system. The validity of the isotropy of scattering can very well be applied to nuclear reactor neutrons, because only very few of the fission neutrons exceed an energy of $\sim$10 Mev, the approximate upper limit for isotropic scattering. Figure 6.13 shows the experimental results with carbon nuclei.

Omitting from now on the suffix "1" from the energy after a collision, we can differentiate 6.31, and get

$$dE = \tfrac{1}{2}E_0(1 - \alpha) \, d(\cos \phi) \tag{6.39}$$

Combining this expression with 6.38 we have for dW

$$dW = - \frac{dE}{E_0(1 - \alpha)} \tag{6.40}$$

The negative sign appears here because dE is itself a negative quantity, representing an energy loss, so that the probability per unit energy loss, $P(E)$, is a positive quantity as it should be. Hence

$$P(E) = \frac{dW}{dE} = \frac{1}{E_0(1 - \alpha)} \tag{6.41}$$

showing that the energy distribution is a constant. If $P(E)$ is plotted against the possible energies after collision, it is a straight line parallel to the energy abscissa (Fig. 6.12). The line is bounded by the points $E = E_0$, corresponding to a collision with zero energy loss, and $E = \alpha E_0$, referring to a collision with the maximum possible energy loss for the neutron. The entire spectrum of possible energy losses is covered by the interval between these two limits. The probability $P(E) \, dE$ for the neutron to be scattered into an energy range lying between E and $E + dE$ is represented in the figure by the shaded area expressed as a fraction of the whole rectangular area. This fraction is the same as the ratio of the energy interval dE over the total available energy range $E_0(1 - \alpha E_0)$, so that

$$P(E) \, dE = \frac{dE}{E_0(1 - \alpha)} \tag{6.41a}$$

in conformity with 6.41.

Example 6.5. Calculate the mean energy of the scattered neutrons after single collisions, assuming their initial energies to be E_0.

$$\bar{E} = \frac{\displaystyle\int_{\alpha E_0}^{E_0} EP(E) \, dE}{\displaystyle\int_{\alpha E_0}^{E_0} P(E) \, dE}$$

The denominator represents the total probability and is, therefore, equal to unity.

Therefore
$$\bar{E} = \int_{\alpha E_0}^{E_0} E \, \frac{dE}{E_0(1 - \alpha)}$$

$$= \frac{\tfrac{1}{2}}{E_0(1 - \alpha)} \left[E^2 \right]_{\alpha E_0}^{E_0}$$

$$= \tfrac{1}{2}E_0(1 + \alpha)$$

This is the arithmetic mean of the two boundary values E_0 and αE_0, which is the energy at the midpoint of Fig. 6.12, a result which was anticipated.

Example 6.6 Calculate the average fractional energy loss after one collision and apply the result to a graphite moderator.

The fractional energy loss is

$$\frac{\Delta E}{E_0} = \frac{E - E_0}{E_0}$$

Hence,

$$\overline{\left(\frac{E_0 - E}{E_0}\right)} = \frac{\int_{\alpha E_0}^{E_0} \frac{E_0 - E}{E_0} P(E)\, dE}{\int_{\alpha E_0}^{E_0} P(E)\, dE}$$

$$= \int_{\alpha E_0}^{E_0} \left(1 - \frac{E}{E_0}\right) P(E)\, dE$$

$$= 1 - \int_{\alpha E_0}^{E_0} \left(\frac{1}{E_0}\right) E P(E)\, dE$$

since $\int_{\alpha E_0}^{E_0} P(E)\, dE = 1$.

Using the result of the previous example, in which the above integral was evaluated, we get for the final answer that

$$\overline{\left(\frac{\Delta E}{E}\right)} = \frac{1 - \alpha}{2}$$

For graphite $A = 12$, and $(1 - \alpha)/2 = \frac{1}{2}(1 - 11^2/13^2) = 0.1425$.

We see that the average fractional energy loss is independent of the initial energy and, we conclude, that for a given neutron, on the average, the same fraction of its precollision energy will be transferred to the moderator nucleus in each successive collision.

This conclusion is justified for neutron energies well above thermal. As the neutron energy approaches thermal energies, however, the kinetic energy of the moderator nucleus is no longer negligible as compared to that of the neutron, a condition we had previously assumed by postulating a target nucleus at rest, and it becomes possible for the neutron to gain energy in collisions as well as lose it.

6.7 Forward Scattering in the L System

Looking at Fig. 6.9 it is apparent that the scattering angles in the L system are smaller than the scattering angles in the C.M. system because of the velocity component V which is added to the velocity of the scattered neutron, where V is the velocity of the C.M. system in the L system. This added component means in effect that the neutrons show a preferential forward scattering in the L system, although in the C.M. system the scattering is spherically symmetrical or isotropic.

The deviation from spherical symmetry can conveniently be expressed in terms of the average value of the cosines of all possible scattering angles in space.

To evaluate the average value of $\cos \theta$ we again use the distribution function either in the form of Eq. 6.36 or of Eq. 6.41 and follow the standard procedure.

Therefore
$$\overline{\cos \theta} = \frac{\int_{\alpha E_0}^{E_0} \cos \theta \, P(E) \, dE}{\int_{\alpha E_0}^{E_0} P(E) \, dE}$$

$$= \frac{\int \cos \theta \, P(\omega_\phi) \, d\omega_\phi}{\int P(\omega_\phi) \, d\omega_\phi}$$

$$= \frac{\int_1^{-1} \cos \theta \left(-\frac{1}{2}\right) d(\cos \phi)}{\int_1^{-1} \left(-\frac{1}{2}\right) d(\cos \phi)} \qquad \text{by Eqs. 6.36 and 6.37}$$

$$= -\frac{1}{2} \int_1^{-1} \cos \theta \, d(\cos \phi)$$

We now replace $\cos \theta$ in this integral by substituting for it the value as given by 6.33 and so obtain

$$\overline{\cos \theta} = \frac{1}{2} \int_{-1}^{1} \frac{(1 + A \cos \phi) \, d(\cos \phi)}{(1 + A^2 + 2A \cos \phi)^{1/2}}$$

$$= \frac{2}{3A} \qquad\qquad (6.42)$$

Thus, for large A and heavy nuclei the average forward component becomes very small and the scattering is almost isotropic. In collisions with lighter nuclei, however, there will be a pronounced preference for forward scattering in the L system.

6.8 Transport Mean Free Path and Scattering Cross Section

The predominant forward scattering for neutrons in the L system will also affect the mean free path in the sense that the average distance traveled by the neutron before it is scattered through an angle of 90° will be greater than the corresponding average distance for isotropic scattering. When calculating the spatial distribution of neutrons, this preference for traveling in the forward direction must be taken into consideration as, because of it, a neutron will move a greater distance away from its point of origin, on the average, in a given number of collisions than it would do if there were no preferred forward scattering directions.

The increased effective mean free path for nonisotropic scattering is called the **transport mean free path** λ_{tr} and it is related to the scattering mean free path λ_s (4.22) by

$$\lambda_{tr} = \frac{\lambda_s}{1 - \overline{\cos\theta}}$$

$$= \frac{\lambda_s}{1 - 2/3A} \tag{6.43}$$

A corresponding cross section, the **transport cross section** σ_{tr} is defined, in analogy with 4.9, by

$$\sigma_{tr} = \frac{1}{N_0\lambda_{tr}} = \frac{1 - \overline{\cos\theta}}{N_0\lambda_s}$$

$$= \sigma_s(1 - \overline{\cos\theta})$$

$$= \sigma_s(1 - 2/3A) \tag{6.44}$$

Example 6.7. Calculate the transport mean free path for thermal neutrons in hydrogen gas at STP if the scattering cross section is 38 barns per nucleus.

$$\lambda_{tr} = \frac{1}{N_0\sigma_s(1 - 2/3A)}$$

$$= \frac{1}{\dfrac{6.03 \times 10^{23} \text{ molecules/mole}}{22{,}400 \text{ cm}^3/\text{mole}} \times 2 \text{ atoms/molecule}}$$

$$\times \frac{1}{38 \times 10^{-24} \text{ cm}^2 \times (1 - 2/3)}$$

$$= 14.7 \text{ meters}$$

6.9 Average Logarithmic Energy Decrement

When considering the thermalization of fast neutrons, we are faced with the need of being able to predict or estimate the number of collisions that are required for most of the neutrons to have their initial fission energy E_0 reduced to thermal energies E_t. The average energy is no longer a good measure for the average neutron behavior after they have undergone several collisions, as most of the neutrons will then have energies well below the corresponding average energy.

The average fractional energy loss per collision, $-\Delta E/E$, however, does not depend on the energy the neutron had before the collision (compare Example 6.6). Since $-\Delta E/E \cong -\Delta(\log E)$,† the use of $\log E$, instead of

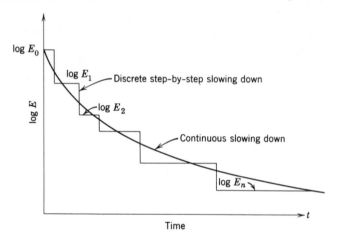

FIG. 6.14. The continuous slowing-down approximation.

E, suggests itself as a possibly more convenient variable. This new variable u, called the **lethargy** of the neutron is defined in terms of its differential du.

$$du = -\frac{dE}{E} = -d(\log E) \tag{6.45}$$

Therefore
$$u = -\int_{E_0}^{E} d(\log E)$$

$$= \log\left(\frac{E_0}{E}\right) = \log E_0 - \log E \tag{6.46}$$

where E_0 is some constant initial reference value.

If $\log E$ is evaluated after each collision, the difference $-\Delta(\log E) = \log E_n - \log E_{n+1}$ for two successive collisions will, on the average, be the same for all collisions that the neutron makes in its passage from high energy to thermal energy (Fig. 6.14).

† This follows from the relation $\Delta y \cong (dy/dx)\Delta x$ with $y = \log x$, $dy/dx = 1/x$ and $\Delta y = \Delta(\log x)$.

The average change in log E between two successive collisions is called the **average logarithmic energy decrement per collision** and is commonly represented by ξ, so that

$$\xi = \overline{\Delta(\log E)}$$

$$= \overline{\log E_n - \log E_{n+1}}$$

$$= \overline{\log \left(\frac{E_n}{E_{n+1}}\right)} = \overline{\Delta u} \tag{6.47}$$

To calculate $\overline{\log (E_n/E_{n+1})}$ we would have to know the distribution function for the neutrons after n collisions. Since we can take ξ to have the same value after n collisions as it has after the first collision, we can simplify our work and evaluate it instead with respect to neutrons that have undergone their first collision. We know the energy distribution for these neutrons, which is given by 6.41, and can, therefore, proceed directly:

$$\xi = \overline{\log \left(\frac{E_0}{E}\right)} = \frac{\displaystyle\int_{\alpha E_0}^{E_0} \log (E_0/E) P(E)\, dE}{\displaystyle\int_{\alpha E_0}^{E_0} P(E)\, dE}$$

$$= -\int_{\alpha E_0}^{E_0} \log \left(\frac{E}{E_0}\right) \frac{d(E/E_0)}{1 - \alpha}$$

$$= -\frac{1}{1 - \alpha}\left[\frac{E}{E_0} \times \log \left(\frac{E}{E_0}\right)\right]_{\alpha E_0}^{E_0}$$

$$= 1 + \frac{\alpha \log \alpha}{1 - \alpha} \tag{6.48}$$

In terms of the atomic mass number A, this becomes

$$\xi = 1 + \frac{(A - 1)^2}{2A} \log \frac{A - 1}{A + 1} \tag{6.49}$$

For $A > 10$, an approximation good to within 1% is the following:

$$\xi \doteq \frac{2}{A + 2/3} \tag{6.50}$$

For very large A, ξ approaches zero, so that practically no energy is lost by a neutron in a collision with a heavy nucleus. This is in line with our previous finding that heavy elements are poor moderators. For hydrogen, ξ is defined as the limiting value of 6.49 for $A = 1$, which is 1. Both ξ and

$\cos \theta$ are independent of neutron energy only if isotropic scattering in the C.M. system can be assumed; otherwise both are energy-dependent.

Example 6.8. Calculate the average energy loss for neutrons that have made one collision with carbon nuclei, using $\xi = 0.158$ for carbon.

$$\left(\overline{\frac{E_0}{E}}\right) = e^{\xi}$$

Therefore
$$\left(\overline{\frac{E_0 - E}{E_0}}\right) = 1 - e^{-\xi} = 1 - e^{-0.158} = 0.1462$$

This result compares with that found in Example 6.6 of 0.1425 where we used the "mean value of E_0/E" instead of the "mean value of log (E_0/E)" as in the present solution. This result shows, therefore, that it is incorrect to use ξ which is the "mean value of the log" and not the "log of the mean value," for finding the average energy loss per collision.

A knowledge of the average logarithmic energy decrement enables us to calculate the number of collisions, n, required to reduce the initial neutron energy E_0 to a final energy $\tilde{E}_t$. We only have to divide the entire logarithmic interval, log (E_0) − log$(\tilde{E}_t)$, by the average logarithmic decrement per collision to arrive at the number of collisions required for the neutron to pass from an energy E_0 to an energy $\tilde{E}_t$. We are now assuming that $\overline{\log E_t} \simeq \log \tilde{E}_t$. Then

$$n = \frac{\log (E_0) - \log (\tilde{E}_t)}{\xi} = \frac{1}{\xi} \log \frac{E_0}{\tilde{E}_t} \tag{6.51}$$

Starting out with a group of neutrons of initial energy E_0, we shall arrive at an energy $\tilde{E}_t$, after the neutrons have made n collisions, which is a representative average value for the group. This representative average value for the energy is very close to the median value for the group, so that about half the neutrons that have started out with energy E_0 will have been slowed down to below the energy $\tilde{E}_t$.

Example 6.9. Calculate the number of collisions required to reduce fast fission neutrons with an average initial energy of 2 Mev to an energy $\tilde{E}_t = 0.025$ ev (thermal energy) in a Be-moderated assembly. For Be, $\xi = 0.209$.
From 6.51

$$n = \frac{\log (2 \times 10^6/0.025)}{0.209} = \frac{2.30 \times \log_{10} (8 \times 10^7)}{0.209} = \frac{2.30 \times 7.903}{0.209} = 87$$

Example 6.10. What would be the energy of neutrons that have made 40 collisions with Be nuclei, starting with an initial energy of 2 Mev? From 6.51

$$\tilde{E}_t = E_0 e^{-n\xi}$$
$$= 2 \times 10^6 \times e^{-40 \times 0.209}$$
$$= 2 \times 10^6 \times 0.00023 = 460 \text{ ev}$$

Example 6.11. How many collisions are required for neutrons to lose, on the average, 99 % of an initial energy of 2 Mev in graphite? Compare this with the total number of collisions required to reach thermal energies (0.025 ev). For carbon, $\xi = 0.158$.

$$n = \frac{1}{\xi} \log \left(\frac{100}{1}\right) = \frac{2.30 \times 2}{0.158} = 29$$

The number of collisions required to reduce the energy to 0.025 ev is

$$n = \frac{1}{0.158} \times \log (8 \times 10^7)$$

$$= \frac{18.18}{0.158} = 115$$

This shows that the energy loss in the earlier collisions is considerably greater than that in the later ones, with almost three times as many more collisions needed to dissipate the last 1 % of excess energy. It should be borne in mind, however, that the percent energy loss (on the average) for any one collision is the same as for any other collision, whatever the neutron energy may be.

6.10 Slowing-Down Power and Moderating Ratio

The efficacy of a substance as a moderator is determined not only by ξ and σ_s but also by the number of scattering centers per unit volume (cm³), N_0. This makes the choice of a solid substance preferable to that of a gas. The three quantities ξ, σ_s, and N_0 jointly determine the slowing-down ability of a moderator, and their product is called the **slowing-down power** (sdp).

$$\begin{aligned} \text{sdp} &= \xi N_0 \sigma_s \\ &= \xi \Sigma_s \\ &= \frac{\xi}{\lambda_s} \end{aligned} \tag{6.52}$$

Hence, it is possible to interpret the sdp as the average loss in the logarithm of the energy per unit distance of travel in the moderator, or average change in the lethargy of the neutron per unit distance of travel.

To give a complete description of the suitability of a substance as moderator, we must also specify its absorption properties for (thermal) neutrons. A substance would not be suitable as a moderator if its absorption cross section were so high that it absorbed more than a minimum of neutrons. A good moderator must have a large sdp and a small absorption cross section.

The relative sizes of the scattering dependent qualities and the absorption dependent qualities will be a more satisfactory determinant for the suitability of a particular substance for the purpose of moderation. We therefore use the **moderating ratio** (mr) as an over-all criterion because it incorporates this information in a convenient manner. The moderating ratio is defined as the ratio of sdp over the macroscopic absorption cross section Σ_a.

$$mr = \frac{sdp}{\Sigma_a}$$

$$= \xi \frac{\Sigma_s}{\Sigma_a} \tag{6.53}$$

When a moderator is not a one-element substance, but consists of a combination of elements (for example, H_2O) or of a mixture of elements, the appropriate value of ξ must be found by weighting and averaging it over the constituent components of the compound or mixture. The weighted average value for ξ is given by

$$\bar{\xi} = \frac{\xi_1\Sigma_s^{(1)} + \xi_2\Sigma_s^{(2)} + \cdots}{\Sigma_s^{(1)} + \Sigma_s^{(2)} + \cdots} \tag{6.54}$$

where the superscripts refer to the various nuclear components that jointly make up the moderator.

If we use this value and Σ_s as given by Eq. 4.24, we get for the slowing-down power of a compound the numerator of Eq. 6.54.

$$sdp = \xi_1\Sigma_s^{(1)} + \xi_2\Sigma_s^{(2)} + \xi_3\Sigma_s^{(3)} + \cdots \tag{6.55}$$

and for the moderating ratio,

$$mr = \frac{\xi_1\Sigma_s^{(1)} + \xi_2\Sigma_s^{(2)} + \xi_3\Sigma_s^{(3)} + \cdots}{\Sigma_a^{(1)} + \Sigma_a^{(2)} + \Sigma_a^{(3)} + \cdots} \tag{6.56}$$

Some of the properties of commonly used moderator materials are listed in Table 6.2.

Example 6.12. Calculate ξ for heavy water (D_2O), using these epithermal cross sections: $(\sigma_s)_D = 6.0$ barns, $(\sigma_s)_O = 4.2$ barns. Applying Eq. 6.49, we find for $\xi_D = 0.725$ and $\xi_O = 0.121$, so that

$$\xi_{D_2O} = \frac{\xi_D \sigma_D 2N_0 + \xi_O \sigma_O N_0}{2N_0\sigma_D + N_0\sigma_O}$$

$$= \frac{0.725 \times 12 + 0.121 \times 4.2}{12 + 4.2} = 0.554$$

TABLE 6.2†

	H_2O	D_2O	Be	BeO	C
$N_0 \times 10^{-24}$	0.0334	0.0334	0.1229	0.0713	0.0803
ξ	0.927	0.510	0.209	0.174	0.158
$\sigma_{a(\text{thermal})}$	0.66	0.00092	0.009	0.0092	0.0045
$\Sigma_{a(\text{thermal})}$	0.022	0.0000307‡	0.00111	0.000656	0.000362
$\sigma_{s(\text{thermal})}$	110	14.5	6.9	9.8	4.8
$\sigma_{s(\text{epithermal})}$	49	10.6	5.9	9.7	4.7
$\xi\Sigma_{s(\text{epithermal})}$	1.36	0.180	0.153	0.120	0.060
$\dfrac{\xi\Sigma_{s(\text{epithermal})}}{\Sigma_{a(\text{thermal})}}$	62	5860	138	183	166

† D. J. Hughes and R. B. Schwartz, *Neutron Cross Sections*, BNL-325, 2nd ed.;
ANL-5800 *Reactor Physics Constants*; H. Hetherington, *Nuclear Engineering Handbook*,
McGraw-Hill; M. V. Davis and D. T. Hauser, "Thermal Neutron Data," *Nucleonics*,
16, 3 (March 1958).
‡ For D_2O the numerical value of Σ_a is greatly affected by light water contamination.
If x is the weight percentage of H_2O admixture,

$$\Sigma_a \doteq 0.000031(1 + 6.56x)$$

6.11 Slowing-Down Density

The rate at which the neutrons per unit volume of a moderator slow
down past a particular energy E is called the **slowing-down density** and it is
denoted by $q(E)$.

Owing to the discontinuous nature of the slowing-down process which
causes the neutron energy to change in finite steps after each collision with
a moderator nucleus and because of the presence of absorption resonances
for neutrons of discrete energies, the variation of q with energy is not
expected to be simple. However, when the average energy loss per collision
is small enough, as is indeed the case with sufficiently heavy moderator
nuclei, we can simplify the problem by treating the slowing down as a
virtually continuous process (Fig. 6.14).

We shall make this assumption and, by means of this continuous
slowing-down model, shall proceed to obtain some information about the
energy distribution of the neutrons during their passage from high energies
to thermal energies. We shall also assume that the production of fission
neutrons occurs uniformly throughout the assembly and that a steady state
prevails; this means that the rate at which neutrons enter an energy interval
between E and $E + \Delta E$ is equal to the rate at which neutrons leave it
(Fig. 6.15).

If the rate of production of neutrons with an initial high energy E_0 is
constant and equal to Q, and if no neutrons are lost either by escaping

from the assembly (i.e., leakage) or through being absorbed by the materials of the assembly before they have reached thermal energies, the slowing-down density $q(E)$ will remain the same at all energies and it will be equal to Q. We can reduce the neutron leakage to negligible proportions by using a very large amount of moderator material, so that neutron absorption will remain as the sole cause of neutron loss with which we shall have to contend.

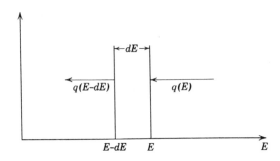

FIG. 6.15. The slowing-down density is the rate at which the neutron density crosses the energy E.

Let us, in the first instance, deal with the case of zero neutron absorption, $\Sigma_a = 0$.

We can then set

$$q(E) = Q = \text{constant} \tag{6.57}$$

The number of neutrons per cm³ whose energies lie between E and $E + \Delta E$ is given by Eq. 6.2 and Eq. 6.3 as equal to $n(E)\Delta E$. If we now interpret Δt as the time that is needed by the neutrons to transit through the energy interval ΔE, the number of neutrons that are within this energy interval at a given time will be equal to the product of rate of flow $q(E)$ and time interval Δt. Therefore

$$-q(E)\Delta t = n(E)\Delta E \tag{6.58}$$

The negative sign is introduced because $\Delta E < 0$, corresponding to the decrease in energy with increasing time during the slowing down.

The neutron density that crosses the energy E per second, $q(E)$, can also be evaluated by taking the product of the neutron density that crosses E per collision with an energy loss ΔE per collision, and the number of collisions this neutron group makes per second. Thus

$$\text{Neutron density crossing } E \text{ per collision} = n(E)\Delta E$$

$$\text{Number of collisions per second} = \frac{v}{\lambda_s} = v\Sigma_s$$

Hence,

$$q(E) = [n(E)\Delta E][v\Sigma_s] \tag{6.59}$$

If we choose ΔE small enough, we can use the relation

$$\frac{\Delta E}{E} = \Delta(\log E) \doteq \xi$$

and eliminate ΔE from Eq. 6.59 by substituting $\Delta E = \xi E$, so that we get the result

$$q(E) = n(E)E\xi v\Sigma_s$$
$$= \phi(E)E\xi\Sigma_s\dagger \tag{6.60}$$

where $\phi(E) = n(E)v$ is the neutron flux per unit energy. Since, in the absence of neutron absorption, $q(E) = Q$, we have

$$\phi(E) = \frac{Q}{E\xi\Sigma_s} \tag{6.61}$$

so that the slowing-down neutron flux per unit energy is inversely proportional to the energy E.

By restating Eq. 6.61 in the form

$$\phi(E)\Sigma_s\Delta E = \frac{Q}{E\xi}\Delta E \tag{6.62}$$

we can give it the following physical interpretation: The left-hand-side of Eq. 6.62 represents the number of neutrons within the energy interval ΔE (per cm³) that undergo scattering collisions with the moderator nuclei and are scattered out of it per second (compare Eq. 4.28).

In a steady state, the number of neutrons scattered out of the energy interval ΔE per second per cm³ must be replaced by an equal number of neutrons scattered into this energy interval per second per cm³. This condition can be expressed (per cm³ per second), by

$$\text{Scattering loss} = \text{neutron influx gain}$$

As the left-hand side of 6.62 has already been identified as the scattering loss, the right-hand side must represent the rate of neutron influx.

The quantity $\phi(E)\Sigma_s$ is called the **collision density**.

Example 6.13. Calculate the flux per unit energy at an energy of 100 ev in a uranium-graphite assembly, assuming a fission rate equivalent to a steady neutron source of 5×10^{10} neutrons/sec cm³.

† It can be shown that the slowing-down density and the neutron flux at any given energy have the same spatial distribution, so that energy and space variables are separable, a fact we shall use later.

We use Eq. 6.61 and have, using for $\xi_{graphite} = 0.158$; $\Sigma_{s(graphite)} = 0.385$

$$\phi = \frac{5 \times 10^{10} \text{ sec}^{-1} \text{ cm}^{-3}}{100 \text{ ev} \times 0.158 \times 0.385 \text{ cm}^{-1}}$$

$$= 8.2 \times 10^9 \text{ neutrons/cm}^2 \text{ sec ev}$$

6.12   Slowing-Down Time

By combining Eqs. 6.58 and 6.60 we can obtain the **slowing-down time,** which is the time required for the neutrons to slow down from an initial energy E_0 to a final energy E_t. Therefore

$$\Delta t = -\frac{\Delta E}{E \xi v \Sigma_s} \tag{6.63}$$

If we can assume that ξ and Σ_s remain fairly constant over the slowing-down range of energy, expression 6.63 can be integrated to give for the slowing-down time T

$$T = \int_0^T \Delta t = -\frac{1}{\xi \Sigma_s} \int_{E_0}^{E_t} \frac{\Delta E}{vE} \tag{6.64}$$

By means of the relation $E = \frac{1}{2}mv^2$, where m is the neutron mass, the integral can be brought to a form which can be readily evaluated. Thus

$$T = -\frac{(\tfrac{1}{2}m)^{1/2}}{\xi \Sigma_s} \int_{E_0}^{E_t} E^{-3/2} \Delta E$$

$$= \frac{(2m)^{1/2}}{\xi \Sigma_s} \left[\frac{1}{E_t^{1/2}} - \frac{1}{E_0^{1/2}} \right] \tag{6.65}$$

Example 6.14. Calculate the slowing-down time in graphite for neutrons starting with an initial energy of 2 Mev and terminating at thermal energies (0.025 ev).

Since $E_0 \gg E_t$, we can neglect the second term of 6.65 as compared to the first term. Therefore

$$T = \frac{1}{\xi \Sigma_s} \left(\frac{2m}{E_t} \right)^{1/2}$$

$$= \frac{1}{\xi \Sigma_s c} \left(\frac{2mc^2}{E_t} \right)^{1/2} \qquad \text{(where } c = 3.10^{10} \text{ cm/sec and } mc^2 = 931 \text{ Mev)}$$

$$= \frac{(2 \times 931 \times 10^6/0.025)^{1/2}}{0.385 \times 0.158 \times 3 \times 10^{10}} = 1.5 \times 10^{-4} \text{ sec}$$

6.13   Resonance Escape Probability

If the moderator has a measurable macroscopic absorption cross section Σ_a—previously we had assumed $\Sigma_a = 0$—the slowing-down density q will no longer be constant and equal to Q, but will now depend on the neutron energies.

The change in q, as the neutrons pass from an energy E to an energy $E - \Delta E$, and which is ascribable to neutron absorptions, is equal to the rate of neutron absorptions per cm³. This rate is given by 4.28, so that we can set

$$\text{Absorption loss} = \Delta q = n(E)\Delta E v \Sigma_a$$
$$= \phi(E)\Delta E \Sigma_a \tag{6.66}$$

This expression for the absorption loss is seen to be formally analogous to the scattering loss as given by the left-hand side of Eq. 6.62.

The slowing-down density with absorption present, $q(E)$, will be only a fraction of its value Q in the absence of absorption. We can express this mathematically by saying that

$$q(E) = Qp(E) \tag{6.67}$$

where $p(E) < 1$ is a measure of the fraction of neutrons that have escaped absorption and still survive after having been slowed down from their initial energy E_0 to an energy E.

The neutron absorptions are primarily the result of the various neutron resonances which are predominant in the epithermal region of energies for the moderator and the thermally nonfissionable components (for example, U^{238}) of the fuel materials of the reactor. The factor $p(E)$ measures the extent to which the neutrons are successful in evading these resonance traps and is thus called the **resonance escape probability.**

The steady-state condition within the energy interval ΔE, when neutron absorption is included, must now be modified to read

$$\text{Scattering loss} + \text{absorption loss} = \text{influx}$$

Substituting Eq. 6.66 for the absorption loss, and the left-hand side of Eq. 6.62 for the scattering loss, we are led to the steady-state condition

$$\phi(E)\Sigma_s \Delta E + \phi(E)\Sigma_a \Delta E = \frac{q(E)}{E\xi}\Delta E \tag{6.68}$$

When this is combined with Eq. 6.66, we get the relation

$$\frac{\phi(E)\Sigma_a \Delta E}{\phi(E)\Sigma_a \Delta E + \phi(E)\Sigma_s \Delta E} = \frac{\Delta q E\xi}{q(E)\Delta E} \tag{6.69}$$

or

$$\frac{\Sigma_a}{\Sigma_s + \Sigma_a}\frac{\Delta E}{E\xi} = \frac{\Delta q}{q(E)} \tag{6.70}$$

The physical meaning of the left-hand sides of Eqs. 6.69 and 6.70 is apparent. In the former we have the number of neutron collisions terminating in an absorption divided by the total number of collisions, i.e., both those leading to absorptions and those leading to a scattering event, so that $\Sigma_a/(\Sigma_a + \Sigma_s)$ represents the probability of a neutron capture per collision. The factor $\dfrac{\Delta E/E}{\xi} = \dfrac{\Delta(\log E)}{\xi}$ is the average number of collisions corresponding to an increase in the neutron lethargy by an amount Δu (compare Eq. 6.51), so that the product of the two factors on the left-hand side of Eq. 6.70 represents the probability of a neutron absorption, as the neutron energy changes by an amount corresponding to a change in lethargy of $\Delta u = \Delta(\log E)$.

On integrating Eq. 6.70 between the limits of neutron energies E and E_0, we get

$$\int_E^{E_0} \frac{\Sigma_a}{\Sigma_a + \Sigma_s} \frac{\Delta(\log E)}{\xi} = \log \frac{q(E_0)}{q(E)} \tag{6.71}$$

with the integral being merely a summation of the partial probabilities of a neutron absorption; thus we can say that we have here the **total probability per neutron of being absorbed as it is moderated from an initial energy E_0 to a final energy E.**

Calling the probability on the left-hand side of Eq. 6.71 P_a, we can write that equation now as

$$q(E) = q(E_0) \exp{(-P_a)} \tag{6.72}$$

where

$$P_a = \int_E^{E_0} \frac{\Sigma_a}{\Sigma_a + \Sigma_s} \frac{\Delta(\log E)}{\xi} \tag{6.73}$$

Since the initial slowing-down density $q(E_0)$ is equal to the neutron production rate Q, we can substitute this in Eq. 6.72 and get instead

$$q(E) = Q \exp{(-P_a)} \tag{6.74}$$

Comparison of this result with Eq. 6.67 shows that we have

$$p(E) = \exp{(-P_a)} \tag{6.75}$$

In all practical cases the exponent is small, so that we can expand it and, neglecting higher terms than the second, obtain the result

$$p(E) = 1 - P_a \tag{6.76}$$

As P_a is the neutron absorption probability, $1 - P_a$ must be probability of the neutron escaping absorption during its passage between the energies E_0 and E, an interpretation which is consistent with the description of $p(E)$ as the resonance escape probability.

6.14   The Effective Resonance Integral

The exponent in Eq. 6.72 as given by Eq. 6.73 is known as the **resonance integral** and, under the assumption of ξ and Σ_s remaining fairly constant over the range of integration, can be written in the convenient form

$$P_a = \int_E^{E_0} \frac{\Sigma_a}{\Sigma_a + \Sigma_s} \frac{d(\log E)}{\xi} = \frac{1}{\xi\Sigma_s} \int_E^{E_0} \frac{\Sigma_a}{1 + \Sigma_a/\Sigma_s} \frac{dE}{E}$$

$$= \frac{N_0}{\xi\Sigma_s} \int_E^{E_0} \frac{\sigma_a}{1 + N_0\sigma_a/\Sigma_s} \frac{dE}{E} \qquad (6.77)$$

The resonance escape probability can therefore be expressed by

$$p = \exp\left[-\frac{N_0}{\xi\Sigma_s} \int_E^{E_0} \frac{\sigma_a}{1 + N_0\sigma_a/\Sigma_s} \frac{dE}{E} \right] \qquad (6.78)$$

The integral in this expression is known as the **effective resonance integral**

$$\int_E^{E_0} \frac{\sigma_a}{1 + N_0\sigma_a/\Sigma_s} \frac{dE}{E} \equiv \int_E^{E_0} (\sigma_a)_{\text{eff}} \frac{dE}{E} \qquad (6.79)$$

and the integrand

$$\frac{\sigma_a}{1 + N_0\sigma_a/\Sigma_s} \equiv (\sigma_a)_{\text{eff}} \qquad (6.80)$$

as the **effective absorption cross section.** The latter represents a smoothed-out effective value of the absorption cross section in a region where the actual absorption cross section varies in a very complicated manner because of the presence of pronounced resonances for neutrons of particular energies (Fig. 7.1). The limits of integration in the effective resonance integral are the energies (or their logarithms) that bound the resonance absorption region. Experimentally, one finds for uranium that $\log E_0 - \log E = 5.6$.†

Similarly, since the resonance absorptions of the various fuels that are of interest in reactor assemblies vary in an irregular manner, the value of the resonance integral must be found empirically. It depends mainly on the ratio of fissionable to moderator material as well as on other factors determined by the type of reactor employed. We shall return to a fuller consideration of these points when we discuss some representative types of reactors and calculate some of the relevant parameters.

The number of nuclei per cubic centimeter, N_0, which appears in Eqs. 6.78, 6.79, and 6.80, refers to the number of resonance absorber nuclei

† More recent investigations indicate that a value of 2.60 gives better over-all agreement with experimental results. (F. L. Fillmore, *Nucl. Sci. and Engin.*, **1**, 355, 1956.)

present; thus if all resonance absorption is ascribable to uranium, N_0 is simply the number of uranium nuclei per cm³.

When the neutrons encounter scattering collisions with several different kinds of nuclei, as is the case when the moderator is a mixture or compound of elements, the product $\xi\Sigma_s$ in the denominator of Eq. 6.78 must be replaced by the sum of terms $\xi_i\Sigma_{si}$ for each type i of scatterer present in accordance with Eq. 6.55.

Since the effect of scattering by the uranium nuclei can be neglected because of the very small value of ξ, which is 0.0084 for U^{238}, and also because these nuclei are only a small fraction of the total number of scatterers present $\Sigma_{su} \ll \Sigma_{sm}$. We can, therefore, set $\Sigma_s = \Sigma_{sm}$.†

PROBLEMS

(1) Obtain the microscopic absorption cross sections σ_a for 1 ev neutrons for the nuclides of Table 6.1 by using the tabulated values for 0.0253 ev neutrons and applying the not $1/v$ factors.

(2) Calculate the de Broglie wavelength in Angstroms (10^{-8} cm) for neutrons of 0.025 ev energy and compare this energy with the X-ray energy (in ev) of equal wavelength. Would these neutrons be suitable for crystal diffraction experiments?

(3) A 2 Mev neutron collides with a Be^9 nucleus and is scattered through an angle of 30°. It then hits a second Be^9 nucleus and is again scattered through 30° but in an opposite direction so that the neutron continues in its original direction. Calculate the neutron energy after the second collision.

(4) Calculate the effective absorption cross section of B^{10} for neutrons with a Maxwell-Boltzmann energy distribution corresponding to a temperature of 440° K.

(5) Calculate the average energy and the most probable energy for neutrons thermalized at liquid nitrogen temperature −196° C.

(6) It is desired to reduce the intensity of a thermal neutron beam by a factor of 1000 by interposing a cadmium foil. Calculate the required foil thickness to achieve this.

(7) A certain $(1/v)$ absorber reduces the intensity of a thermalized neutron beam of effective temperature $T = 300°$ K by 10%. What would be the reduction in intensity if the same experiment were done at a temperature of 327° K?

(8) Derive the energy distribution 6.2 from the velocity distribution 6.1. How do you explain the fact that $E_0 \neq \frac{1}{2}mv_p{}^2$?

(9) Calculate the flux density per unit velocity for the thermal neutron distribution and show that the most probable neutron flux occurs for a value of the velocity $v = v_{rms}$.

(10) Derive Eq. 6.26 by combining Eqs. 6.22 and 6.25 and show that it is equivalent to Eq. 6.31.

† For further details and additional information see, Weinberg and Wigner, op. cit., pp. 300-303.

(11) Calculate the smallest value of A for which the maximum fractional energy loss can be approximated by $4/A$ to within an error of 1%.

(12) Prove that $\displaystyle\int_{\alpha E_0}^{E_0} P(E)\,dE = 1$.

(13) Evaluate the integral in 6.42 and confirm the value $2/3A$ for it.

(14) Calculate the scattering angle in the L system for a neutron colliding with a proton in terms of the scattering angle ϕ in the C.M. system. What is the largest possible angle of scattering in the L system?

(15) (a) By means of Eq. 6.49 calculate ξ for $A = 1$ (hydrogen), following the instructions in the text; (b) what is the average energy lost by a neutron in an elastic collision with a proton?

(16) Evaluate ξ for a Be^9-moderator.

(17) Calculate the sdp and the mr for D_2O, using these numerical values: density of $D_2O = 1.10$ gram/cm^3; $\sigma_s = 10.6$ barns, $\sigma_a = 0.001$ barn.

(18) Derive the result 6.16 for $\bar{\sigma}_a$ by averaging over the energy distribution 6.2 and show that this procedure is equivalent to averaging over the neutron flux distribution.

(19) Calculate $\bar{\sigma}_s$ for the neutron flux between fission energies E_0 and thermal energies E_t, assuming the flux distribution 6.61 for the slowing-down neutrons.

(20) The value of $\overline{\cos\theta}$ for a mixture or compound is obtained by weighting the individual values $2/3A$ with the probability of scattering by each component of the mixture. Derive an expression for $\overline{\cos\theta}$ for a mixture, and by means of it calculate the transport mean free path for fast neutrons in H_2O, assuming the following scattering cross sections: $\sigma_O = 2$ barns; $\sigma_H = 3$ barns.

(21) Calculate the lethargy for 0.025 ev neutrons, assuming zero lethargy for 10 Mev neutrons.

BIBLIOGRAPHY

Curtiss, L. F.: *Introduction to Neutron Physics*, van Nostrand, 1958.

Fermi, E.: *Nuclear Physics*, University of Chicago Press, 1950.

Glasstone, S.: *Principles of Nuclear Reactor Engineering*, van Nostrand, 1955.

Glasstone, S., and M. C. Edlund: *The Elements of Nuclear Reactor Theory*, van Nostrand, 1952.

Halliday, D.: *Introductory Nuclear Physics*, Wiley, 1955.

Hughes, D. J.: *Pile Neutron Research*, Addison-Wesley, 1953.

Hughes, D. J., and R. B. Schwartz: *Neutron Cross Sections*, BNL-325, 2nd ed.

Kaplan, I.: *Nuclear Physics*, Addison-Wesley, 1955.

Littler, D. J., and J. F. Raffle: *An Introduction to Reactor Physics*, Pergamon Press, 1957.

Segrè, E. (Ed.): *Experimental Nuclear Physics*, vol. II, part VII, Wiley, 1953.

Soodak, H., and E. C. Campbell: *Elementary Pile Theory*, Wiley, 1950.

Weinberg, A. M., and E. P. Wigner: *The Physical Theory of Neutron Chain Reactors*, University of Chicago Press, 1958.

Westcott, C. H.: "Effective Cross Sections for Thermal Spectra," *Nucleonics*, **16**, No. 10 (October 1958).

Westcott, C. H.: "The Specification of Neutron Flux and Nuclear Cross Sections in Reactor Calculations," *Jour. of Nucl. Energy*, **2**, 59 (1955).

chapter **7**
The Nuclear Chain Reaction

7.1 Introduction

We have now reached the central theme of our discussion, which is the nuclear chain reaction. By the term *chain reaction*, one understands a self-sustaining process that, once started, needs no additional agents to keep it going. The particular processes with which we are concerned are nuclear fission reactions initiated by neutrons that result in the destruction of fissionable nuclei, the liberation of useful nuclear energy, and the production of a fresh supply of neutrons to replace those that have been used up in previous fission reactions and other processes.

In this chapter we shall follow the life history of a group of neutrons and develop a numerical criterion for a nuclear chain reaction to be possible and apply it to various types of nuclear reactors.

7.2 Neutron Cycle and Multiplication Factor

A self-sustaining chain reaction is possible if v, the number of neutrons released per fission, is sufficiently greater than 1 to compensate for neutron loss due to a variety of causes. Since v is a constant of nature for a given fissionable material and, therefore, beyond human control, the only alternative is to reduce and bypass the various causes which are responsible for the loss of neutrons in a given assembly.

Consider, for example, a natural uranium assembly in which some fission reactions have been initiated and follow the life history of a typical neutron from the instant of its creation as a fast fission neutron, listing the various possible events that may occur during its lifetime.

1. It may be absorbed by U^{238} while its energy is still greater than the threshold energy for U^{238} fission and it may cause a fission of a U^{238} nucleus.

2. It may be absorbed by U^{238} without leading to a fission, i.e., radiative capture. This is most likely to happen for a neutron whose energy has been reduced by elastic collisions to the epithermal region ($\sim$1000 ev to 5 ev), where U^{238} has pronounced absorption resonances (Fig. 7.1).

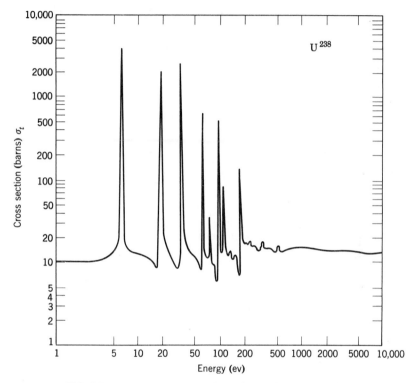

FIG. 7.1. The U^{238} resonance absorption region. (BNL-325.)

3. It may be absorbed by a U^{235} nucleus causing a fission.

4. It may be absorbed by a U^{235} nucleus without causing fission.

5. It may be absorbed by other materials and impurities that are part of the assembly without causing a fission.

6. It may escape from the assembly and be lost by what is called "leakage."

Events (1) and (3) are positive contributions to the neutron economy i.e., they create new neutrons, whereas events (2), (4), (5), and (6) are negative contributions, i.e., they remove available neutrons from the assembly.

Assume we start with n_0 fast neutrons which have just been produced in a uranium assembly. Some of them will cause fissions in U^{238} (event 1), with a consequent increase in the number of fast neutrons. Let us take account of this small increase by means of a factor $\varepsilon > 1$, called the **fast fission factor**.

The number of fast neutrons has now increased to

$$n_0\varepsilon$$

The energy of the fast neutrons is being reduced steadily by collisions with the other nuclei in the assembly until they eventually enter the epithermal energy region with its strong U^{238} absorption resonances (Fig. 7.1). Some of the neutrons will be absorbed by U^{238} (event 2), whereas most of them will escape resonance absorption. The number of neutrons that will pass through this region without being absorbed can be obtained by multiplying the number that enter the region by the resonance escape probability p (6.67). Hence, the number of neutrons surviving thus far is

$$n_0\varepsilon p$$

These neutrons will next reach thermal energies, where their impending fate may be either absorption in U^{235} (events 3 and 4) or absorption in materials other than U^{235} (event 5).

The fraction of thermal neutrons absorbed by the fuel as compared to all thermal neutron absorptions in the assembly is called the **thermal utilization factor** f.

If we now multiply by f the previous number of thermal neutrons, we shall obtain the number of thermal neutrons that are actually absorbed by the fuel, which is

$$n_0\varepsilon pf$$

This number of thermal neutron absorptions will yield a number of fast fission neutrons that is η times as large. Hence, having started with an initial number of n_0 fast neutrons, we have now obtained a new generation of fast neutrons whose total number is

$$n_0\varepsilon pf\eta$$

Hence,

$$\frac{\text{Final number of fast neutrons}}{\text{Initial number of fast neutrons}} = \frac{n_0\varepsilon pf\eta}{n_0}$$

$$= \varepsilon pf\eta \qquad (7.1)$$

This ratio is called the **reproduction** or **multiplication factor** and is denoted by k_∞. The relation

$$k_\infty = \varepsilon p f \eta \qquad (7.2)$$

is known as the **four-factor formula**.

Expression 7.1 can also be interpreted as the ratio of thermal neutrons created per second to the number of thermal neutrons destroyed per second. A schematic picture of the neutron cycle as we have just traced it is shown in Fig. 7.2.

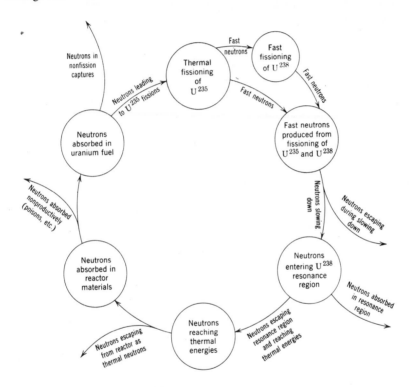

FIG. 7.2. Neutron cycle.

7.3 The Thermal Utilization Factor

When defining f, we conventionally consider the uranium mixture as the fuel, although the thermal neutrons can produce fissions with the U^{235} component only. We must then also use the numerical value for η which applies to the uranium mixture. For the natural mixture this would be $\eta = 1.34$.

Thus, if σ stands for the thermal absorption cross sections and the suffix i referring to all nonuranium materials and impurities and employing an obvious notation, we can write for a natural uranium fuel mixture that

$$f_{(\text{nat})} = \frac{N_{0(235)}\sigma_{(235)} + N_{0(238)}\sigma_{(238)}}{N_{0(235)}\sigma_{(235)} + N_{0(238)}\sigma_{(238)} + N_{0i}\sigma_i} \qquad (7.3)$$

Here, the numerator represents the thermal neutron absorptions by the two uranium isotopes only, and the denominator represents, similarly, the total number of thermal neutron absorptions in the assembly.

Also, by Eq. 5.3

$$\eta_{(\text{nat})} = \frac{\sigma_{f(\text{nat})}}{\sigma_{a(\text{nat})}} \, \nu_{(235)}$$

$$= \frac{N_{0(235)}\sigma_{f(235)}\nu_{(235)}}{N_{0(235)}\sigma_{a(235)} + N_{0(238)}\sigma_{a(238)}} \qquad (7.4)$$

Hence, by multiplying Eqs. 7.3 and 7.4,

$$\eta_{(\text{nat})}f_{(\text{nat})} = \frac{N_{0(235)}\sigma_{f(235)}\nu_{(235)}}{N_{0(235)}\sigma_{a(235)} + N_{0(238)}\sigma_{a(238)} + N_{0i}\sigma_i} \qquad (7.5)$$

Alternatively, considering only the U^{235} portion of the natural uranium mixture as the fuel, we have

$$f_{(235)} = \frac{N_{0(235)}\sigma_{a(235)}}{N_{0(235)}\sigma_{a(235)} + N_{0(238)}\sigma_{a(238)} + N_{0i}\sigma_i} \qquad (7.6)$$

$$\eta_{(235)} = \frac{\sigma_{f(235)}}{\sigma_{a(235)}} \, \nu_{(235)} \qquad (7.7)$$

Therefore $f_{(235)}\eta_{(235)} = \dfrac{N_{0(235)}\sigma_{f(235)}\nu_{(235)}}{N_{0(235)}\sigma_{a(235)} + N_{0(238)}\sigma_{a(238)} + N_{0i}\sigma_i}$

$$= f_{(\text{nat})}\eta_{(\text{nat})} \qquad \text{by Eq. 7.5.}$$

Therefore

$$f_{(\text{nat})}\eta_{(\text{nat})} = f_{(235)}\eta_{(235)} \qquad (7.8)$$

which shows that it is immaterial whether we consider the U^{235} isotope alone or the uranium mixture as a whole as the fuel, provided we match the correct η with the adopted utilization factor f in the four-factor formula.

7.4   Neutron Leakage and Critical Size

In the preceding derivation of the multiplication factor we omitted completely the possibility of leakage from the assembly (event 6) and tacitly assumed zero leakage during the neutron cycle. This omission is tantamount to the assumption of an infinite size for the assembly, because only then can there be no neutron leakage from the system. For that reason, in order to remind us of the implied assumption of an assembly of infinite extent, the suffix ∞ was added to k.

For an assembly of finite dimensions, the **effective reproduction constant** k_{eff} will be less than k_∞ by a factor L, $(L < 1)$, which is determined by the neutron leakage from the system.

$$k_{eff} = k_\infty L \qquad (7.9)$$

We conveniently separate the total leakage effect into two components, a **fast neutron nonleakage factor** l_f, and a **thermal neutron nonleakage factor** l_{th}. This separation is suggested by diffusion theory, which treats the diffusion of fast neutrons and that of thermal neutrons separately. We, therefore, set

$$L = l_f l_{th} \qquad (7.10)$$

The two nonleakage factors are a measure of the fraction of neutrons that do not escape from an assembly of finite size. Hence,

$$k_{eff} = k_\infty l_f l_{th} \qquad (7.11)$$

k_{eff}, for a given reactor system, is the ratio of the number of neutrons (at corresponding stages of the neutron cycle) in successive generations.

This self-multiplication of neutrons is the essential feature of a nuclear chain reaction. The magnitude of k_{eff} determines the speed with which the number of neutrons builds up and the rate at which nuclear fissions occur in the assembly. In a nuclear bomb type of assembly, this build-up must take place very rapidly, whereas in industrial and research reactors this self-multiplication must be slow enough to allow the fission rate to remain always under the control of the operator.

If $k_{eff} > 1$, the assembly continues to produce more neutrons than it consumes and is then said to be **supercritical**.

For $k_{eff} < 1$, fewer neutrons are produced than are consumed. Such an assembly is said to be **subcritical**.

For $k_{eff} = 1$, the rate of neutron production is exactly balanced by the rate of neutron consumption and, in this case, the assembly is called a **critical** one.

If we start with an assembly for which $k_{eff} > 1$, we can decrease k_{eff} by progressively reducing the reactor size, thereby increasing the neutron loss through leakage from the assembly. If this reduction in the dimensions of the assembly is continued until $k_{eff} = 1$, the reactor size of the assembly at that point is called its **critical size**. Thus, the critical size of an assembly is that size for which the rate of neutron loss due to all causes is exactly equal to the rate of neutron production in the assembly.

The fundamental problem in the design of a nuclear reactor is to obtain an assembly with $k_{eff} > 1$. As a first step to this end k_∞ must be calculated and then, by introducing the finite size and geometry of the reactor, k_{eff} can be calculated from the layout and the dimensions of the reactor. Although this plan of action is very straightforward, the actual mathematical work involved can be very complex.

Of the four factors in formula 7.2, η is a constant of nature for a given nuclear fuel† which must be obtained from experimental measurements. The numerical values of this constant for the important nuclear fuels have been listed in Table 5.2. The other three factors allow the nuclear engineer and designer some leeway, as they depend on the physical properties of the fuel as well as on the size of the reactor, its geometry, fuel-arrangement, moderator, as well as on other materials incorporated in the reactor assembly.

If no U^{238} is used as part of the reactor fuel, ε and p differ only very slightly from the numerical value 1; thus the four-factor formula reduces to

$$k_\infty = \eta f \tag{7.12}$$

Although neutron leakage is generally not welcomed by the nuclear engineer, it is important to realize that the critical size requirement for a chain reaction to become possible is a consequence of neutron leakage. It acts as a safeguard against spontaneous chain reactions with small quantities of U^{233}, U^{235}, or Pu^{239} by reducing the number of neutrons from spontaneous fissions to below the minimum number required to sustain continued fission reactions. For these three fuels the number of neutrons generated per neutron absorbed is well above unity (Table 5.2); consequently, in all three materials chain reactions would occur if all the generated neutrons were retained inside the fissionable material.

7.5 Nuclear Reactors and Their Classification

We can classify nuclear reactors according to a variety of characteristic features, such as: (1) type of fuel used; (2) average neutron energy at which the greater part of all fissions occur; (3) moderator material used; (4) arrangement and spatial disposition of fuel and moderator; (5) purpose of the reactor; and (6) other features, such as heat removal methods and coolants employed.

† By changing the composition of the fuel, e.g., increasing the degree of enrichment, a higher value for η could be achieved, but this would no longer be the same given fuel in the sense this term is being used here.

Let us consider and compare some of these features in the given order:

1. The fuels that can be used are uranium containing U^{235} in its natural concentration of 0.715% or in an enriched proportion, U^{233} or Pu^{239}. The fraction of delayed fission neutrons is greatest with U^{235}, which is important from the point of view of reactor control. U^{233} is potentially the most abundant fuel, as the fertile material from which it can be derived, namely, thorium, is about four times as abundant as uranium. Pu^{239} is favored as a fuel in fast breeding reactors (i.e., reactors that convert fertile materials into fissionable materials and create more fuel than they consume) because of its high breeding gain.

U^{233} is the only one of the fuels cited that can sustain a breeding reaction with either thermal or fast neutrons.

2. A fast reactor employs high-energy neutrons to sustain the chain reaction that makes the use of a moderator unnecessary. Enriched uranium and Pu^{239} are suitable fuels for this type of reactor. Natural uranium cannot be used as a fast reactor fuel because it is not possible to achieve a chain reaction with it unless a suitable moderator is also used. An enriched fuel with not less than 25% of fissionable material content (i.e., U^{233}, U^{235}, Pu^{239}) is required for its successful operation. A relatively large amount of fissionable material is needed to reach criticality; however, the critical core size may be only about one foot across because of the elimination of the moderator. This small critical size presents difficult technical problems with respect to the heat removal at high operating power levels.

The main interest in fast reactor design is at present directed towards their application as breeder reactors. Fast reactors require a greater amount of fuel, but parasitic neutron absorption is greatly reduced. The σ_f/σ_c ratio for the fuel is also greater for the fast reactor.

An intermediate reactor uses neutron energies between thermal and several thousand ev, but little information about this type is as yet generally available. †

In a thermal reactor the fissions generally occur at energies that correspond to the temperature of the reactor core. Natural uranium can be used as fuel in this type of reactor if a suitable moderator is employed to assist the neutrons to bypass the U^{238} resonance traps, because the capture cross section of U^{235} for thermal neutrons is considerably greater than any of the competing cross sections.

The thermal reactor was the first type of reactor ever to be assembled and most of the existing reactors are of this type. It still is the backbone of

† Two up-to-date reports have recently joined the declassified list of documents; *Naval Reactors Physics Handbook*, vol. 3 and LAMS-2288, *Physics of Intermediate Reactors* (U. S. Atomic Energy Commission).

reactor engineering and construction and most of the available information is concerned with this type.

3. Commonly used moderators are graphite, light and heavy water, and beryllium or its oxide. The requirements for a good moderator are, as previously noted, light mass of moderator nuclei, small absorption cross section, and large slowing-down power.

Of all moderators, H_2O has the greatest sdp but an appreciable neutron absorption cross section. Heavy water has a very small absorption cross section and the highest moderating ratio of all moderators. Graphite has a very small absorption cross section and the second highest moderating ratio of all moderators. Beryllium, too, has a small absorption cross section and the best sdp of all metals (Table 6.2). Hydrogenous organic compounds have proved to be suitable as moderators and have found some application.

When high concentrations of fissionable materials are used as fuels, moderators are often employed not to improve the neutron balance but to ease the control operations of the nuclear reactor by lengthening the time interval between successive neutron generations.

4. Nuclear reactors are either of the homogeneous type or the heterogeneous type, depending on the fuel moderator arrangement.

In a homogeneous reactor the fissionable material is intimately and uniformly mixed with the moderator, either as a solid mixture, as a slurry, as a liquid solution of a uranium salt in the moderator, or as a solution of uranium in a liquid metal.

In a heterogeneous reactor the fissionable material is concentrated in plates, rods, or hollow cylinders, which are distributed in a regular array according to some geometric pattern or lattice throughout the moderator.

The theory of moderation as outlined earlier assumed a uniform distribution of all materials. It requires some modification in the case of a heterogeneous arrangement which will be introduced later.

Homogeneous thermal reactors employing natural uranium can reach a multiplication factor greater than one only with heavy water as moderator.

However, if the lattice or matrix arrangement (i.e., a heterogeneous system) is employed, a chain reaction becomes possible with natural uranium and graphite as moderator. The increase in the multiplication factor with the heterogeneous arrangement is due mainly to a reduction in the resonance absorption of the neutrons by the U^{238} which results in an increased value for p.

5. The chief purposes for which nuclear reactors have been built are either for research, for thermal or electric power production, for breeding, for propulsion, or for a combination of these with a variety of subdivisions possible.

6. In order to remove the heat that is being generated in the reactor core as a result of the fissioning taking place, materials are employed that are known as **coolants**, which are circulated through the core for the purpose of abstracting the heat and transferring it to the outside of the core where it can be utilized for various purposes. Possible coolants are ordinary water circulated under pressure, heavy water, liquid metal coolants such as sodium or sodium-potassium alloy, and mercury. In some reactor designs, air is circulated at subatmospheric pressure (open cycle), in others, high-pressure gas coolants such as He, CO_2, or N_2 are used. In still others, the heat is removed by pumping the fuel solution through an external heat exchanger and then returning it to the reactor core (closed cycle).

It is obvious from this multiplicity of choice, that numerous possible combinations of the various components described can be selected for the design and planning of a nuclear reactor. Considering the great number of variables that are at the disposal of the nuclear engineer, it should cause little surprise that well over a hundred designs for power reactors alone have been proposed. To these must be added a variety of research reactors and experimental units which have already been built and which still make up the majority of the reactors which have progressed from the planning to the operating stage. In Tables 7.1 to 7.10 are listed some of the better known units of various types to which frequent reference is made in the literature on nuclear reactors.

7.6 Power Reactors

To give a short description of some of them, we shall start with power reactors, and of these we select four main types: (1) the pressurized water reactor (PWR); (2) the boiling water reactor (BWR); (3) the gas-cooled, natural uranium, graphite-moderated reactor; and (4) the homogeneous reactor.

The primary purpose of a power reactor is the utilization of the fission energy which is being produced in the reactor core and to convert it into useful power. The main task of the nuclear engineer consists in devising means and developing designs that will permit the efficient and economical exploitation of this energy source. Some ways by which this conversion can be achieved are indicated in Figs. 7.3, 7.4, and 7.7.†

The Pressurized Water Reactor   (Table 7.1)

Figure 7.3 is a schematic diagram of a pressurized water reactor (PWR). This is a heterogeneous reactor that uses slightly enriched uranium (1.4%

† For a summary survey of power reactor developments, see "Atomic Energy Facts," published by the U. S. Atomic Energy Commission, Chapter 5 and Table 24.

TABLE 7.1　Power Reactors

Pressurized Water Type (PWR)

Name, Location, Comments	Fuel and Fuel Arrangement	Moderator and Reflector	Coolant	Power (kw) (Thermal)	Size
Shippingport, Penn.	93% enriched Zr-U alloy plate elements, natural UO_2 pellets in tubes; 14 tons natural UO_2, 75 kg U^{235}	H_2O	H_2O, 2000 psi	230,000 (60,000 el)	Core: cylinder 6.8 ft diam., 5.9 ft high
Yankee (Rowe, Mass.)	~3% enriched UO_2 rods; 25 tons; pellets assembled in SS-tube to form fuel rod	H_2O	H_2O, 2000 psi	400,000 (130,000 el)	
CETR (Consolidated Edison thorium reactor, Indian Point)	90% enriched UO_2, 1.1 ton; ThO_2 19.2 tons; 4% over-all enrichment, rod-shaped fuel elements	H_2O	H_2O, 1500 psi	585,000 (160,000 el)	
APPR-1 (Army package power reactor)	Flat-plate sandwich-type elements; highly enriched UO_2; SS cladding	H_2O	H_2O, 1200 psi	10,000 (1850 el)	Cylinder ~4 ft high ~7 ft base radius
S1W (STR-1; STR-2), submarine thermal reactor; world's first mobile unit	Enriched uranium-zirconium sheathing; first major use of Zr	H_2O	H_2O	18,000	
N. S. Savannah	4% enriched, sintered UO_2 pellets; 330 kg U^{235}	H_2O	H_2O	74,000	Core: cylinder 5.1 ft diam., 5.5 ft high
BR-3 (Mol, Belgium)	4.5% enriched UO_2; 2.8 tons	H_2O	H_2O	43,000	
NPDR (nuclear power demonstration reactor, Canada)	Natural uranium oxide pellets in zirc-aloy tubes, ~8 tons of uranium oxide, 120 rods of 19 tubes each	D_2O	D_2O	75,000–100,000	Core tank: 10 ft high 12 ft diam.
APS-1 (atomic power station, Russia)	550 kg of 5% enriched uranium; fuel tubes in concentric cooling channel tubes	H_2O and graphite	H_2O, 100 atm	50,000 (5×10^{13} thermal flux)	Core size: 5 ft diam., $5\frac{1}{2}$ ft high

TABLE 7.2 Power Reactors
Boiling Water Type (BWR)

Name, Location, Comments	Fuel and Fuel Arrangement	Moderator	Reflector	Coolant	Power (kw) (Thermal)	Flux (Thermal)	Size
BER-1 ("Borax") (boiling reactor experiment, Arco, Idaho) destroyed in "runaway" test	30 MTR-type fuel elements; fuel core 2 ft × 2 ft × 2½ ft test	H_2O	H_2O, 16 in.	H_2O	1200	10^{13}	Tank: 4 ft diam., 13 ft high
BER-2 as above	Similar to BER-1	H_2O	H_2O, 7 in.	H_2O	6400	3.5×10^{13}	Similar to BER-1
BER-3 (Arco, BWR power plant prototype)	MTR-type fuel elements, 54 cm core rad., 65 cm high	H_2O	H_2O, 5 in.	H_2O	12,000	3×10^{13}	Similar to BER-1
EBWR (experimental BWR, Argonne NL)	Sandwich-type plates assembled into 112 fuel elements of 6 plates each over-all enrichment 1.44%; 75 kg U^{235}, 4535 kg U^{238}	H_2O	H_2O, 1½ ft	H_2O, 600 psi	20,000 (5000 el)	10^{13}	Core cylinder: 4 ft diam., 4 ft high
SPERT-1 (special power excursion reactor test, Arco, Idaho)	MTR-type plates of highly enriched uranium; 168 kg U^{235}	H_2O	H_2O, 15 in.	H_2O, normal pressure	10^6		Steel tank: 4 ft diam., 10 ft high
VBWR (Vallecitos)	90% enriched fuel plates; 30 kg UO_2	H_2O	H_2O	H_2O	30,000		
Dresden power station (Morris, Ill.)	66 ton UO_2, 1.5% enriched Zr-clad rods	H_2O	H_2O	H_2O, 1000 psi	650,000 (180,000 el)		
Norwegian power reactor (Halden)	Slightly enriched uranium	D_2O	D_2O	D_2O	20,000		
ALPR (Argonne low power reactor)	40 plate-type elements; 91% enriched; 14 kg U^{235} Al-Ni cladding	H_2O	H_2O	H_2O	3000	7.5×10^{12}	Core size: cylinder 2½ ft diam., 2 ft high

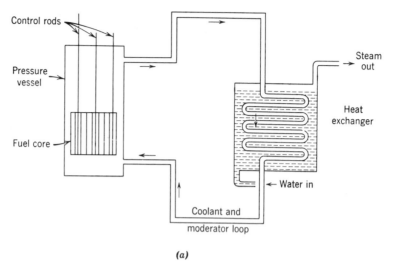

(a)

FIG. 7.3a. Schematic diagram of a pressurized water reactor.

to 2% of U^{235}) as fuel and light water as moderator and coolant.† The core is contained in a pressure vessel under a pressure of 1000 to 2000 psi, with water being circulated by means of a pump through the core and an external heat exchanger.

The purpose of the heat exchanger is the abstraction of heat energy from the coolant in order to make it available for conversion into other forms of energy in a (for the engineer) conventional manner. The maintenance of a high pressure in the core and coolant loop is essential in order to raise the boiling point of the coolant to a high enough temperature (300 to 400° C) which will permit a satisfactory thermodynamic efficiency to be achieved for the heat transfer cycle.

Examples of this reactor type are the Shippingport, Pennsylvania, installation and the reactor unit on the U.S.S. Nautilus (Table 7.1).

An interesting variant of this reactor type is the nuclear power demonstration reactor (NPDR) being built in Canada which is designed to employ D_2O as moderator-coolant instead of the more traditional light water (Table 7.1).

The Boiling Water Reactor   (Table 7.2)

Figure 7.4a shows a boiling water reactor diagram which also uses light water as moderator-coolant. In contrast to the PWR, however, steam is

† With light water as moderator a minimum enrichment of ~1% is required.

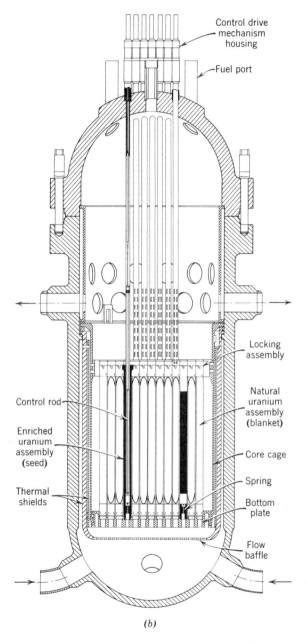

FIG. 7.3*b*. The Shippingport PWR fuel core assembly and pressure vessel.

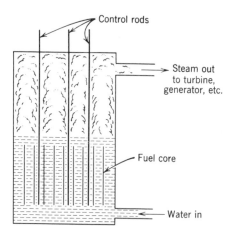

FIG. 7.4. Boiling water reactor. (*a*) Schematic diagram.

generated in the reactor core itself with this unit, which is then passed directly to the turbines without having to go first through an intermediate heat exchanger. Enriched uranium is used to fuel this reactor with a possible degree of enrichment that can vary within rather wide limits. Working examples of this type are the BORAX reactors, one of which was used to supply light and power to Arco, Idaho, for about an hour in 1955.

The experimental boiling water reactor (EBWR) at Argonne National Laboratory, which develops a power of 5000 kw (electrical), was the first of the reactors to be completed under the AEC's nuclear power development program (Fig. 7.4*b*).

The first BWR which uses D_2O as moderator is the Halden (Norway) reactor which has a designed thermal power of 20,000 kw. This reactor is the only D_2O moderated BWR that has been constructed so far. An important advantage of the D_2O moderated BWR is the high **conversion ratio**, i.e., the number of new fissionable or fuel nuclei produced per fuel nucleus consumed in the reactor. With natural uranium a ratio of nearly unity can be reached in this reactor.

Extensive tests have shown that the BWR is a comparatively safe reactor type and that a properly designed BWR is largely self-regulatory. A sudden power surge, should it occur, will induce the formation of steam bubbles or steam voids in the liquid moderator, thus reducing the thermalization of neutrons while increasing the neutron leakage rate. As a consequence, the fissioning rate and, hence, the power production will fall.

There is, however, some evidence that under certain conditions of operation power oscillations with increasing amplitudes can occur so that the claim of inherent stability of these reactors should be regarded with

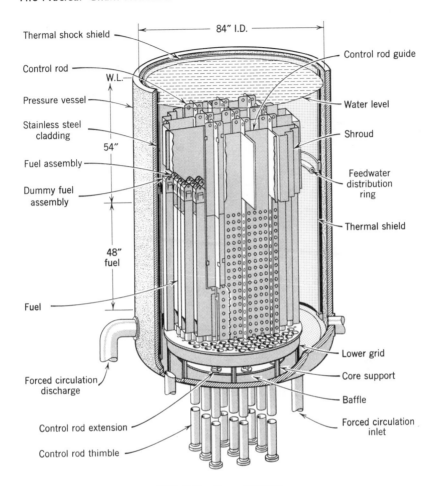

FIG. 7.4*b*. Core of EBWR.

some reservation until sufficient information about the origin and cause of these power oscillations becomes available (see J. A. Thie, *Nucleonics*, **16**, No. 3, 102 (1958)).

Many of the designed power reactors which are fueled with enriched uranium are of the heterogeneous type to ensure a maximum contact area between fuel and coolant for the effective transfer of heat from the fuel to the circulating coolant.

FUEL ELEMENTS. The fuel elements that have been used in reactor design are of two main types, the cylindrical rod type with or without a fin attachment, and the plate or sandwich type (Fig. 7.5). For reactors

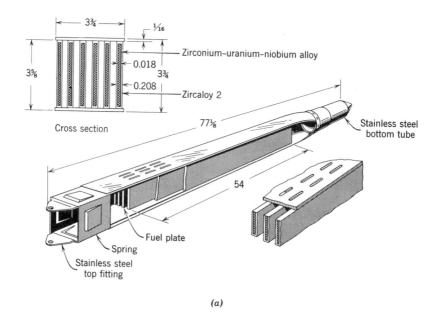

(a)

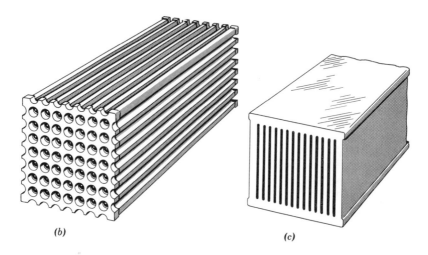

(b)   (c)

FIG. 7.5. Typical fuel element shapes. (a) EBWR fuel element. (b, c) Fuel elements for the Shippingport PWR. b—Uranium oxide pellets in tubing of zircaloy with coolant able to flow through tubes. c—U^{235} used as fuel with zircaloy cladding, with coolant flowing through channels. (d) Cross sectional view of sandwich-type fuel element as used in MTR. (e) Cross section through a fuel element of the Halden (Norway) heavy water reactor.

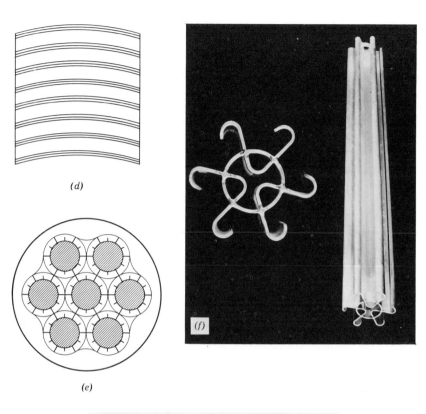

(d)

(e)

(f)

(g)

FIG. 7.5ƒ. New, enriched fuel elements of the Brookhaven National Laboratory uranium–graphite reactor. (Courtesy of Brookhaven National Laboratory). (g) Fuel element cross sections of the Canadian NRX-reactor (rod elements) and NRU-reactor (plate-type elements). (Courtesy of Atomic Energy of Canada Limited.)

operating at fairly high power levels the former are less suitable because of their relatively small contact area with the coolant, which is not sufficient for the required rate of heat removal from the core; the sandwich type is generally preferred.

The fuel elements must be "canned," i.e., they must be completely enclosed by cladding materials and sealed in to prevent corrosion of the fuel material by contact with the coolants, and also to retain the radioactive fission products and prevent their escape into the exposed parts of the unit. Aluminum and, to an increasing extent, zirconium are being widely used as cladding material.

The fuel elements can be either pure uranium metal or uranium oxide, UO_2. The advantages of the oxide are its longer fuel life and its compatibility with hot water. The pure unalloyed metal undergoes violent chemical reactions when it comes in contact with hot water. On the other hand, the main drawback in the employment of the oxide fuel element is its rather low thermal conductivity as compared to that of the pure metal.† Nevertheless, the use of UO_2 as a fuel in large power reactors is very likely to increase in the further development of the preceding class of reactors.

Water-cooled and -moderated reactors of the type so far described employ lattices of relatively low moderator to fuel ratio, and enriched fuel is required for their successful operation. All existing designs necessitate the use of pressure vessels to contain the core, but their size can be of a reasonable diameter for relatively high power output because of the high fuel to moderator ratio used. They have generally relatively high power densities (i.e., power per unit volume) and high specific powers (i.e., power per unit mass of fuel).

The Gas-Cooled, Natural Uranium-Graphite Reactor   (Table 7.3)

A third type of power reactor which, together with the previous two, can be considered to have become more or less standardized is the gas-cooled, natural uranium-graphite-moderated reactor (Fig. 7.6). It holds a special attraction because it can be constructed and operated without the use of fuel or moderator that requires isotope separation. The graphite moderator must be of a high degree of purity, containing a minimum amount of parasitic absorbers, and the fuel must be of uranium metal. As a coolant either nitrogen or carbon dioxide can be used. The fuel to moderator ratio must be chosen close to the value giving maximum k for the reactor geometry selected. The fuel elements are inserted in fuel channels that pass through the graphite moderator at regularly repeating intervals. The

† It has been found that the addition of small amounts of Y_2O_3 or Nb_2O_5 to the uranium oxide greatly improves its thermal conductivity (see *Nucleonics*, **17**, No. 11, p. 156).

TABLE 7.3 Power Reactors

Graphite-Moderated, Natural Uranium Reactors

Name, Location, Comments	Arrangement	Fuel and Fuel Arrangement	Moderator	Coolant	Power (Mw) (Thermal)
Calder Hall, England	Heterogeneous	Natural uranium, 130 tons, finned, cylindrical fuel elements, 1.15 in. diam., 3.5 ft long; Mg-alloy clad; core size 31 ft diam., 21 ft high	Graphite, 3 ft graphite reflector	CO_2 under pressure	8×180
Windscale, England, BNL-type, (optimized for Pu production)	Heterogeneous	Similar to BEPO 235 tons, finned cylinder fuel-elements; Al-clad	Graphite, graphite reflector	Air at atm pressure	160
G-1, Marcoule, France (Pu production 15 kg/year)	Heterogeneous	Similar to BNL reactor, 100 ton natural uranium, Mg-clad fuel elements, 2.6 cm diam., 10 cm long; cylindrical core, 32 ft diam., 29 ft long	Graphite, 2 ft of graphite reflector	Air at atm pressure	40, 5.5×10^{12} thermal neutron flux
G-2 (Marcoule, France) Pu-production	Heterogeneous	Similar to G-1	Graphite	CO_2 under pressure	150 (30 el)
G-3, Marcoule, France	Heterogeneous	Similar to G-1	Graphite	CO_2 under pressure	150 (30 el)
EDF-1, France	Heterogeneous	140 tons natural uranium	Graphite	CO_2 under pressure	300

FIG. 7.6. Fuel loading face of G-1 Marcoule reactor—natural uranium—graphite-moderated. (Courtesy Commissariat à l'Energy Atomique, through French Embassy Press and Information Division.)

gas coolant passes through the fuel channels and carries away the heat generated in the fuel elements.

The British Calder Hall reactor with a power of 182,000 kw belongs to this category of power reactors. Another important function of this reactor, besides the generation of power, is the production of Pu^{239}.

The Oak Ridge National Laboratory reactor of this type with a power of 700,000 kw uses partly enriched fuel in the form of UO_2 fuel elements and He-gas as coolant.

The French reactors at Marcoule, the G1, G2, and G3, are dual-purpose reactors designed for plutonium production and for the production of electrical power.

The Homogeneous Reactor (Table 7.4)

A homogeneous reactor is shown schematically in Fig. 7.7. The active solution of uranylsulfate (or nitrate) in light or heavy water circulates directly through the heat-exchanger and back to the active core which is contained in a stainless steel sphere. The size of this sphere is large enough to contain a sufficient amount of material for a chain reaction to be possible in the core itself (i.e., critical mass) but nowhere else in the system. The system as a whole is kept under pressure to enable the liquid to reach an operating temperature which is well above the normal boiling point of the solvent.

An attractive feature of this type of reactor is the continuous operation that is possible without the need for periodic shutdowns to replenish the burnt-up fuel or to remove the Pu^{239} produced. A portion of the solution can be withdrawn for reprocessing and additional fuel can be introduced to compensate for fuel consumed without interfering with the continued operation of the reactor. It is essentially self-regulating and stable during operation, which obviates the need for elaborate control mechanisms. The operating power level is determined by the rate of heat removal from the reactor, and if this remains steady the reactor maintains a steady operating temperature also.[†]

The use of a highly enriched fuel solution makes possible the attainment of a high neutron flux and of a power level of several thousand kilowatts for a relatively small reactor size. Its small critical size with its high power density and specific power are distinct advantages of this class of reactors.

By surrounding the active core with a blanket of fertile material this type of reactor can also be used as a breeder reactor of relatively high breeding ratio.

† The corrosive effect of the solution on the reactor components presents a problem and gold or platinum cladding must be used for their protection. In addition, the high activity of the circulating fuel solution ($\sim 10^9$ curies) requires effective shielding of the primary cooling system, which is a major difficulty.

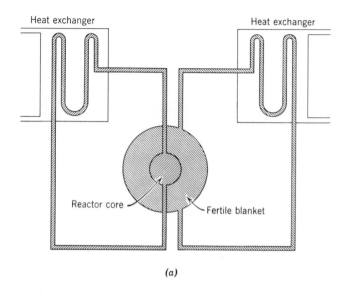

Heat exchanger

Heat exchanger

Reactor core

Fertile blanket

(a)

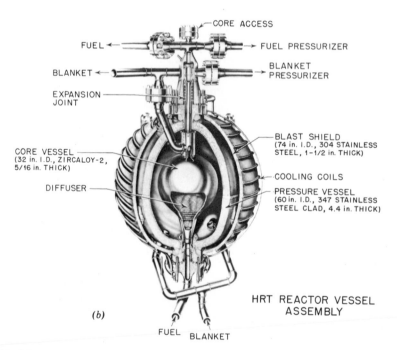

CORE ACCESS

FUEL

FUEL PRESSURIZER

BLANKET

BLANKET
PRESSURIZER

EXPANSION
JOINT

BLAST SHIELD
(74 in. I.D., 304 STAINLESS
STEEL, 1-1/2 in. THICK)

CORE VESSEL
(32 in. I.D., ZIRCALOY-2,
5/16 in. THICK)

COOLING COILS

DIFFUSER

PRESSURE VESSEL
(60 in. I.D., 347 STAINLESS
STEEL CLAD, 4.4 in. THICK)

HRT REACTOR VESSEL
ASSEMBLY

(b)

FUEL   BLANKET

FIG. 7.7. Homogeneous reactor. (*a*) Schematic diagram. (*b*) Reactor vessel assembly of the HRE-2. (Courtesy of Oak Ridge National Laboratory.)

TABLE 7.4 Power Reactors

Homogeneous, Enriched Uranium Type

Name, Location, Comments	Fuel and Fuel Arrangement	Moderator	Reflector	Coolant	Power (kw) (Thermal)	Flux (Thermal)	Size
HRE-1 (homogeneous reactor exper.), Oak Ridge NL (dismantled 1954)	Over 90% enriched uranium sulfate solution; 3 kg U^{235}, pressurized to 1000 psi	H_2O	D_2O, 10 in.	Fuel solution is pumped through external heat exchanger	1000 (140 el)	1.9×10^{13}	Stainless steel sphere $1\frac{1}{2}$ ft diam.
HRE-2 (HRT), Oak Ridge NL	90% enriched uranylsulfate, 4 kg U^{235}, 2000 psi	D_2O	D_2O, 14 in.	As above	5000 to 10,000 (300 el)		$2\frac{2}{3}$ ft diam. sphere
LAPRE-1 (Los Alamos power reactor exp.) dismantled in 1957 after mechanical failure	90% enriched uranyl-phosphate solution; 4.2 kg U^{235} in core, 4000 psi	H_2O	Steel (3 in.) and H_2O	Fuel solution forced through heat exchanger	2000	1.7×10^{13}	Cylinder core: 15 in. diam.,16 in. high
LAPRE-2, Los Alamos	As above; 2.8 kg U^{235}; gold (or Pt)-cladding necessary to withstand corrosive effect of fuel solution	H_2O	Graphite, 11 in.	Natural circulation of fuel solution	1000	1.2×10^{13}	Core cylinder: 15 in. diam., 2 ft high

The HRE (homogeneous reactor experiment) at Oak Ridge National Laboratory is the prototype of a homogeneous power reactor, and its forerunner, the HRE-1 (later dismantled), was one of the earliest power reactors to produce electrical power from nuclear fission energy.[†] That reactor operated at a power of 1000 kw using a 93% enriched uranium sulfate solution contained in a stainless steel sphere of 18 in. diameter.

ORGANIC MODERATORS (Table 7.5). The employment of water as moderator-coolant has certain drawbacks such as the need of high pressurization for reactors which must operate at high temperatures in order to prevent the water from boiling, as well as the need to use special materials to contain the water because of the highly corrosive property of pure hot water. Some of these drawbacks can be circumvented by the employment of organic moderator-coolants such as polyphenyls or their derivatives. These substances have high enough boiling points to permit their use at fairly high steam temperatures without the need for pressurization.

The prototype of this arrangement is the OMRE (organic moderated reactor experiment) which is designed to operate at power levels of 5000 to 16,000 kw.

An additional advantage of some significance which ought to be mentioned in connection with organic moderator-coolants is the low induced radioactivity in the pure materials.[‡]

7.7 Reactor Control

Reactor control provisions are included in all reactor designs, the most common being control by means of movable neutron absorbing control rods which can be inserted in the core or the reflector (see page 267) of the reactor installation. Control by means of control rods is normally of three degrees of effectiveness: (1) a fine control by means of "regulating rods"; (2) a coarse or "shim" control; and (3) an emergency or "scramming" control, which shuts down the reactor immediately.

Other methods of control are available in the form of fuel control or configuration control. In the former method fuel is either added or withdrawn; in the latter method the neutron multiplication of the system is altered by changing the reflector configuration or that of other movable reactor parts, thus affecting the neutron leakage loss. .

Control by the insertion or the withdrawal of strong neutron absorbing

---

† The first reactor to produce electricity from nuclear energy was the Argonne National Laboratory's EBR-1 in Idaho.

‡ See C. A. Trilling, "OMRE Operating Experience," *Nucleonics*, **17**, No. 11, November 1959.

TABLE 7.5 Power Reactors

Miscellaneous Types

Name, Location, Comments	Fuel and Fuel Arrangements	Moderator and Reflector	Coolant	Power (kw) (Thermal)	Size
SRE (sodium reactor experiment, Calif.)	2.8% enriched uranium, 62.5 kg U^{235}; 2190 kg U^{238}; slugs in stainless steel jacket tubes	Graphite	Sodium	20,000 (6000 el) (3.5 × 10^{13} thermal neutron flux)	Cylinder core: 6 ft diam., 6 ft high
LMFR (liquid metal fuel reactor, homogeneous type) prototype, BNL design	90% enriched uranium dissolved in Bi. Later, U^{233} to be used. Thorium blanket around fuel loop	Graphite	U-Bi solution circulating, transferring heat to intermediate and Na loops	10,000	
OMRE (organic moderated reactor experiment; Arco, Idaho)	Highly enriched (∼90%) UO$_2$ stainless steel fuel plates, sandwich-type, stainless steel cladding. 25.5 kg U^{235}	Diphenyl and terphenyl	Diphenyl and terphenyl, 300 psi	16,000 (thermal neutron flux: 3 × 10^{13})	Core: 22$\frac{1}{2}$ in. square by 36 in. high; pressure vessel: 4.5 ft diam. by 24 ft high

materials in the shape of rods or strips is particularly suited to the control of thermal reactors because of the high thermal neutron cross sections of the materials that are incorporated in the control rods, such as boron, cadmium, or hafnium.

The fuel control method is best suited for homogeneous or liquid fuel reactors, where this method presents no difficulty. The addition of "poisons," such as a boron salt solution, is difficult to reverse and is normally employed only as a shutdown measure.

7.8   Reactor Shielding

All nuclear reactors, except those operating near zero power level, are sources of intense neutron and γ-radiation and represent, therefore, a serious health hazard to the operating personnel and research workers. Provisions for their health protection must therefore be made by surrounding the reactor core and active components with a radiation shield. This consists usually of about 6 to 8 ft of high density concrete or of an equivalent thickness of other suitable materials. Because of this shield's primary function of health protection it is generally known as the **biological shield**. Through the absorption of neutrons and γ-radiation, that part of the shield which is in immediate contact with the core can heat up considerably and may require special cooling facilities in order to prevent it from cracking or suffering other heat damage. For this reason, the inner portion of the shield generally known as the **thermal shield**, is usually constructed of steel plates.

7.9   Research Reactors

The design of research reactors is aimed at providing relatively high neutron flux densities for experimental work and making the neutrons accessible to the experimenter. In contrast with power reactors, the power produced here in the form of heat is an undesirable by-product which should be kept to a minimum in order to eliminate the need for elaborate cooling arrangements.

By starting with Eq. 4.28, it follows easily that the average thermal flux ϕ and the reactor power P for U^{235} fuel are related by the expression

$$\phi = \frac{P\,(\text{watts})}{m\,(\text{grams})} \times 4 \times 10^{10}\ n/\text{cm}^2\ \text{sec}$$

which indicates that the flux ϕ is determined by the **specific power** P/m of the reactor. Since m is proportional to the volume of the reactor core, it is seen that, to achieve a given flux ϕ, the necessary power can be reduced by making the core volume smaller. With a good moderator like D_2O and enriched fuel a very compact size (linear dimensions of the order of 1 ft) is possible without falling below the critical size requirement.

A somewhat more realistic estimate of the neutron flux, instead of the optimum expression given earlier, is about one-third less, so that one can take the average thermal flux to be given approximately by

$$\phi_{th} = 2.6 \times 10^{10} \times \frac{P\,(\text{watts})}{m\,(\text{grams})}$$

where m is the critical mass of the reactor fuel U^{235}.

Experimental facilities are provided by openings that lead into the reactor core ("glory hole") or into the lattice where the neutron flux will be composed of the entire reactor spectrum, with fast neutron flux and thermal neutron flux in about equal proportions. If openings are provided leading into the moderator region where no fuel is present, the neutron flux will be preponderantly thermal, with some admixture of fast neutrons, however, since the fission neutron flux decreases exponentially with distance from the fuel.

If well-thermalized neutrons are required, use is made of a **thermal column**, which is an extension of the moderator against a portion of one side of the reactor from which the reactor shielding has been removed.

We shall here describe four main types of research reactors: (1) the water boiler (Table 7.6); (2) the swimming pool (Table 7.7); (3) the tank-type reactor (Tables 7.8 and 7.9); and (4) the graphite-moderated reactor (Table 7.10).

The Water Boiler   (Table 7.6)

The water boiler (Fig. 7.8) is usually a homogeneous mixture of a highly enriched uranium salt dissolved in ordinary water and contained in a small stainless steel vessel surrounded by a reflector and shield. Unless the reactor is run at a very low power (a few watts), a stainless steel cooling coil must be provided inside the core. Furthermore, the vessel must also be provided with a gas circulation and recombination system because considerable amounts of H_2 and O_2 are dissociated during the operation of the reactor due to the intense ionizing radiation in the core.

A good example of this type of reactor is the SUPO at Los Alamos which has been in operation since 1951. It is run at about 50 kw and provides a neutron flux of $\sim 10^{12}$. The fuel solution normally contains about 1 kg of highly enriched uranium salt in a total volume of 15 liters.

This reactor type is not to be confused with the BWR described earlier,

FIG. 7.8. The Armour Research Foundation water boiler reactor. (*a*) Stainless steel reactor core with coolant circulating coils.

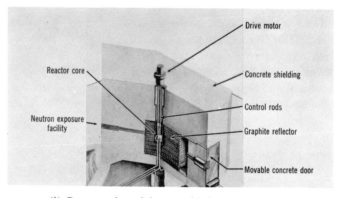

(*b*) Cutaway view of the assembled reactor facility.

although the similarity in denotation may be misleading. The reason for the term "water boiler" is because of the fact that a sudden increase in power will cause the formation of steam bubbles in the solution, which in turn will quickly shut down the reactor. This behavior is an important safety feature of this reactor type. Under normal operating conditions boiling does not occur, since the temperature of the fuel solution is generally kept below 80° C by a water coolant circulating through the coils inside the core vessel.

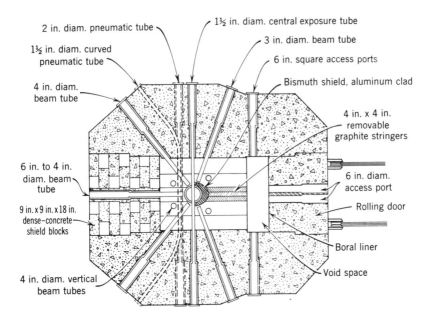

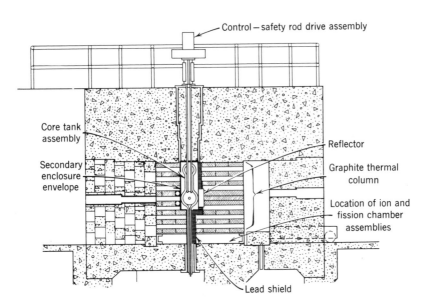

FIG. 7.8c. Cross sections through the installation. (Courtesy of Armour Research Foundation.)

TABLE 7.6 Water Boiler Research Reactors

Enriched Uranium, Homogeneous Type

Name, Location, Comments	Fuel and Fuel Arrangement	Moderator	Reflector	Coolant	Power (kw) (Thermal)	Thermal Flux	Size
LOPO (low power water boiler, world's first water boiler), Los Alamos	Enriched uranyl sulfate solution; 15 liters; 580 grams U^{235}, 3380 grams U^{238}	H_2O	BeO and graphite	H_2O	5×10^{-5}		One ft diameter stainless steel sphere, 15 liter
HYPO (high power WB, replaced LOPO), Los Alamos	Enriched U-nitrate solution, 897 grams U^{235}, 5341 grams U^{238}	H_2O	BeO and graphite	H_2O	6	3×10^{11}	As above
SUPO (super power WB, replaced HYPO) Los Alamos	90% enriched U-nitrate, 0.8 kg in 13 liters	H_2O	Graphite	H_2O	35–45	1.7×10^{12}	As above
WBNS (water boiler neutron source) NAA, Calif.	90% enriched uranyl nitrate solution, 700 grams U^{235}	H_2O	Graphite	—	0.005	2×10^8	As above
Water boiler, Livermore, Cal.	UO_2SO_4-solution, 694 grams U^{235}, 2950 grams U^{238}	H_2O	Graphite	H_2O	0.1–0.5	$10^9 - 2 \times 10^{10}$	As above
North Carolina State College reactor, (first university reactor)	90% enriched UO_2SO_4 solution, 848 grams U^{235} 14 liters	H_2O	Graphite	H_2O	10	5×10^{11} (average 2×10^{11})	Stainless steel cylinder $10\frac{3}{4}$ ft diam., 11 ft high
HRE-1 (homogen. reactor exper.) Oak Ridge NL, replaced by HRE-2	90% enriched uranyl sulfate under 1000 psi pressure	H_2O	D_2O	solution circulat. through heat exch.	1000		$1\frac{1}{2}$ ft stainless steel sphere
ARR (Armour research reactor) Chicago	88% enriched uranyl sulfate	H_2O	Graphite	H_2O	50	10^{12}	15 liter spherical core
KEWB (kinetic exper. WB), Atomics Internl., Calif.	90% enriched uranyl sulfate 1750 grams U^{235}	H_2O	Graphite	H_2O	50	9×10^{11}	$1\frac{1}{4}$ ft diam. stainless steel sphere
Proserpine (Saclay, France)	Plutonium salt in light water solution	H_2O	BeO and graphite	—	0.001	5×10^7	

The Swimming Pool Reactor   (Table 7.7)

This reactor (Fig. 7.9) contains a large amount of highly purified water (100 to 200 meters^3) in a concrete tank into which is immersed the fuel assembly attached to a steel framework and suspended from a bridge which spans the width of the swimming pool.

The fuel core consists of a rectangular assembly of plate type fuel elements made up of highly enriched uranium alloy and clad with aluminum which is immersed from 5 to 7 meters below the water surface. The total amount of fuel is about 3 kg of uranium.

The water in the pool plays the triple role of moderator, coolant, and shield. Convective cooling is sufficient for power levels up to 100 kw. Beyond that, resort must be had to forced cooling by means of pumps to cause a downward flow of the water. This is necessary because of the $O^{16}(n, p)N^{16}$ reaction which is of considerable practical importance with water-cooled reactors in general. The product nucleus of this reaction, N^{16}, is short-lived, having a half-life of 7.35 sec, and emits a very penetrating γ-radiation of 6.2 Mev energy in 82% of the disintegrations. The downward draft of the forced circulation prevents the radioactive N^{16} from reaching the surface and contaminating the air.

At a power level of 100 kw the neutron flux available for experimentation is 10^{12}. The first reactor of this type at Oak Ridge was designed with the view of allowing radiation effects on bulky materials to be observed by immersing them in the water surrounding the core. The mobility of the reactor core is very convenient for the preparation and rearrangement of experimental set-ups.

The BSF (bulk shielding facility) at Oak Ridge and the NRLR (Naval Research Laboratory reactor) are large open pool reactors of this type.

The Tank-Type Reactor   (Tables 7.8 and 7.9)

This reactor (Fig. 7.10) is very similar to the swimming pool as regards the reactor core, but the size of the pool has been reduced considerably to that of a tank. With proper heat removal equipment the operating power of these reactors can be pushed high enough to provide a neutron flux of 10^{14}. The highest experimental flux attained so far is made available in the MTR (materials testing reactor) at Arco, Idaho, which uses 4 kg of highly enriched uranium assembled in standard fuel elements with aluminum cladding. It is a water-cooled and moderated tank-type reactor, with an available average neutron flux of 2×10^{14} at a reactor power of 30,000 kw.

A number of tank-type research reactors employ D_2O instead of light water as moderator-coolant as, for example, the CP-5 at Argonne National Laboratory, which uses about 1 to 2 kg of 90% enriched uranium, alloyed and assembled with aluminum. At an operating power of 1000 kw this

(c) The University of Michigan Ford Reactor is a swimming pool type that has two compartments and a movable core. (Courtesy University of Michigan.)

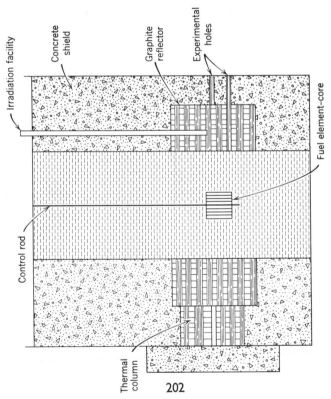

Irradiation facility

Concrete shield

Graphite reflector

Experimental holes

Control rod

Fuel element-core

Thermal column

FIG. 7.9a. Schematic side view of swimming pool reactor.

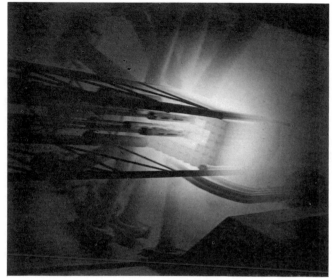

(d) Fuel core of reactor during full power operation. (Courtesy of Dr. J. L. Shapiro, University of Michigan, Dept. of Nuclear Engineering.)

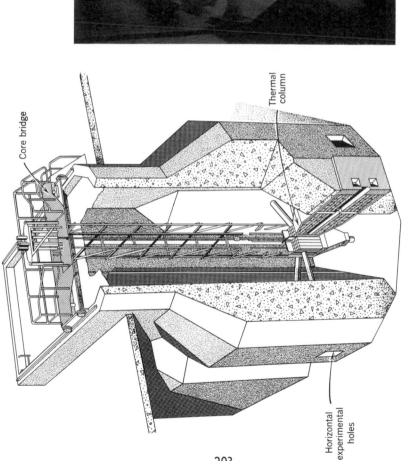

Core bridge

Thermal column

Horizontal experimental holes

FIG. 7.9b. Two compartment swimming pool reactor. (Courtesy of Bendix Aviation Corporation.)

TABLE 7.7 Research Reactors

Light-Water-Moderated, Enriched Uranium Reactors—Swimming Pool Type

Name, Location, Comments	Fuel and Fuel Arrangement	Moderator	Reflector	Coolant	Power (kw) (Thermal)	Thermal Flux	Size
BSR (The original swimming pool reactor) BSF(bulk shielding facility Oak Ridge N. L.	MTR-sandwich type fuel elements over 90% enrichment Al-cladding; 3.5 kg of U^{235}. Fuel core 1 ft × 1 ft × 2 ft	H_2O	BeO or H_2O	H_2O	100–1000	$1 - 2 \times 10^{13}$	20 ft × 20 ft × 40 ft
NRLR (Naval research lab. reactor, Washington, D.C.)	MTR type fuel elements; fuel core, 21 in. × 21 in. × 24 in.	H_2O	H_2O or graphite	H_2O	100–1000	10^{12}	49 ft × 32 ft × $28\frac{1}{2}$ ft
Battelle research reactor	MTR-type elements 2.8 kg U^{235}	H_2O	H_2O or graphite	H_2O	1000	1.4×10^{13}	
Univ. of Mich. Ford nuclear reactor	BSF fuel elements; 3 kg U^{235}	H_2O	H_2O or graphite	H_2O	1000	10^{13}	10 ft × 27 ft × 27 ft
Penn. State Univ. reactor	MTR-type elements; 90% enriched	H_2O	H_2O or graphite	H_2O	100	0.7×10^{12}	15 ft × 30 ft × 21 ft
Swiss reactor (Geneva exhibit.)	23 MTR-type fuel assemblies	H_2O	H_2O	H_2O	10–100	10^{11}	10 ft diam., 21 ft deep
LIDO (Harwell, England)	U-Al alloy, 46% enriched; 3.3 kg U^{235} MTR-type elements	H_2O	H_2O	H_2O	100	10^{12}	28 ft × 8 ft × 24 ft
Melusine (Grenoble, France)	Enriched uranium	H_2O	H_2O	H_2O	1000	10^{13}	
Triton (Fontenay, France)	Enriched uranium	H_2O	H_2O	H_2O	1000	10^{13}	
Minerve (Fontenay, France)	Enriched uranium	H_2O	H_2O	H_2O	Very low	10^{11}	
RS-1 (Italy)	20% enriched U-Al alloy, Al-canned, 3.5 kg of U^{235}	H_2O	H_2O	H_2O	1000–5000	10^{13}	

reactor provides an average thermal neutron flux of 10^{13} for experimental purposes. Other examples are the Canadian NRX and NRU reactors shown in Figs. 7.11 to 7.13.

The Graphite-Moderated Natural Uranium Reactor   (Table 7.10)

This reactor was the prototype of all reactors, starting with the CP-1 (Chicago pile) built under Fermi's direction in Chicago. Similar assemblies,

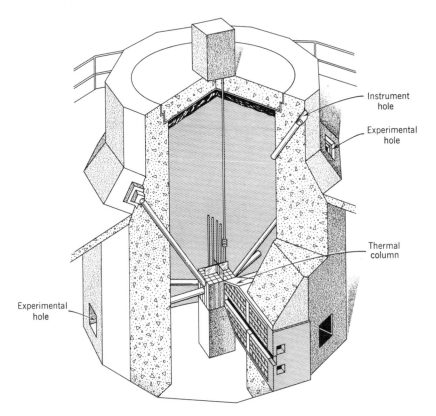

FIG. 7.10. Tank-type water-reflected reactor. (Courtesy Bendix Aviation Corporation.)

like the GLEEP (graphite low energy experimental pile) and BEPO (British experimental pile) at Harwell, England, and the X-10 Clinton pile at Oak Ridge and one at Brookhaven (Fig. 7.14) are well-known examples as they have been the "work horses" of reactor technology and research. Their importance for research has lessened since the advent of the other types of research reactors which were described earlier. Primary interest in this

TABLE 7.8 Research Reactors

Tank Type—Enriched Uranium, Water-Moderated and Water-Cooled

Name, Location, Comments	Arrangement	Fuel and Fuel Arrangement	Moderator	Reflector	Coolant	Power (kw) (Thermal)	Neutron Flux (Thermal)	Size
MTR (materials testing reactor); Arco, Idaho	Heterogeneous	Sandwich-type, >90% enriched fuel elements of U-Al alloy, 19 curved vertical fuel plates, contained in 3 × 3 × 24 in. box. About 4.5 kg U^{235} in Al-tank, 54 in. diam. with side extension to form water well	H_2O	Be and graphite	H_2O	40,000	5.5×10^{14} (maximum) 2.7×10^{14} (average)	Overall: 32 ft × 34 ft × 40 ft reactor tank: 56 in. diam., 30 ft high; fuel assembly: 16 in. × 28 in. × 24 in.
LITR (low intensity test reactor) Oak Ridge Natl. Lab.	Heterogeneous	MTR-type, 3.4 kg of U^{235}	H_2O	Be	H_2O	3000	2×10^{13}	26 ft × 26 ft × 22 ft
RMF (reactivity measuring facility) Arco	Heterogeneous	30 MTR-type fuel elements	H_2O	H_2O	—	0.005–0.1		8 ft × 10 ft × 18 ft
ORR (Oak Ridge research reactor)	Heterogeneous	MTR-type 3–4 kg U^{235} 51 fuel elements 19 plates per element	H_2O	H_2O	H_2O	20,000	10^{14}	Core tank: 5.3 ft diam., 14.8 ft high, immersed in swimming pool
OWR (Omega West reactor) Los Alamos	Heterogeneous	MTR-type, over 90% enriched, 3 kg of U^{235}	H_2O	H_2O	H_2O	1000–5000	10^{13}	Core in stainless steel tank: 25 ft × 8 ft diam.
ETR (engineering test reactor) Arco, Idaho	Heterogeneous	49 MTR-type fuel elements 4 kg U-Al alloy more than 90% enriched	H_2O	Be and graphite	H_2O	175,000	3×10^{14} (average)	32 in. diam., 36 in. high

TABLE 7.8 (Continued)

Name, Location, Comments	Arrangement	Fuel and Fuel Arrangement	Moderator	Reflector	Coolant	Power (kw) (Thermal)	Neutron Flux (Thermal)	Size
WTR (Westinghouse test reactor), Pittsburgh	Heterogeneous	60 MTR-type fuel assemblies	H_2O	H_2O	H_2O	20,000	10^{14}	Core: 28 in. diam., 36 in. high
TTR (thermal test reactor) Knolls Lab., Schenectady	Heterogeneous	U-Al alloy disks stacked in slug tubes, 2 in. × 24 in., 2.8 kg U^{235}	H_2O	Graphite, $2\frac{1}{2}$ ft	—	0.1 (30) (improved version)	3.4×10^9 (10^{12}) (improved version)	Al tank: 1 ft diam.
ARGONAUT Argonne N.L. University training reactor	Heterogeneous	20% enriched U_3O_8-Al fuel plates; 4 kg U^{235}	H_2O	Graphite and H_2O	H_2O	10	5×10^{11}	
HFR (high flux reactor) Petten, Netherlands	Heterogeneous	90% enriched MTR-type fuel elements; 4.2 kg	H_2O	H_2O	H_2O	20,000	4×10^{14}	
BR-2 (Mol, Belgium)	Heterogeneous	Over 90% enrichment, MTR-type elements, 4 kg U^{235}	H_2O and Be	H_2O and Be	H_2O	25,000–50,000	8×10^{14}	
RFT (USSR)	Heterogeneous	10% enriched fuel elements, 3.5 kg U^{235}, 32 units of 24 subunits, 16 fuel elements per subunit	H_2O	H_2O	H_2O	300	2×10^{12}	Cylindrical core: 40 cm diam., 50 cm high
TRR (USSR)	Heterogeneous	Similar to RFT				2000		

TABLE 7.9   Heterogeneous, D_2O-Moderated, Tank-Type Reactors

Name, Location, Comments	Fuel and Fuel Arrangement	Moderator	Reflector	Coolant	Power (kw) (Thermal)	Neutron Flux (Thermal)	Size
CP-3 Argonne N.L. (first heavy water reactor)	120–136 U rods, Al-clad, 1.1 in. diam., 6 ft long; 3 ton of natural U	D_2O, 6½ tons	Graphite 2 ft	D_2O	300	10^{12} (average 5×10^{11})	Al tank: 6 ft diam., 8¾ ft high
CP-3′ (ANL) improved version of CP-3; replaced by CP-5	U-Al alloy fuel rods, highly enriched; 4.2 kg U^{235}	D_2O, 6½ tons	Graphite 2 ft	D_2O	300	3×10^{12}	Al tank: 6 ft diam., 8¾ ft high
CP-5 (ANL)	U-Al alloy, over 90% enriched, sandwich-type fuel plates, 1.7 kg of U^{235}	D_2O, 7 tons	2 ft D_2O and 2 ft of graphite	D_2O	2000–4000	4×10^{13}	Core: 2 ft high 2 ft diam.
ZEEP (Chalk River, Can.) (Zero Energy exper. pile)	Nat. U slugs, 1.285 in. diam., 6 in. long in Al jackets; 148 rods holding 9 slugs	D_2O, 10 tons	Graphite 2½ ft	—	0.01–0.03	10^8	Steel tank: 6¾ in. diam., 8½ ft high
NRX (Chalk River, Canada)	176 natural U rods Al-clad. 10.5 tons natural U	D_2O, 18 tons	2 ft 9 in. of graphite	H_2O, air and circulation of D_2O	30,000–40,000	6.8×10^{13}	10 ft high, 8 ft diam. cylinder
NRU (Chalk River, Canada)	200 natural U fuel rods	D_2O	H_2O, 1 ft	D_2O	200,000	3×10^{14}	Al vessel: 11½ ft diam., 12 ft high
JEEP (Kjeller Norway)	65–76 natural U fuel rods, 35.5 kg per rod, Al tubes	D_2O, 7 tons	Graphite 70 cm	D_2O	100–350	10^{12}	Tank: 2 meters diam.

TABLE 7.9 (Continued)

Name, Location, Comments	Fuel and Fuel Arrangement	Moderator	Reflector	Coolant	Power (kw) (Thermal)	Neutron Flux (Thermal)	Size
R-1 (Stockholm, Sweden) SLEEP (Swedish low energy experimental pile)	126 natural U rods, 2.9 cm diam., canned in very pure Al alloyed with $\frac{1}{2}\%$ Mg, ("reflectal")	D_2O	Graphite 90 cm	D_2O, recirculation, and air	300–600	$3 - 8.7 \times 10^{11}$	Reflectal tank: 1.85 meters diam., 2.54 meters high
ZOE (Chatillon, France)	UO_2 tablets in Al tubes. Replaced by U rods (1.9 tons of U)	D_2O	Graphite and some D_2O	D_2O	150	10^{12} maximum	Al-vessel: 1.8 meters diam., 2.35 meters high
P-2 (Saclay, France)	136 U rods, 1.1 in. diam., 7 ft long in 4 concentric Al cylinders, 3 tons of U	D_2O, 6.3 tons	Graphite 90 cm, some D_2O	N_2 or CO_2 passing between concentric Al fuel cylinders	1500–2000	7×10^{12} maximum	Al-tank: 2.5 meters high 2 meters diam.
DIMPLE (deuterium-moderated pile low energy) Harwell, England	Variable, or similar, to DIDO, below	D_2O, 15 tons	Graphite, 3 ft	D_2O	0.3 maximum	3×10^8 maximum	Al tank: 10 ft high, $8\frac{1}{2}$ ft diam.
DIDO (Harwell, England)	90% enriched U-Al alloy plates Al-clad, arranged in boxes, 9 plates per box, 2.5 kg U^{235}	D_2O, 10 tons	Graphite, 2 ft	D_2O	10,000	10^{14}	Al tank: 6 ft 7 in. diam.
E-443 (Harwell, England)	Similar to DIDO; 2.5 kg of U^{235}	D_2O	Graphite, 2 ft	D_2O	10,000	10^{14}	Al tank: 2 meters high, 2 meters diam.
EL-2 (Saclay, France)	Natural U	D_2O	Graphite	D_2O	2500	10^{13}	
EL-3 (Saclay, France)	Slightly enriched U	D_2O	Graphite	D_2O	15	10^{14}	
ISPRA-1 (Italy)	20% enriched U-Al alloy, 2.5 kg U^{235}	D_2O	D_2O	D_2O	5000	10^{14}	

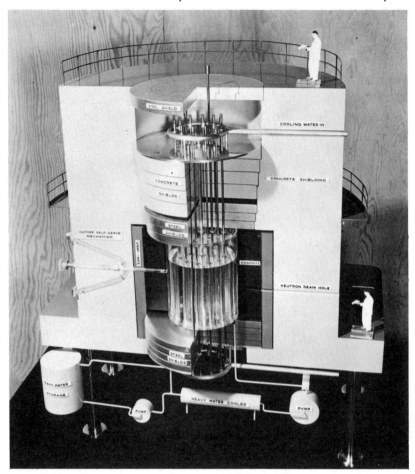

FIG. 7.11. Model of the NRX, which is a heavy water-moderated, light water-cooled tank type research reactor. (Courtesy Atomic Energy of Canada Limited.)

reactor type has now shifted to their adaptation and development as power reactors.

They all use natural uranium as fuel (20 to 50 tons) in the shape of cylindrical rods, or variations on this shape, clad usually in aluminum. Several hundred tons of graphite are used as moderator·and reflector, with several hundred cylindrical channels passing right through the mass of graphite to allow the introduction and positioning of the fuel elements. Cooling gas (air or CO_2) is made to pass over the elements and through the channels, usually at low pressure.

The power and neutron flux range from 100 kw and $\sim 4 \times 10^{10}$ for the

FIG. 7.12. The NRX-reactor and neutron research facilities at the left, radioisotope producing equipment at right. (Courtesy Atomic Energy of Canada Limited.)

GLEEP to 30,000 kw and $\sim 4 \times 10^{12}$ for the Brookhaven reactor. The X-10 is also used partly for the production of Pu^{239} and for the preparation of radioisotopes.

A heavy water-moderated reactor can be made much smaller than a graphite-moderated reactor of the same power, because the amount of D_2O required to moderate the fission neutrons is much smaller than that of

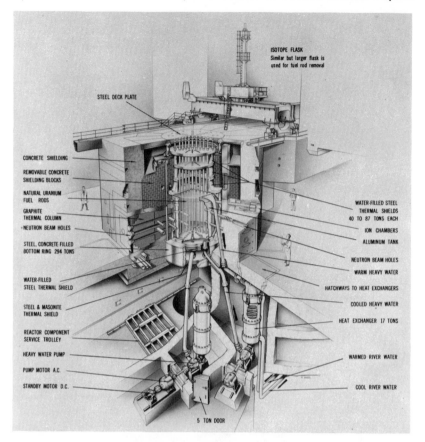

FIG. 7.13. Cutaway of NRU reactor. It is similar to NRX, but it uses heavywater as moderator-coolant. In addition to its research facilities and isotope-producing function it is also a plutonium-producing reactor. (Courtesy Atomic Energy of Canada Limited.)

graphite. Since the neutron flux is determined by the power density, D_2O-moderated reactors, with their smaller volumes, can thus achieve a high neutron density, which is one of the advantages of that type of reactor. This fact explains the extensive use the D_2O-moderated reactor has found as a research tool, as a test reactor, and as a Pu-production reactor, although its application as a power producing reactor is as yet limited to a single prototype, the Halden reactor in Norway. A very general classification of research reactors is given in Table 7.11.†

† For an up-to-date compilation of chain reacting assemblies in the United States, see *Nuclear Reactors, Built, Building or Planned*, TID-8200, U. S. Atomic Energy Commission.

TABLE 7.10 Graphite-Moderated Natural Uranium Reactors
Research and Testing Reactors

Name, Location, Comments	Arrangement	Fuel and Fuel Arrangement	Moderator Reflector	Coolant	Power (kw) (Thermal); Neutron Flux (Thermal)	Size
CP-1 (Chicago pile, Fermi's original pile; Chicago; dismantled and used as basis for CP-2)	Heterogeneous	Uranium (6 tons) uranium oxide (40 tons) spherical lumps, $2\frac{1}{4}$ in. diam. at $8\frac{1}{4}$ in. cubical spacing	Graphite, 1 ft		0.2	9 ft × 9 ft × 12 ft
CP-2, Argonne Natl. Lab. modified version of CP-1, dismantled	Heterogeneous	Similar to CP-1, 10 tons uranium metal, 42 tons uranium oxide	Graphite, 1 ft		0.2–2 3×10^8	18 ft × 19 ft × 20 ft
X-pile (ORNL) Oak Ridge (oldest of all operating reactors)	Heterogeneous	Uranium slugs (49 tons) 1.1 in. diam., 4 in. long, 8 in. spacing, diamond shaped fuel channels, Al-clad	Graphite, 2 ft	Air	1000–3800 $\sim 10^{12}$	20 ft cube
GLEEP (Graphite low energy exper. pile); Harwell, England	Heterogeneous	Uranium slugs 0.97 in. diam., 12 in. long, $7\frac{1}{4}$ in. spacing, Al-clad	Graphite, 2 ft	Air at sub-atmospheric pressure	100 3.7×10^{10}	Cylinder: $9\frac{1}{2}$ ft diam., 17 ft long
BNL (Brookhaven* National Lab.) reactor	Heterogeneous	Uranium slugs (100 tons) 1.1 in. diam., 4 in. long, 8 in. spacing, Al-clad	Graphite, $4\frac{1}{2}$ ft	Air at sub-atmospheric pressure	30,000 4×10^{12}	25 ft cube
BEPO (British experimental pile), Harwell, England	Heterogeneous	Uranium slugs, 0.9 in. diam., 12 in. long, $7\frac{1}{4}$ in. spacing, Al-clad	Graphite, 3 ft	Air	4000–6000 10^{12}	Cylinder: 20 ft diam., 20 ft long
Hanford-305	Heterogeneous	Natural uranium	Graphite		6	Cubic, 18–20 ft
BR-1 (Mol. Belgium)	Heterogeneous	Natural uranium, 24 tons	Graphite	Air	4000 2×10^{12}	

* The BNL-reactor is being reloaded with enriched uranium. The new fuel elements are shown in Fig. 7.7. (See Second Geneva Conference Report P/2366, Vol. 12, p. 685.)

FIG. 7.14. Model of the Brookhaven graphite reactor core with the 5 ft heavy concrete shielding removed. At the right is the loading face showing large number of cylindrical holes into which uranium slugs or materials to be irradiated can be inserted. The round ports at the left are exit holes for neutron beams to be used for experiments. (Courtesy of Brookhaven National Laboratory.)

TABLE 7.11

Research Reactors

Reactor Type	Fuel	Moderator	Reflector	Coolant	Thermal Power (kw)	Thermal Neutron Flux
Natural uranium–graphite	Natural uranium	Graphite	Graphite	Gas	4000–30,000	5×10^{11}–5×10^{12}
Natural uranium–D_2O	Natural uranium	D_2O	D_2O Graphite	D_2O H_2O	300–40,000	5×10^{11}–6×10^{13}
Swimming pool	20%–90% enriched uranium	H_2O	H_2O Graphite	H_2O	100–5000	10^{12}–5×10^{13}
Light water tank	20%–90% enriched uranium	H_2O	H_2O Graphite Beryllium	H_2O	3000–30,000	10^{13}–2×10^{14}
Heavy water tank	20%–90% enriched uranium	D_2O	D_2O Graphite	D_2O	3000–20,000	10^{13}–10^{14}
Homogeneous	U^{235} in solution	H_2O	Graphite	H_2O	10–50	10^{11}–2×10^{12}

7.10   Calculation of k_∞ for a Homogeneous Reactor

The Fast Fission Factor ε

For a homogeneous system ε is practically unity because the fast fission neutrons, upon creation, almost immediately collide with the atoms of the moderator and suffer a reduction in their energy. This will reduce the neutron energy to below the threshold energy for U^{238} fission before they have had a significant chance to make a collision with a U^{238} nucleus.

The Thermal Utilization Factor f

For a homogeneous assembly that uses either natural or enriched uranium uniformly mixed with a moderator, f can be obtained immediately from its definition

$$f = \frac{\Sigma_{a(\text{uranium})}}{\Sigma_{a(\text{uranium})} + \Sigma_{a(\text{moderator})} + \Sigma_{a(\text{other})}} \tag{7.13}$$

This expression gives the fraction of thermal neutrons absorbed per cm^3 by the uranium (numerator) as compared to all thermal neutron absorptions (denominator). The last term in the denominator takes account of the thermal neutron absorptions by foreign bodies in the assembly, such as impurities ("poisons") and structural components which, although not directly contributing to the chain reaction, are nevertheless essential for circulating the coolants, which in turn are required for removing the heat generated inside the core of the reactor.

By writing Eq. 7.13 in the form

$$f = \frac{1}{1 + \dfrac{\Sigma_{a(\text{moderator})}}{\Sigma_{a(\text{uranium})}} + \dfrac{\Sigma_{a(\text{other})}}{\Sigma_{a(\text{uranium})}}} \tag{7.14}$$

it becomes evident that, in order to achieve as large an f as possible, the reactor should be designed so as to keep the last term in the denominator as small as possible and to make the uranium/moderator ratio as large as possible.

The Resonance Escape Probability p

For a given resonance absorber—we are here primarily interested in U^{238}—the effective resonance integral (Eq. 6.78) is seen to depend on Σ_s/N_0, which represents the **scattering cross section of the mixture per atom of absorber.** This is not the same as σ_s (absorber) because Σ_s is the scattering cross section of the fuel-moderator mixture as a whole, $\Sigma_s = \Sigma_s$ (fuel) $+$ Σ_s (moderator). In general, the scattering contribution of the uranium can be neglected as will become apparent from the numerical examples that will be given presently. The $1/E$ spectrum of the neutron flux (6.61) will be considerably depressed in the neighborhood of an absorption resonance and the flux will be depleted after having crossed the resonance energy by an amount which depends on Σ_s/N_0 (Fig. 7.15).

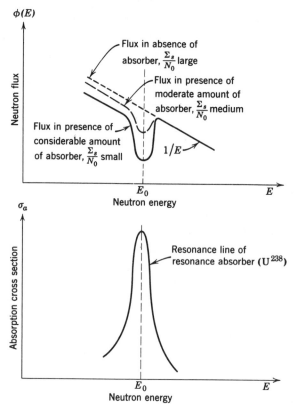

FIG. 7.15. Neutron flux near a resonance line of absorber and its dependence on Σ_s/N_0. The flux is depressed in the neighborhood of an absorption resonance and has a minimum for an energy which is very nearly the same as that for which σ_a is a maximum.

The value of the effective resonance integral and its dependence on Σ_s/N_0 must be determined experimentally and, as a result of such experiments, it was found that the effective resonance integral is essentially independent of the mass of the moderator atom, so that the dependence can be taken to be the same for all commonly used moderators. For a given fuel, its value depends only on the fuel/moderator ratio.

For U^{238} the empirical relation between the effective resonance integral and Σ_s/N_0 that was found to be very satisfactory for $\Sigma_s/N_0 \leqslant 1000$ barns is as follows:

$$\int_E^{E_0} (\sigma_a)_{\text{eff}} \frac{dE}{E} = 3.85 \left(\frac{\Sigma_s}{N_0}\right)^{0.415} \tag{7.15}$$

The integral is shown as a function of Σ_s/N_0 in Fig. 7.16 for U^{238} and Th^{232}.

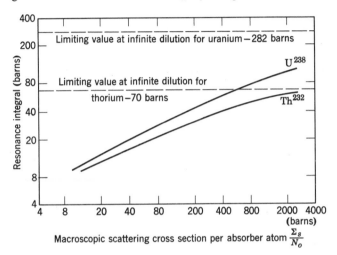

FIG. 7.16. The effective resonance absorption integrals of U^{238} and Th^{235} at 300°K for various moderators. The curves summarize experimental results with the absorber in the form of pure metal or oxide and diluted with graphite, sucrose, light water, or heavy water. (After Dresner, *Nucl. Sci. and Engin.*, **1**, 68 (1956).)

For U^{238} the integral approaches a limiting value of 282 barns at infinite dilution, and this value is used when calculating p for highly diluted fuels. For the pure U^{238} metal the value of the integral is 9.25 barns.

The numerical value of the resonance escape probability for these two limits can be obtained directly from 6.75, from which it follows that for infinite dilution, $N_0/\Sigma_s \to 0$, the exponent approaches zero, so that $p \to 1$. For the pure U^{238} metal p, of course, approaches zero.

The important conclusion is the requirement of increasing dilution, i.e., decreasing fuel content, for increasing the value of the resonance absorption p, which is just the opposite of the requirement we had found to be necessary in order to increase the thermal utilization factor f. Thus, the conditions for a maximum p and a maximum f are seen to lead to contradictory demands on the fuel/moderator ratio. An optimum ratio must, therefore, be chosen when designing an assembly, which will lead to a maximum value of the product pf.

For a natural uranium-moderator assembly of the homogeneous type the four-factor formula reduces to the following condition for a chain reaction to be possible.

$$k_\infty = \varepsilon \eta p f = 1 \times 1.34 \times p f \geqslant 1$$

Therefore

$$p f \geqslant \frac{1}{1.34} = 0.746 \qquad (7.16)$$

In Table 7.12 are listed two of several other possible empirical relations for the calculation of the effective resonance integral that have been proposed (see L. Dresner, *Nucl. Sci. and Engin.*, **1**, 68 (1956)).

TABLE 7.12

Material	Effective Resonance Integral	Range of Validity
Uranium	$3.04(\Sigma_s/N_0)^{0.475}$	$\Sigma_s/N_0 < 800$ barns
Thorium	$3.20(\Sigma_s/N_0)^{0.430}$	$\Sigma_s/N_0 < 800$ barns

Example 7.1. Calculate k_∞ for a homogeneous, natural uranium-graphite-moderated assembly which contains 300 moles of graphite per mole of uranium. Assume natural uranium to contain one part of U^{235} to 139 parts of U^{238}, and use these constants:

Natural uranium
$\sigma_{a(U)} = 7.68$ barns
$\sigma_{s(U)} = 8.3$ barns

Graphite
$\sigma_{a(M)} = 0.0032$ barn
$\sigma_{s(M)} = 4.8$ barns
$\xi = 0.158$

If N_u is the number of uranium atoms per cubic centimeter, and N_0 is the number of U^{238} atoms only per cubic centimeter, then

$$N_0 = \frac{139}{140} \times N_u \qquad \text{Also,} \quad \frac{N_m}{N_u} = 300$$

Therefore

$$\frac{N_m}{N_0} = 300 \times \frac{140}{139} = 302.2$$

1. Thermal utilization f:

$$f = \frac{\sigma_{a(U)}}{\sigma_{a(U)} + \sigma_{a(M)}} = \frac{1}{1 + \dfrac{N_m}{N_u} \dfrac{\sigma_{a(M)}}{\sigma_{a(U)}}}$$

$$= \frac{1}{1 + 300 \times \dfrac{0.0032}{7.68}} = \frac{1}{1.125}$$

$$= 0.889$$

2. Resonance escape probability p:

$$\frac{\Sigma_s}{N_0} = \frac{\Sigma_{s(U)} + \Sigma_{s(M)}}{N_0} = \sigma_{s(U)} + \frac{N_m}{N_0} \sigma_{a(M)}$$

$$= 8.3 \text{ barns} + 302.2 \times 4.8 \text{ barns}$$

$$= 1458 \text{ barns}$$

Assuming the validity of the empirical expression 7.15 for this high value of Σ_s/N_0, we get for the effective resonance integral

$$3.85(1458)^{0.415} = 80 \text{ barns}$$

If we had omitted the scattering contribution of the uranium, this would not have been reflected in the accuracy of this numerical result. The influence of the uranium scattering is even less significant in the $\xi\Sigma_s$ product of expression 6.77, where, according to 6.55, we should use $\xi_U\Sigma_{s(U)} + \xi_M\Sigma_{s(M)}$.

Therefore
$$p = \exp\left(-\frac{80}{1450 \times 0.158}\right)$$

$$= \exp(-0.3495) = 0.705$$

Hence

$$k_\infty = 1 \times 1.34 \times 0.705 \times 0.889 = 0.840$$

This assembly is therefore not capable of sustaining a chain reaction. Similar computations for other ratios of moderator/uranium lead to the results tabulated in Table 7.13, which are also shown in the graph of Fig. 7.17, from which the opposing trends of f and p with varying fuel concentrations are quite apparent.

TABLE 7.13

N_m/N_u	Σ_s/N_0	$\int (\sigma_a)_{\text{eff}} \frac{dE}{E}$	f	p	k_∞
100	483	50	0.960	0.523	0.673
200	967	67	0.923	0.647	0.800
300	1450	80	0.889	0.706	0.840
400	1932	88	0.858	0.751	0.864
500	2418	98	0.828	0.774	0.859
600	2900	106	0.800	0.795	0.852

It is to be noted that since k_∞ is always less than unity, even with the most favorable product pf, it is not possible for a homogeneous natural uranium-graphite-moderated reactor to become critical. This conclusion was reached before the first reactor (CP-1, the Fermi pile) was built, and led to the concept of the heterogeneous reactor where the fuel and moderator are separated from each other.

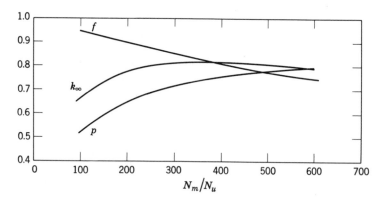

FIG. 7.17. Graph showing variation of f, p, and k_∞ with different molar ratios of moderator/fuel for a homogeneous mixture of natural uranium and graphite.

Example 7.2. Repeat the previous calculations for a heavy water-moderated assembly with $N_m/N_u = 50$. For D_2O, we use the following cross sections: $\sigma_a = 0.00092$ barn; $\sigma_s = 10.6$ barns; and $\xi = 0.570$.
   1. Thermal utilization f:

$$f = \frac{1}{1 + \dfrac{50 \times 0.00092}{7.68}} = 0.994$$

   2. Resonance escape probability p:

$$\frac{\Sigma_s}{N_0} = \frac{N_m}{N_0}\sigma_{s(M)} = 50 \times \frac{140}{139} \times 10.6 = 530 \text{ barns}$$

Therefore $\displaystyle\int (\sigma_a)_{\text{eff}}\frac{dE}{E} = 3.85(530)^{0.415} = 60.2 \text{ barns}$

Therefore $p = \exp\left(-\dfrac{60.2}{530 \times 0.57}\right) = \exp(-0.199) = 0.820$

Hence

$$k_\infty = 1 \times 1.34 \times 0.994 \times 0.820 = 1.09$$

This shows that a chain reacting system is possible if heavy water is used as moderator with natural uranium as fuel (see Fig. 7.18).

In the following examples, we shall find that a chain reaction is possible with graphite or light water as moderators if enriched uranium is used as the nuclear fuel.

Example 7.3. Calculate k_∞ for an enriched uranium-graphite-moderated assembly, using 400 moles of graphite to 1 mole of uranium and a U^{238}/U^{235} ratio of 70, which is about twice the natural concentration.

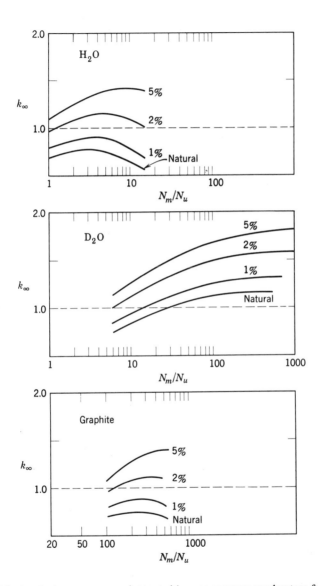

FIG. 7.18. k_∞ for homogeneous mixtures with some common moderators for different molar ratios and various degrees of enrichment.

We shall first have to find the absorption cross section $\sigma_{a(U)}$ and the number of fission neutrons per neutron absorbed, η_u for the enriched fuel.

We apply 4.24 and proceed as in Example 5.2.

$$\sigma_{a(U)} = \frac{N_{(235)}\sigma_{a(235)} + N_{(238)}\sigma_{a(238)}}{N_{(235)} + N_{(238)}}$$

$$= \frac{\sigma_{a(235)} + \dfrac{N_{(238)}}{N_{(235)}}\sigma_{a(238)}}{1 + \dfrac{N_{(238)}}{N_{(235)}}}$$

$$= \frac{698 + 70 \times 2.75}{1 + 70} = 12.54 \text{ barns}$$

$$\eta_u = \frac{N_{(235)}\sigma_{f(235)}}{N_{(235)}\sigma_{a(235)} + N_{(238)}\sigma_{a(238)}}\,\nu$$

$$= \frac{\nu\sigma_{f(235)}}{\sigma_{a(235)} + \dfrac{N_{(238)}}{N_{(235)}}\sigma_{a(238)}}$$

$$= \frac{2.46 \times 590}{698 + 70 \times 2.75}$$

$$= 1.63$$

1. Thermal utilization:

As in the previous example,

$$f = \frac{1}{1 + (400 \times 0.0032)/12.54} = 0.907$$

2. Resonance escape probability p:

$$\frac{\Sigma_s}{N_0} = \frac{N_m}{(70/71)N_u}\,\sigma_{s(M)}$$

$$= 1948 \text{ barns}$$

Therefore   Effective resonance integral $= 3.85(1948)^{0.415} = 88$ barns

Therefore $p = \exp\left(-\dfrac{88}{1948 \times 0.158}\right) = 0.751$

Hence

$$k_\infty = 1 \times 1.63 \times 0.751 \times 0.907 = 1.11$$

and the assembly is self-sustaining (Fig. 7.18).

The increased k_∞, when enriched uranium is used, is seen to be attributable to an increase in the values of η and of f. The increase in f is caused by the greater absorption cross section of the enriched uranium. The effect on p is clearly negligible and its value is the same as that for the natural uranium for the same moderator to fuel ratio (compare Example 7.1). This conclusion is valid for slightly enriched fuels, as in this example, where the enrichment is $\sim 1.5\%$.

The effect on p of a high degree of enrichment will be illustrated in the next example.

Example 7.4. The world's first "water boiler" reactor was the LOPO nuclear reactor at Los Alamos which used an enriched uranium sulfate solution made up as follows:

		σ_a (barn)	σ_s (barn)
U^{235}	580 grams	698	10
U^{238}	3378 grams	2.75	8.3
S	534 grams	0.49	1.1
O	14,068 grams	0.0002	4.2
H	1573 grams	0.33	20

Calculate k_∞ for this reactor.

The isotopic concentration of U^{235}, which is a measure of the degree of enrichment, is

$$\frac{U^{235}}{U^{235} + U^{238}} = \frac{580}{3958} = 14.65\%$$

1. Thermal utilization f:

$$f = \cfrac{1}{1 + \cfrac{N_{(238)}\sigma_{a(238)}}{N_{(235)}\sigma_{a(235)}} + \cfrac{N_{(S)}\sigma_{a(S)}}{N_{(235)}\sigma_{a(235)}} + \cfrac{N_{(O)}\sigma_{a(O)}}{N_{(235)}\sigma_{a(235)}} + \cfrac{N_{(H)}\sigma_{a(H)}}{N_{(235)}\sigma_{a(235)}}}$$

We tabulate these ratios as follows:

$$\frac{N_{(238)}}{N_{(235)}} = \frac{3378/238}{580/235} = 5.75 \qquad \frac{\sigma_{a(238)}}{\sigma_{a(235)}} = \frac{2.75}{698} = 0.00394$$

$$\frac{N_{(S)}}{N_{(235)}} = \frac{534/32}{580/235} = 6.76 \qquad \frac{\sigma_{a(S)}}{\sigma_{a(235)}} = \frac{0.49}{698} = 0.000715$$

$$\frac{N_{(O)}}{N_{(235)}} = \frac{14,068/16}{580/235} = 356 \qquad \frac{\sigma_{a(O)}}{\sigma_{a(235)}} = \frac{0.0002}{698} = 0.0000286$$

$$\frac{N_{(H)}}{N_{(235)}} = \frac{1573/1}{580/235} = 637 \qquad \frac{\sigma_{a(H)}}{\sigma_{a(235)}} = \frac{0.33}{698} = 0.000473$$

Therefore
$$f = \frac{1}{1 + 0.0023 + 0.0048 + 0.0102 + 0.3018}$$

$$= \frac{1}{1.3191} = 0.754$$

2. Resonance escape probability:

$$\frac{\Sigma_s}{N_0} = \frac{N_{(O)}}{N_{(238)}}\sigma_{s(O)} + \frac{N_{(H)}}{N_{(238)}}\sigma_{s(H)}$$

$$= \frac{356}{5.75} \times 4.2 + \frac{637}{5.75} \times 20$$

$$= 2475 \text{ barns}$$

The scattering contribution of the other components is negligible as is verified by inspection.

Assuming the validity of the empirical expression for this rather high value, we have

$$3.85(2475)^{0.415} = 99 \text{ barns}$$

and for

$$
\frac{N_0}{\xi\Sigma_s} = \frac{1}{\xi_{(O)}\sigma_{s(O)}\dfrac{N_{(O)}}{N_0} + \xi_{(H)}\sigma_{(H)}\dfrac{N_{(H)}}{N_0}}
$$

$$
= \frac{1}{0.120 \times 4.2 \times 356/5.75 + 1 \times 20 \times 637/5.75}
$$

$$
= \frac{1}{2249}
$$

Therefore $\quad p = \exp\left(-\dfrac{99}{2249}\right) = \exp(-0.044) = 0.957$

This value of p is considerably greater than the values obtained for natural uranium in the previous examples. With increasing enrichment, p approaches unity and for high degrees of enrichment $p \simeq 1$. Since f was evaluated with respect to absorption in U^{235} only, the matching value for η to be used now is $\eta = 2.08$. Hence

$$k_\infty = 1 \times 2.08 \times 0.957 \times 0.754 = 1.50$$

7.11   Heterogeneous Reactors

Although the construction of homogeneous reactors might appear simpler than that of heterogeneous reactors, the majority of those that have so far been built are of the latter type. The reason for this preference is because it is impossible to build a chain-reacting homogeneous assembly with natural uranium as fuel, unless heavy water is used as a moderator; whereas a heterogeneous assembly can be made chain reacting with natural uranium and the more economical graphite as moderator. In addition, the heterogeneous arrangement has certain technical advantages, as well as some important practical considerations that recommend themselves to the nuclear engineer, some of which will be mentioned in what follows.

The theoretical problems involved, however, when calculating the various design parameters become more complicated when a lattice arrangement for the fuel elements is to be employed. The multiplication factor k_∞ for this kind of arrangement depends on the geometry and the linear dimensions of the representative "lattice cell." By this term we describe a representative fuel element together with its associated mass of moderator and components. By combining a large number of such cells in proper juxtaposition we arrive at the final built-up reactor. Such a typical build-up from square or hexagonal lattice cells is shown in Fig. 7.19.

When dealing with such a lattice, in order to simplify the mathematical aspect of the problem, we replace the rectilinear lattice cells by equivalent cylindrical cells, which are so chosen, that the cross-sectional areas of the

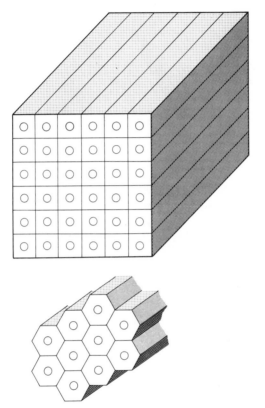

FIG. 7.19. Lattices as made up from a square unit cell and a hexagonal unit cell.

actual and the substituted cells are equal (Fig. 7.20). This method is reliable for fuel elements in the shape of cylindrical rods, for which the simplified mathematical approach leads to satisfactory agreement with experiment.†

The difficulties encountered in an exact calculation of the parameters lie chiefly in the complicated variation of the thermal neutron flux across a heterogeneous assembly. This is best seen from Fig. 7.21 which shows the variation of the thermal neutron flux as one passes from one edge across

† See, for example, E. R. Cohen, *Nucl. Sci. and Engin.*, **1**, 268 (1956).

the reactor to the opposite edge in a qualitative manner. The flux distribution reveals the presence of rhythmic depressions as we move across the lattice. These depressions appear at those portions of the graph that correspond to the locations of the fuel elements. They are caused by the

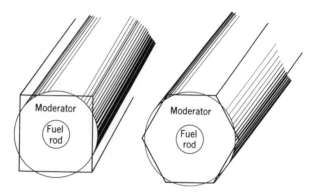

FIG. 7.20. Equivalent cylindrical cells for a square and a hexagonal lattice cell.

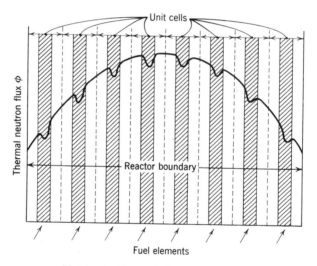

FIG. 7.21. Flux variation across reactor.

much larger thermal neutron absorption in the fuel elements as compared to that in the moderator and materials surrounding them. The increased neutron absorption by the fuel element causes a noticeable reduction in the neutron flux at that location.

If the depressions in the flux distribution at the centers of the individual cells are small enough, we can regard the over-all flux distribution, considering the reactor as a whole, as essentially the same as that for a homogeneous assembly upon which the relatively minor variations within the individual cells have been superimposed.

This assumption is made in the calculation of the critical size of a heterogeneous assembly which allows one to apply the equations for a homogeneous reactor to the case of the heterogeneous reactor, provided some necessary modifications are introduced in the interpretation of specific terms. We shall make use of this procedure subsequently and fill in some pertinent explanations.

For the time being we can reformulate the conditions and procedures which we have just outlined in the following simple mathematical terms.[†]

The neutron flux $\phi(r)$ across the heterogeneous reactor can be written as the product of two functions of the space coordinate r as follows.

$$\phi(r) = F(r)f(r)$$

where $F(r)$ is the smooth macroscopic flux across the assembly and $f(r)$ is the superimposed "fine structure" modulation representing the neutron flux variation within the individual lattice cells. It is then assumed that

1. the form of $f(r)$ is repeated periodically as one goes from one lattice cell to the next and that it is identical in each lattice cell;

2. the neutron current (see Appendix B) across intercell boundaries is zero;

3. the rate of thermal neutron production in the moderator is constant;

4. no thermal neutrons are produced in the fuel elements; and

5. the reactor lattice cell can be replaced by an equivalent cylindrical lattice cell.

7.12   Effect of Heterogeneous Arrangement on p, f, and ε

Resonance Escape Probability

An assembly where uranium lumps either in the shape of spheres or, more commonly, cylindrical rods are distributed in a regular array throughout the moderator, can achieve a higher resonance escape probability than a comparable homogeneous arrangement because the resonance capture of neutrons is reduced considerably with a lattice structure. The explanation for this reduction of resonance absorption is twofold.

By concentrating the regions of resonance absorption, as represented by the U^{238} lumps, most of the slowing down can take place in the moderator,

---

† See Geneva Conf. Proc., S. M. Feinberg, P/669; A. D. Galanin, P/663 and P/666, **5** (1955).

which is a region completely free of resonance absorber material. This gives the neutrons a good chance of having their energies reduced below the U^{238} resonances through collisions with moderator nuclei before they will re-enter a uranium lump and be able to interact with these nuclei.

An even more important reason is that any neutrons of resonance energies, on encountering a uranium lump, will be absorbed in the surface layer of the lump so that the neutron flux entering its interior will be practically free of neutrons whose energies coincide with the U^{238} resonance energies. The U^{238} resonances occur, as Fig. 7.1 shows, for energies of 6.7 ev, 21 ev, 37 ev, and higher. They have very large and narrow peaks, so that U^{238} appears practically opaque for neutrons with energies close to these resonance energies. No neutrons with these resonance energies arise inside the uranium fuel elements because neutrons are slowed down only in the moderator. Neutrons having these resonance energies can enter the fuel only from the outside. As they do so they are rapidly absorbed in a surface layer of uranium before they have an opportunity to penetrate deeper into the fuel.

A thin surface layer of U^{238} acts as a nearly impenetrable screen which shields the interior of the uranium lump against neutron resonance absorption. This phenomenon is often referred to as "self-protection."

Thus, neutron resonance absorption becomes mainly a surface effect, as the U^{238} atoms in the inner portion of the fuel element have little opportunity to encounter neutrons of resonance energies. By employing large lumps the surface to volume ratio is reduced and resonance absorption can thereby be kept to a minimum.

It should be noted, however, that this surface absorption effect reduces not only the resonance neutron flux but also the thermal neutron flux in the interior of the lump. Experimental measurements as well as theoretical considerations show, however, that the reduction in resonance absorption is numerically much more significant than the reduction in the thermal absorption caused by a diminished thermal neutron flux, so that a net gain in the neutron economy results from the lumping arrangement.

Thermal Utilization

The decrease of the thermal flux as a result of the lattice arrangement of the fuel elements with the consequent lowering of the thermal utilization, as just mentioned, is a distinct disadvantage of the heterogeneous assembly. The thermal neutron flux distribution in the vicinity of a fuel element is shown on an enlarged scale in Fig. 7.22. As the thermal neutron flux enters the uranium lump it decreases with increasing penetration because of the continuing absorption of thermal neutrons by the uranium without a corresponding and compensating production of thermal neutrons. The uranium acts throughout as a neutron sink for thermal neutrons and, consequently, the average thermal neutron flux inside the uranium lumps is considerably smaller than the average thermal neutron flux in the moderator. With a graphite moderator the average thermal flux in uranium is only about two-thirds of that in the moderator because of the high thermal neutron absorption in the uranium element.

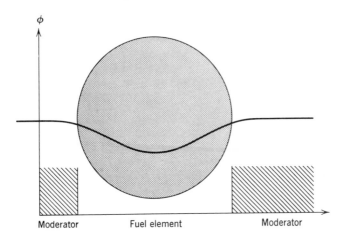

FIG. 7.22. Flux in vicinity and inside fuel element.

The ratio of the average thermal neutron flux in the moderator $\bar{\phi}_m$ and the average thermal neutron flux in the uranium lump $\bar{\phi}_u$ is called the **thermal disadvantage factor.**[†]

Fast Fission Factor

The fast fission factor will make a small but distinct contribution to the number of fissions in a heterogeneous assembly because the fission neutrons will have a fair chance of causing fast fissions with U^{238} before they leave a uranium lump and enter the moderator.

The uranium lump size for a graphite-moderated assembly is usually chosen so as to give a value for ε close to 1.03. For a given lattice arrangement ε is usually determined by experiment because of intrinsic difficulties in calculating an exact value.[‡]

The effect a heterogeneous arrangement has on the neutron economy of the assembly can be summarized by stating that it causes an increase in the

[†] See J. B. Hoag, *Nuclear Reactor Experiments*, Chapter 6 and C. E. Wikdahl and F. Akerhielm, Second Geneva Conference Reports (1958), P/162, vol. 12, p. 377.

[‡] See B. I. Spinrad, "Fast Effect in Lattice Reactors," *Nucl. Sci. and Engin.*, **1**, 455 (1956).

resonance escape probability and an increase of $\sim 3\%$ in the fast fission factor. The numerical increase in these two factors is, however, partially offset by a decrease in the thermal utilization factor. The variation of k_∞ with fuel to moderator ratio and fuel cylinder radius for a natural uranium-graphite assembly is shown in Fig. 7.27.

7.13   Calculation of k_∞ for a Heterogeneous Reactor

Thermal Utilization Factor f

In addition to the different values for the average thermal neutron flux in the regions occupied by the fuel and the moderator respectively, we must also bear in mind that the volumes occupied by these components of the reactor assembly are not equal, and due allowance must be made for this difference in the absorption rate of thermal neutrons. If we let V_u and V_m stand for the respective volumes of fuel and moderator, we can obtain the thermal neutron absorption rate by applying Eq. 4.28 to each part separately, so that we have for the absorption rate in the fuel

$$\Sigma_{au}\bar{\phi}_u V_u$$

and for the absorption rate in the moderator

$$\Sigma_{am}\bar{\phi}_m V_m$$

The fraction of thermal neutrons absorbed by the uranium fuel as compared to the total number of thermal neutron absorptions in the assembly is, therefore,

$$f = \frac{\Sigma_{au}\bar{\phi}_u V_u}{\Sigma_{au}\bar{\phi}_u V_u + \Sigma_{am}\bar{\phi}_m V_m} \tag{7.17}$$

$$= \frac{1}{1 + \dfrac{\Sigma_{am}\bar{\phi}_m V_m}{\Sigma_{au}\bar{\phi}_u V_u}} \tag{7.18}$$

Other causes of thermal neutron absorptions such as "poisons," structural materials, coolants, etc., would be represented by similar terms in the denominators of Eq. 7.17 or 7.18. Comparing expression 7.18 with the corresponding relation for the homogeneous arrangement 7.14, we see that 7.14 is a simplified version of 7.18 because of the equalities of the neutron fluxes and of the volumes for the homogeneous system. Since the thermal disadvantage factor $\bar{\phi}_m/\bar{\phi}_u > 1$, as was shown previously, and also $V_m/V_u > 1$, it is apparent that $f_\text{het} < f_\text{hom}$, or that the thermal utilization factor for a heterogeneous assembly is smaller than that for a homogeneous assembly, with both using the same amounts of fuel and moderator.

The value of the disadvantage factor varies with the size of the fuel elements and the lattice spacing. For a given fuel to moderator ratio the thermal disadvantage factor increases with the diameter of the cylindrical fuel element, and the thermal utilization factor must, therefore, decrease as a consequence. Figure 7.23 shows f as a function of the fuel element radius r_0 and the radius r_1 of the equivalent cylindrical unit cell.

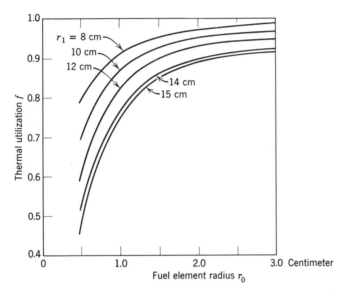

FIG. 7.23. Graphs showing the behavior of f with fuel element radius for equivalent cylindrical unit cells of different radii.

Example 7.5. Calculate f for a heterogeneous lattice made up of cylindrical uranium metal rods of 3 cm diameter which are spaced at regular intervals of 18 cm in graphite. Assume a thermal disadvantage factor of 1.6 and these constants for the materials.

Uranium density $\rho_u = 18.7$ gram/cm^3; graphite density $\rho_m = 1.62$ gram/cm^3

$\sigma_{au} = 7.68$ barns $\sigma_{am} = 4.5 \times 10^{-3}$ barns

Therefore $\dfrac{\Sigma_{am}}{\Sigma_{au}} = \dfrac{N_m}{N_u} \times \dfrac{\sigma_{am}}{\sigma_{au}} = \dfrac{\rho_m/A_m}{\rho_u/A_u} \times \dfrac{\sigma_{am}}{\sigma_{au}}$

$= \dfrac{1.62/12}{18.7/238} \times \dfrac{4.5 \times 10^{-3}}{7.68} = 1.01 \times 10^{-3}$

$\dfrac{V_m}{V_u} = \dfrac{18^2 - \pi(1.5)^2}{\pi(1.5)^2} = \dfrac{(18/1.5)^2}{\pi} - 1 = 44.8$ (Fig. 7.24)

$\dfrac{\bar{\phi}_m}{\bar{\phi}_u} = 1.6$

Therefore

$$f = \frac{1}{1 + (1.01 \times 10^{-3}) \times 44.8 \times 1.6}$$

$$= \frac{1}{1.0721} = 0.933$$

Example 7.6. Find f for the previous lattice by using the data of Fig. 7.23 and compare this value with that obtained in the previous example. Calculate the disadvantage factor from the data of the figure.

In order to be able to use the graph we must first find the equivalent cell radius of the unit cell (Fig. 7.24).

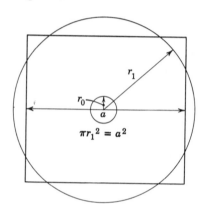

$$\pi r_1^2 = a^2$$

FIG. 7.24. Unit cell and equivalent cell radius.

Area of unit cell

$$A = \pi r_1^2$$

$$= 18 \times 18 \text{ cm}^2$$

Therefore

$$r_1 = \frac{18}{\pi^{1/2}} = 10.13 \text{ cm}$$

For $r_0 = 1.5$ cm and $r_1 = 10.1$ the graph gives a value for $f = 0.93$.

The thermal disadvantage factor $\bar{\phi}_m/\bar{\phi}_u$ as obtained from this numerical value of f is

$$\frac{\bar{\phi}_m}{\bar{\phi}_u} = \frac{1/f - 1}{(\Sigma_{am}/\Sigma_{au}) \times (V_m/V_u)}$$

$$= \frac{0.07/0.93}{1.01 \times 10^{-3} \times 44.8}$$

$$= 1.66$$

Resonance Escape Probability

As was seen earlier, the increase in k_∞ that is brought about by the heterogeneous method of fuel-moderator arrangement is primarily due to a decrease in the resonance absorption of neutrons by U^{238}. A rigorous calculation of p for the heterogeneous assembly is almost impossible because all the U^{238} resonances are not known with sufficient accuracy to permit this, so that the integral in the expression for p must be replaced as shown earlier by an effective resonance integral.

When evaluating the effective resonance integral we can proceed on the assumption that it can be considered to consist of two partial contributions: (1) a surface contribution which is proportional to the surface area of the uranium fuel element, and (2) a volume contribution which is proportional to the volume of the uranium lump.

The mathematical theory is simplified by this separation which, from the physical point of view amounts to this, that one ascribes to surface absorption alone the absorption of those neutrons which have been slowed down in the moderator to an energy corresponding to a strong U^{238} absorption line, whereas all other absorptions are treated as a volume absorption effect which takes place inside the uranium lump exclusively.

Taking the volume part first, we can readily see that it should be the same as would apply to the homogeneous case under the extreme condition of pure uranium fuel without moderator. The volume part contribution to the effective resonance integral is, therefore, given by 7.15 with Σ_s referring to uranium. Hence,

$$\int_E^{E_0} (\sigma_a)_{\text{eff}} \frac{dE}{E} = 3.85 \left(\frac{\Sigma_s}{N_0}\right)^{0.415}$$

$$= 3.85(\sigma_{su})^{0.415}$$

$$= 3.85(8.3)^{0.415} = 9.25 \text{ barns}$$

To this must be added the surface contribution to the resonance absorption which will be proportional to the surface area of the fuel element that is exposed to the resonance neutron flux.

For cylindrical uranium rods the surface contribution is given very satisfactorily by $24.7(S/M)$ barns, where S is the surface area expressed in cm², and M the mass of the fuel element in gram.

Combining the two contributions we get for the effective resonance integral

$$\int_E^{E_0} (\sigma_a)_{\text{eff}} \frac{dE}{E} = 9.25 \left(1 + 2.67 \frac{S}{M}\right) \text{ barns}$$

$$= \left(9.25 + 24.7 \frac{S}{M}\right) \text{ barns} \qquad (7.19)$$

$$\left(\begin{array}{c}\text{volume}\\\text{part}\end{array}\right) + \left(\begin{array}{c}\text{surface}\\\text{part}\end{array}\right)$$

(This formula is limited to uranium rods with diameter greater than 0.6 cm.)

The limit of this expression for $S/M \to 0$ would correspond to infinitely large lumps of fuel or, what is the same, to pure uranium. This limiting value is seen to be equal to 9.25 barns, the value we found also by comparing this extreme case with that obtained for pure uranium in the homogeneous arrangement. The limiting value for great dilution of fuel should similarly lead to the same result as the corresponding limiting value for a homogeneous assembly, which is 282 barns.

For thin rods, Untermeyer has proposed a modified and slightly more general expression† which, in terms of the numerical constants of 7.19, can be written as

$$\text{Effective resonance integral} = 9.25\left[1 + \frac{2.67}{(M/S) + r_0}\right] \quad (7.19a)$$

This expression reduces to the classical form 7.19 for $r_0 = 0$. The numerical value of r_0 is determined by the condition that for infinite dilution, i.e., $M/S = 0$, the effective resonance integral should yield 282 barns, which is the case for $r_0 = 0.11$.

Other empirical expressions similar to 7.19 and suitable for uranium oxide fuel rods are listed in Table 7.14.

TABLE 7.14

Material	Effective Resonance Integral
U_3O_8	$12.0\left(1 + 1.67\dfrac{S}{M}\right)$
UO_2	$11.51\left(1 + 1.92\dfrac{S}{M}\right)$

Russian scientists have developed alternative expressions for the effective resonance integrals which have some merit on the basis of theoretical considerations also and which have recently gained some favor amongst reactor designers of other countries. They are listed in Table 7.15.

From what has been described earlier, it is clear that the resonance neutron flux is not the same in the moderator as in the interior of the uranium lumps, being smaller inside the fuel elements because of the surface screening action of the uranium. This difference in resonance neutron flux for the scattering region (moderator region) and absorption region (uranium region) must be taken into account in the expression for p.

† See R. L. Macklin and H. S. Pomerance, Geneva Conference P/833, vol. 5, page 98 (1955). For the effective resonance integral of thorium and thorium oxide, see J. E. Dayton and W. G. Pettus, *Nucl. Sci. and Engin.*, **3**, 286 (1958).

We must also take account of the fact that the volume occupied by the fuel elements and that occupied by the moderator are not equal in the heterogeneous lattice arrangement as was the case with the homogeneous assembly.

TABLE 7.15

Material	Effective Resonance Integral	Range of Validity
Uranium metal	$2.51\left(1 + 9.85\sqrt{\dfrac{S}{M}}\right)$	$0.05 < \dfrac{S}{M} < 0.70$
UO_2	$3.85\left(1 + 6.91\sqrt{\dfrac{S}{M}}\right)$	$0.15 < \dfrac{S}{M} < 0.55$

I. I. Gurevich, and I. Y. Pomeranchuk, Geneva Conference P/649, **5**, 466; see also E. Hellstrand, *Journ. Appl. Phys.*, **28**, 1493 (1957) and Weinberg and Wigner, *op. cit.*, p. 660.

If we let $\bar{\phi}_0$ denote the average resonance flux in the uranium lump and $\bar{\phi}_m$ that in the moderator, with V_0 and V_m the respective volumes, the resonance escape probability for a heterogeneous assembly, with these weighting factors included, becomes now

$$p = \exp\left[-\frac{N_0 V_0 \bar{\phi}_0}{\xi \Sigma_s V_m \bar{\phi}_m} \int_E^{E_0} (\sigma_a)_{\text{eff}} \frac{dE}{E}\right] \tag{7.20}$$

It is easy to see that if $V_0 = V_m$ and $\bar{\phi}_0 = \bar{\phi}_m$, which holds for a homogeneous assembly, the last expression becomes identical with 6.75 and 6.77 for a homogeneous assembly.

The ratio $\bar{\phi}_m/\bar{\phi}_0$ is called the **disadvantage factor for resonance neutrons**. (Although the same symbol is used, it should be noted that the flux here refers to neutrons with energies in the resonance region, whereas the flux in the thermal disadvantage factor refers to neutrons of thermal energies.)

As a first approximation we can set $\bar{\phi}_m/\bar{\phi}_0 \simeq 1$ so that the expression 7.20 simplifies to

$$p = \exp\left[-\frac{N_0 V_0}{\xi \Sigma_s V_m} \int_E^{E_0} (\sigma_a)_{\text{eff}} \frac{dE}{E}\right] \tag{7.21}$$

This approximation is sufficient in many calculations where an error of $\sim 1\%$ is permissible.

For fuel elements of uranium in the shape of long cylinders the end areas can be neglected as compared to the mantle area of the cylinder, so that

$$\frac{S}{M} = \frac{2\pi r l}{\pi r^2 l \rho} = \frac{2}{r\rho} \quad (\rho = 18.7 \text{ grams/cm}^3)$$

which, when used in 7.19 and 7.20, gives for the resonance escape probability in this particular case

$$p = \exp\left[-\frac{V_0\bar{\phi}_0 N_0(9.25 + 49.4/r\rho)}{V_m\bar{\phi}_m\xi\Sigma_s}\right] \qquad (7.22)$$

(Note that the term in parentheses is in units of barns.)

Inspection of this expression shows that increasing the size of the fuel elements by increasing r, but keeping the V_0/V_m ratio unchanged, decreases the $1/r$ term in the exponent of 7.22, so that p must increase. In addition, increasing r causes an increased resonance neutron absorption by the fuel element because of its greater surface area, and this in turn causes a further depression of $\bar{\phi}_0$, so that as a result, $\bar{\phi}_0/\bar{\phi}_m$ decreases also. This will lead to a further decrease of the exponent, so that p must increase.

As we know, the filtering action of the uranium surface layer causes also a decrease of the thermal neutron flux in the interior of the fuel element, so that increasing the radius r of the fuel element must increase the thermal disadvantage factor. Inspection of 7.18 shows that, as a consequence of this, f must become smaller. This indicates that changing the fuel element size affects p and f in opposite ways, increasing one and decreasing the other.

When designing a heterogeneous reactor, a judicious choice of fuel element size and lattice spacing must, therefore, be made in order to balance these opposing trends and to arrive at an optimum arrangement. Figure 7.25 shows the variation of p with r_0 and r_1.

The resonance escape probability is often written in this form:

$$p = \exp\left(-\frac{f_r}{1 - f_r}\right) \qquad (7.23)$$

where f_r is the **resonance utilization** which in turn is defined by

$$f_r = \frac{V_0\bar{\phi}_0 N_0 \displaystyle\int_E^{E_0} (\sigma_a)_{\text{eff}} \frac{dE}{E}}{V_0\bar{\phi}_0 N_0 \displaystyle\int_E^{E_0} (\sigma_a)_{\text{eff}} \frac{dE}{E} + \xi\Sigma_s V_m\bar{\phi}_m} \qquad (7.24)$$

This expression is formally analogous to expression 7.17 for the thermal utilization, with the integral term taking the place of the neutron absorption in the fuel and the scattering term here corresponding to the neutron absorption in the moderator there. The analogy is purely formal, and the reason for expressing p in the form of 7.23 is because of the convenience of being able to apply calculating methods that have been worked out for f to the calculation of f_r.

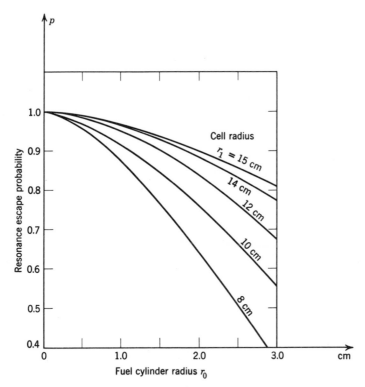

FIG. 7.25. Variation of p with fuel cylinder radius for different equivalent cylindrical cell radii.

Example 7.7. Calculate p for a lattice consisting of natural uranium fuel rods of circular cross section, diameter 3 cm, and spaced 25 cm apart in a graphite moderator.

Assuming $\bar{\phi}_m/\bar{\phi}_0 = 1$ and applying 7.22 we get

$$\frac{V_m}{V_0} = \frac{25^2 - \pi r_0^2}{\pi r_0^2} = \frac{(25/1.5)^2}{\pi} - 1 = 87.5$$

$$\frac{N_m}{N_0} = \frac{1.62/12}{18.7/238} = 1.72$$

$$\frac{9.25 + 49.4/r\rho}{\sigma_s} = \frac{9.25 + \dfrac{49.4}{18.7 \times 1.5}}{4.8} = 2.29$$

Therefore $\qquad p = \exp\left(-\frac{1}{87.5} \times \frac{1}{1.72} \times \frac{2.29}{0.158}\right) = \exp\,(-0.0963)$

Therefore $\qquad\qquad\qquad\qquad p = 0.908$

From Fig. 7.25 we get for $r_0 = 1.5$ cm and $r_1 = 25/\pi^{1/2} = 14.1$ cm, $p = 0.93$, which is about 2% off our calculated value. The discrepancy is explained by the limitation set by the graph and by the assumption of unity for the resonance flux ratio.

Fast Fission Factor ε

The chance that a fast neutron will cause a fission before it leaves the uranium lump increases with increasing lump size, as might have been expected.

If P is the probability that a fission neutron created anywhere inside the fuel element will make a single collision with a uranium nucleus before it can escape from the fuel element into the moderator, the fast fission factor ε can be shown to be related to P by

$$\varepsilon = 1 + \frac{(\nu - 1)\sigma_f - \sigma_c}{\sigma_t - (\nu\sigma_f + \sigma_s)P} P \tag{7.25}$$

When we substitute the appropriate numerical values for the cross sections and ν for fast neutron fission in natural uranium, this becomes

$$\varepsilon = 1 + \frac{0.0952P}{1 - 0.521P} \tag{7.26}$$

The fast fission values to be used in 7.25 are listed in Table 7.16.

TABLE 7.16

ν	σ_f	σ_c	$\sigma_{s(\text{elastic})}$	σ_t
2.55	0.29 barn	0.04 barn	1.5 barns	4.3 barns

The probability function for solid uranium cylinders and ε are tabulated in Table 7.17 as a function of the cylinder radius r_1 and P is also shown graphically in Fig. 7.26.

TABLE 7.17

Fuel Element Radius (cm)	P	ε
1	0.2096	1.022
2	0.3543	1.041
3	0.4566	1.057
4	0.5368	1.071
5	0.5972	1.083

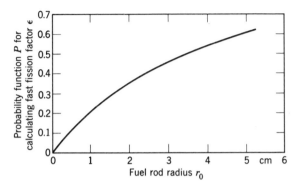

FIG. 7.26. The probability function P for solid uranium cylinders as a function of fuel rod radius.

Example 7.8. Calculate k_∞ for a Brookhaven type reactor, which is a heterogeneous, graphite-moderated reactor, using aluminum clad uranium metal rods spaced at regular intervals of 20.3 cm apart. Each fuel slug is 2.8 cm in diameter, 10.2 cm long, and encased in Al of 1 mm thickness. The fuel channels into which the fuel elements are inserted have a circular cross section of 36 cm² and allow air to be passed through them to act as a coolant.

We tabulate the relevant data as follows:

	Volume	Number of Atoms/cm³	Atomic Weight	Density gram/cm³	σ_a	σ_s
Uranium	V_0	N_0	238	18.7	7.68	
Graphite	V_1	N_1	12	1.62	0.0032	4.8
Aluminum	V_2	N_2	27	2.70	0.23	
Air (at 100° C assumed temp.)	V_3	N_3	15	9×10^{-4}	1.50	

$$\frac{N_1}{N_0} = \frac{1.62/12}{18.7/238} = 1.72 \qquad \frac{V_1}{V_0} = \frac{(20.3)^2 - 36}{\pi(1.4)^2} = 61.2$$

$$\frac{N_2}{N_0} = \frac{2.70/27}{18.7/238} = 1.27 \qquad \frac{V_2}{V_0} = \frac{\pi \times 2.8 \times 0.1}{\pi(1.4)^2} = 0.143$$

$$\frac{N_3}{N_0} = \frac{9 \times 10^{-4}/15}{18.7/238} = 0.00076 \qquad \frac{V_3}{V_0} = \frac{36 - (1.4)^2\pi}{(1.4)^2\pi} = 4.85$$

$$\frac{\sigma_{a1}}{\sigma_{a0}} = 4.16 \times 10^{-4} \qquad \frac{\sigma_{a2}}{\sigma_{a0}} = 0.03 \qquad \frac{\sigma_{a3}}{\sigma_{a0}} = 0.195$$

For the thermal disadvantage factor we assume 1.6, and for the resonance disadvantage factor a value of 1.

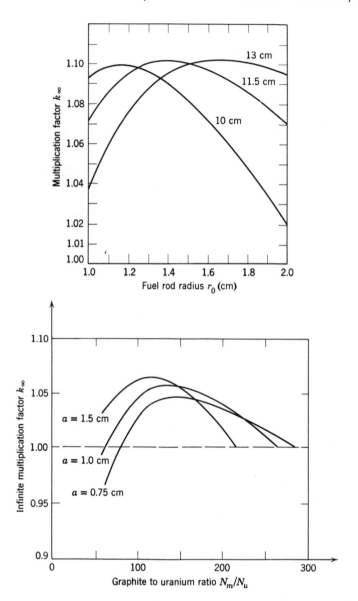

FIG. 7.27a. The variation of k_∞ with fuel rod radius for equivalent cell radii of 10 cm, 11.5 cm, and 13 cm for a natural-uranium graphite lattice. (*b*) k_∞ for a heterogeneous natural uranium–graphite assembly for various molar ratios of graphite and uranium for different fuel rod radii (*a* = fuel rod radius in centimeters). (According to data from E. A. Guggenheim, and M. H. Pryce, "Uranium–Graphite Lattices," *Nucleonics*, **11**, No. 2, 50 (1953).)

1. Thermal utilization f:

$$f = \cfrac{1}{1 + \cfrac{N_1 V_1 \sigma_{a1} \bar{\phi}_m}{N_0 V_0 \sigma_{a0} \bar{\phi}_0} + \cfrac{N_2 V_2 \sigma_{a2} \bar{\phi}_m}{N_0 V_0 \sigma_{a0} \bar{\phi}_0} + \cfrac{N_3 V_3 \sigma_{a3} \bar{\phi}_m}{N_0 V_0 \sigma_{a0} \bar{\phi}_0}}$$

$$= \frac{1}{1 + 0.072 + 0.0087 + 0.0012} = \frac{1}{1.082} = 0.924$$

2. Resonance escape probability p:

$$p = \exp\left[- \frac{N_0 V_0 \bar{\phi}_0 (9.25 + 49.4/r\rho)}{N_1 V_1 \bar{\phi}_1 \xi \sigma_{s1}} \right]$$

$$= \exp\left(- \frac{11.14}{1.72 \times 61.2 \times 0.158 \times 4.8} \right)$$

$$= \exp(-0.139) = 0.870$$

3. Fast fission factor ε:
ε is obtained from Fig. 7.12 and is seen to be 1.03 for $r_0 = 1.4$ cm.
4. η for natural uranium is 1.34. Hence

$$k_\infty = 1.03 \times 1.34 \times 0.870 \times 0.924 = 1.11$$

The behavior of k_∞ for different fuel rod radii, molar ratios, and equivalent cell dimensions for a heterogeneous natural uranium-graphite lattice is shown in Fig. 7.27.

PROBLEMS

(1) Calculate the thermal utilization factor for an aqueous fuel solution containing 10% (by weight) of U^{235}.

(2) Find the fast fission factor for solid cylindrical uranium elements of 1.2 cm radius.

(3) Use the latest available numerical values for the constants in 7.25 to compute ε and compare your result with that quoted in 7.26. What would be the change in ε if a new measurement of ν would change its numerical value by -2%?

(4) Starting a neutron cycle with 1000 fast fission neutrons, calculate
(a) the number of neutrons produced by fast fissions
(b) the number of neutrons absorbed in uranium fuel before reaching thermal energies
(c) the number of neutrons reaching thermal energies
(d) the number of thermal neutrons absorbed in fuel
(e) the number of neutrons escaping through fast leakage
(f) the number of neutrons escaping through thermal leakage if $\varepsilon = 1.029$; $p = 0.889$; $f = 0.910$; $l_f = 0.956$; $l_{th} = 0.945$; $\eta = 1.34$.

(5) Calculate k_∞ and k_{eff} for a reactor having the numerical constants as in Problem 4.

(6) Calculate k_∞ for a homogeneous graphite-uranium assembly using enriched uranium with 25% U^{235} content, and tabulate the results for the moderator/uranium ratios: 50, 100, 200, 300, 400, 500.

(7) Calculate p for a homogeneous natural uranium-BeO assembly with a 200/1 moderator to fuel molar ratio.

(8) Calculate the thermal utilization factor for a reactor with square lattice spacings of 6 in., using natural uranium slugs of 1.285 in. in diameter, encased in aluminum cans of 1.295 in. internal diameter and 0.040 in. thickness, which are immersed in a heavy water moderator.

(9) Calculate k_∞ for the reactors in Problems 7 and 8.

(10) A solution of uranyl nitrate, $UO_2(NO_3)_2$, of 100% enrichment, in ordinary water, has an infinite multiplication factor of $k_\infty = 1.10$. What is the molar fuel/moderator ratio of the solution?

(11) Recalculate Examples 7.3 and 7.4 in the text by using the more recent numerical values of the relevant nuclear quantities as quoted in Tables 4.2 and 5.2.

BIBLIOGRAPHY

Amouyal, A., and B. Benoist: "New Method of Determining the Thermal Utilization Factor of a Cell," *Journ. Nucl. Energy*, **6**, 79 (1957).

Atkinson, I. C., and R. L. Murray: "Optimizing Multiplication Factors of Heterogeneous Reactors," *Nucleonics*, **12**, No. 4 (April 1952).

Beck, C. K.: *Nuclear Reactors for Research*, van Nostrand, 1957.

Bonilla, C. F. (Ed.): *Nuclear Engineering*, McGraw-Hill, 1957.

Catalogue of Nuclear Reactors—1955, AECL-220 (CRR-590).

Borst, L. B.: "Design Comparison of Reactors for Research," *Ann. Rev. Nucl. Sci.*, vol. 5 (1955).

Breazeale, W. M.: "The Swimming Pool," *Nucleonics*, **10**, No. 11 (November 1952); *Nucleonics*, **12**, No. 2 (February 1954).

Charpie, R. A., et al. (Ed.): *Progress in Nuclear Energy*, Series II; *Reactors*, Pergamon Press, 1956.

Chastain, J. W.: *U. S. Research Reactor Operation and Use*, Addison-Wesley, 1957.

Creutz, E., et al.: "Review of Measurements of Resonance Absorption of Neutrons by Uranium in Bulk," *Journ. Appl. Phys.*, **26**, 257 (1955).

Davies, M. V.: "Resonance Absorption of Neutrons by Uranium Cylinders," *Journ. Appl. Phys.*, **28**, 250 (1957).

Dresner, L.: "The Effective Resonance Integrals of U^{238} and Th^{232}," *Nucl. Sci. and Engin.*, I, 68 (1956).

Dunworth, J.: "Fuel Cycles and Reactor Types," *Prog. in Nucl. Energy*, series VIII, vol. I.

Experimental Power and Test Reactors, TID-4562, U. S. Atomic Energy Commission, 1956.

U. S. Research Reactors, TID-7013, U. S. Atomic Energy Commission, 1957.

"Gas-Cooled Reactors," *Nucleonics*, **16**, No. 4 (April 1958).

"Report on Nuclear Fuels," *Nucleonics*, **16**, No. 8 (August 1958).

Ford, G. W. K.: "Power Reactor Projects throughout the World," *Engineering*, October 7, 1955.

Geneva Conf. on the Peaceful Uses of Atomic Energy—1955:

P/888: Barendregt, T. J., et al.: "Practical Experiences with the JEEP Reactor," vol. 2, 259.

P/401: Bretscher, E., et al.: "Research Reactors," vol. 2, 254.

P/834: Callihan, A. D., et al.: "Small Thermal Homogeneous Critical Assemblies," vol. 5, 145.

P/603: Chernick, J.: "The Theory of Uranium Water Lattices," vol. 5, 215.

P/485: Doan, R. L., and J. R. Huffman: "MTR Experimental Program and Reactor Operation," vol. 2, 270.

P/860: Fox, M.: "The Brookhaven Reactor," vol. 2, 353.

P/606: Kaplan, I., and J. Chernick: "Uranium-Graphite Lattices," vol. 5, 295.

P/488: King, L. D. P.: "Design and Description of Water Boiler Reactors," vol. 2, 372.

P/946: Kowarski, L.: "Report on Research Reactors," vol. 2, 233.

P/435: Kruzhilin, G. N.: "Reactor for Physical and Technical Investigations," vol. 2, 435.

P/859: McCorkle, W. H., and W. H. Zinn: "Research Program and Operating Experience on ANL Reactors," vol. 2, 304.

P/833: Macklin, R. L., and H. S. Pomerance: "Resonance Capture Integrals," vol. 5, 96 (also in *Progress of Nucl. Energy*, series I, vol. I).

P/604: Radkowsky, A., and S. Krasik: "Physics Aspects of the Pressurized Water Reactor (PWR)," vol. 5, 229.

P/490: Weinberg, A. M., et al.: "The MTR and Related Research Reactors," vol. 2, 402.

P/387: Yvon, J.: "The Saclay Reactor," vol. 2, 337.

Second Geneva Conference on the Peaceful Uses of Atomic Energy—1958:

P/15: Cutts, B., et al.: "Graphite Moderated Thermal Reactor Calculations for the Calder Hall Reactors," vol. 12, 612.

P/590: Dessauer, G.: "Physics of Natural Uranium Lattices in Heavy Water," vol. 12, 320.

P/1461: Firth, K., et al.: "The Physics of a Medium Flux Research Reactor," vol. 12, 491.

P/336: Girard, Y., et al.: "Natural Uranium—Heavy Water Lattices," vol. 12, 281.

P/591: Niemuth, W. E., and R. Nilson: "Lattice Parameters Derived from Neutron Distributions," vol. 12, 643.

P/630: Williams, R. O., et al.: "Reactor Analysis of the OMRE, vol. 12, 518.

Glasstone, S.: *Principles of Nuclear Reactor Engineering*, van Nostrand, 1955.

Glasstone, S., and M. C. Edlund, *The Elements of Nuclear Reactor Theory*, van Nostrand 1952.

Goodman, C. (Ed.): *Science and Engineering of Nuclear Power*, Addison-Wesley, 1952.

Guggenheim, E. A., and M. H. L. Pryce: "Uranium-Graphite Lattices," *Nucleonics*, **11**, No. 2 (February 1953).

Hellstrand, E.: "Measurements of the Effective Resonance Integral in Uranium Metal and Oxide in Different Geometries," *Journ. Appl. Phys.*, **28**, 1493 (1957).

Hoag, J. B. (Ed.): *Nuclear Reactor Experiments*, van Nostrand, 1958.

Houston, R. W.: "Calculating Thermal Utilization for Large Thermal Reactors," *Nucleonics*, **13**, No. 4 (April 1955).

Huffman, J. R.: "The Materials Testing Reactor," *Nucleonics*, **12**, No. 6 (June 1954).

Klein, D., et al.: "Measurement of Thermal Utilization, Resonance Escape Probability and Fast Effect in Water Moderated, Slightly Enriched Uranium and Uranium Oxide Lattices," *Nucl. Sci. and Engin.*, **3**, 403 (1958).

Kramer, A. W.: *Boiling Water Reactors*, Addison-Wesley, 1957.

Littler, D. J., and J. F. Raffle: *An Introduction to Reactor Physics*, Pergamon Press, 1957.

Murray, R. L.: *Introduction to Nuclear Engineering*, Prentice-Hall, 1954.

Murray, R. L., and A. C. Menius: "Fast Fission Factor for Hollow Natural Uranium Cylinders," *Nucleonics*, **11,** No. 4 (April 1953).

Nuclear Engineering Handbook, McGraw-Hill, 1958.

Reactor Handbook, vol. I—Physics; vol. II—Engineering; AECD-3645,6.

Nuclear Reactor Data, Raytheon Manufacturing Co., Waltham, Mass., 1956.

Pickard, J. K. (Ed.): *Nuclear Power Reactors*, van Nostrand, 1957.

Schumar, J. F.: "Reactor Fuel Elements," *Scientific American*, February 1959.

"Special Report on Pressurized Water Reactors," *Nucleonics*, **16,** No. 4 (April 1958).

Soodak, H., and E. C. Campbell: *Elementary Pile Theory*, Wiley, 1950.

Starr, C., and R. W. Dickinson: *Sodium Graphite Reactors*, Addison-Wesley, 1957.

Stephenson, R.: *Introduction to Nuclear Engineering*, McGraw-Hill, 1957.

Syrett, J. J.: *Nuclear Reactor Theory*, Temple Press, 1958.

Weinberg, A. M., and E. P. Wigner: *The Physical Theory of Neutron Chain Reactors*, University of Chicago Press, 1958.

chapter 8

Neutron Diffusion

8.1 Introduction

In our previous treatment of the slowing down of neutrons we considered only the effect this process has on the energy distribution of the neutrons. A complete description of the neutron gas in a reactor must, however, also include an examination of the spatial distribution of the neutrons during the slowing-down phase as well as during their life as thermal neutrons. The results of such an investigation have an important application in the calculation of critical reactor sizes and of the neutron leakage from nuclear reactor assemblies.

In a nuclear reactor where one has an aggregation of a very large number of neutrons the diffusion of neutrons, i.e., the net passage of neutrons from regions of higher neutron densities to regions of lower neutron densities, must play a significant role in the over-all picture of neutron behavior. Diffusion of neutrons is a consequence of the nonuniform neutron density in the reactor assembly, and as the physical laws of diffusion are familiar from the kinetic theory of gases, many of the results of that theory and their underlying assumptions can justifiably be applied to the behavior of neutrons in a thermal reactor.

As a start we divide the neutrons in a reactor into two main groups, a group of thermalized neutrons and another group of fast neutrons which comprises all those neutrons that have not yet reached thermal equilibrium with their surroundings, and we then describe the diffusion process for each of the two groups separately.

Because the scattering cross section of the moderator is so very much larger than its absorption cross section, those neutrons that have been slowed down to thermal energies will be able to attain a state of thermal equilibrium with the moderator nuclei during their life span as thermal neutrons, long before their final capture by the fissionable material terminates their independent existence. This group can, therefore, very well be treated as a monoenergetic group if one chooses a suitable representative energy for it.

On the other hand, the theory of diffusion for neutrons in the prethermal or slowing-down stage is of necessity more complex because, in addition to a neutron flow in space, we have also to deal with a simultaneous neutron flow in "energy space." A complete distribution function of these neutrons must contain a description of the spatial as well as of the energy dependence of the neutron density. The complete slowing-down diffusion equation which accomplishes this satisfactorily in many respects is known as the **Fermi age equation**.

A detailed reactor theory combines the Fermi age theory for nonthermal neutrons with the diffusion theory for thermal neutrons. We shall first treat thermal neutron diffusion and then continue with the Fermi age theory.

8.2 Thermal Neutron Diffusion

In order to simplify this problem we treat the thermal neutrons as a monoenergetic group. Accordingly, all the neutrons of the group are assumed to have the same (average) energy and neither to gain nor lose energy, on the average, when colliding with the nuclei of the moderator.

The neutron density $n(r)$ at a given point $r(x, y, z)$ of the moderator will then be determined by these three factors. (1) The rate of production of thermal neutrons per unit volume, Q. (2) The rate of thermal neutron absorption per unit volume, $nv\Sigma_a$. (3) The rate of neutron leakage or diffusion per unit volume, $-D\nabla^2 n$.

Here, D is the **diffusion coefficient**† which is given from kinetic theory by

$$D = \lambda_{tr} \frac{v}{3} \qquad (8.1)$$

with λ_{tr}, the transport mean free path (6.43), and v, the appropriate average neutron velocity for the thermal neutron group. The negative sign takes account of the fact that the diffusion process is in a direction opposite to that of increasing neutron density. ∇^2 is the Laplace operator which, in Cartesian coordinates, is $\nabla^2 \equiv \partial^2/\partial x^2 + \partial^2/\partial y^2 + \partial^2/\partial z^2$ (see Appendix B).‡

† The diffusion constant D_0 is often used, where $D_0 = D/v$; (see Appendix B).

‡ The Laplace operator with r as coordinate (when no other dependence occurs) can be written in the form

$$\nabla^2 = (1/r^m)(d^2/dr^2)r^m$$
$$= d^2/dr^2 + (m/r)(d/dr)$$

where

for infinite slab
for infinite cylinder $m = \begin{cases} 0 \\ 1 \\ 2 \end{cases}$
for sphere

The net rate of increase in the neutron density, $\partial n/\partial t$, is determined by the excess of (1) over the sum of (2) and (3). Therefore

$$\frac{\partial n}{\partial t} = \text{production} - \text{leakage} - \text{absorption} \qquad (8.2)$$

Hence,

$$\frac{\partial n}{\partial t} = Q - (-D\nabla^2 n) - nv\Sigma_a$$

$$= Q + \lambda_{tr}\frac{v}{3}\nabla^2 n - nv\frac{1}{\lambda_a} \qquad (8.3)$$

When a steady state has been established—and this we assume to hold for the thermal neutron group—the neutron density n at any given point inside the moderator will no longer vary with the time t. We can, therefore, say that

$$\frac{\partial n}{\partial t} = 0 \qquad (8.4)$$

and the thermal neutron production is then exactly balanced by the combined losses due to leakage and absorption.

This is true at all points of the moderator, except at points which are too close to the boundaries of the moderator. At distances less than a few mean free-path lengths from the boundaries the assumptions underlying the simple diffusion theory are not fulfilled and the results that follow from an application of Eq. 8.3 without due regard to this restriction require· some modification.

The production of thermal neutrons is to be attributed mainly to the slowing down of fast neutrons to thermal energies, so that one can set Q equal to the slowing-down density q.

Rearranging the terms in 8.3 and applying 8.4, the **steady-state equation** can then be written as

$$\nabla^2 n - \frac{3}{\lambda_{tr}\lambda_a}n + \frac{3q}{v\lambda_{tr}} = 0 \qquad (8.5)$$

Since $\phi = nv$ and v is assumed constant, the steady-state equation can also be stated in terms of the neutron flux ϕ in this form.

$$\nabla^2\phi - \frac{3}{\lambda_{tr}\lambda_a}\phi + \frac{3q}{\lambda_{tr}} = 0 \qquad (8.6)$$

Solutions of 8.5 and 8.6 can be found for various physical situations and an outline of the procedure will now be given for two simple cases. (For details of the calculation refer to Appendix B.)

8.3 The Diffusion Equation

The diffusion of a gas is physically very similar to that of heat, although, in the latter case, one usually refers to it as heat conduction. It is therefore not surprising that Eq. 8.6 turns out to be very similar to the basic differential equation of heat conduction. Many of the solutions of the heat equation for various initial and boundary conditions can, with proper interpretation, be applied to neutron diffusion.

The first simple case we shall consider is that of neutron diffusion from a point source that emits Q thermal neutrons per second and which is located in a homogeneous moderator of infinite extension (Fig. 8.1). We want to find the neutron flux distribution in the moderator due to the imbedded point neutron source.

Because neutron production occurs only at the point of location of the neutron source, the neutron production in all regions that exclude this point is zero; thus the neutron production terms in 8.5 and 8.6 disappear for all regions that do not contain the neutron source. The steady-state equation for these regions reduces therefore to:

$$\nabla^2 \phi - \frac{3}{\lambda_{tr}\lambda_a} \phi = 0 \tag{8.7}$$

or, if we set

$$L^2 \equiv \frac{\lambda_{tr}\lambda_a}{3} \tag{8.8}$$

to

$$\nabla^2 \phi - \frac{1}{L^2} \phi = 0 \tag{8.9}$$

To get a solution of 8.9, the Laplacian ∇^2 is expressed in coordinates most appropriate to the geometry of the problem, which, in the present case, are spherical coordinates because of the spherical symmetry of the physical arrangement.

The proper boundary conditions are determined by the physical nature of the situation which precludes the possibility of ϕ becoming infinite anywhere, and which stipulates that the source strength at the origin of the spherical coordinate system ($r = 0$) is to be equal to the actual neutron source strength used in this experiment (see Appendix B).

Following standard-methods, the solution is found to be

$$\phi(r) = \frac{3Q}{4\pi\lambda_{tr}} \times \frac{e^{-r/L}}{r} \tag{8.10}$$

or, in terms of the neutron density $n(r) = \phi(r)/v$,

$$n(r) = \frac{3Q}{4\pi v \lambda_{tr}} \times \frac{e^{-r/L}}{r} \tag{8.11}$$

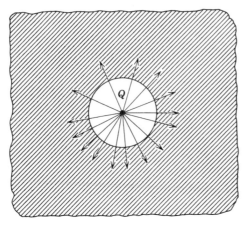

FIG. 8.1. The neutron diffusion from a point source in a homogeneous infinite medium. The solution 8.10 applies to shaded region which does not contain the point source.

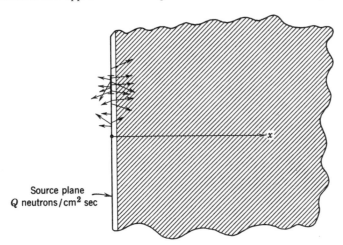

FIG. 8.2. Diffusion of neutrons from plane source. Solution 8.13 applies to region not containing the source, which is shaded in the figure.

The second simple case of interest is the diffusion from a neutron source in the form of an infinite plane that emits Q thermal neutrons per square centimeter per second and which is immersed in a moderator of infinite extension (Fig. 8.2).

The most suitable coordinates in this example are Cartesian coordinates with the source plane coinciding with the coordinate plane $x = 0$. Because the source extends to infinity in the y and z directions, the flux ϕ is dependent on x only, and the steady-state equation 8.6 for regions that do not enclose the source or any part of it now becomes

$$\frac{d^2\phi}{dx^2} - \frac{1}{L^2}\phi = 0 \tag{8.12}$$

where we have again used 8.8.

The boundary conditions are very similar to those in the previous case and the appropriate solution of 8.12 is found to be

$$\phi(x) = \frac{3QL}{2\lambda_{tr}} e^{-x/L} \tag{8.13}$$

or, in terms of the neutron density $n(x)$,

$$n(x) = \frac{3QL}{2v\lambda_{tr}} e^{-x/L} \tag{8.14}$$

8.4 The Thermal Diffusion Length

The quantity L introduced and defined by 8.8 is $3^{-\frac{1}{2}}$ times the geometric mean of λ_a and λ_{tr} and, obviously, has the dimension of a length.

For an infinite planar neutron source L appears in 8.13 and 8.14 as the distance from the source at which the neutron flux is reduced by a factor of $1/e$ and is, therefore, in this particular case, equal to the relaxation length. L is more generally known as the **thermal diffusion length**.

This length is a measure of the air-line distance a neutron travels between the point of its origin as a thermal neutron and the point of its absorption. It is smaller than λ_a, because the latter measures the total zig-zag path that the neutron travels before its final absorption (Fig. 8.3).

Example 8.1. Calculate the average air-line distance traveled by a neutron away from an infinite planar neutron source in a moderator before being absorbed.

The average distance is found by averaging over all distances, using either 8.13 or 8.14. Thus,

$$\bar{x} = \frac{\displaystyle\int_0^\infty x e^{-x/L}\, dx}{\displaystyle\int_0^\infty e^{-x/L}\, dx} = L$$

Hence, L is equal to the mean distance traveled by the neutrons for an infinite planar source.

Example 8.2. Calculate the mean square of the distance traveled, $\overline{x^2}$, for an infinite planar source.

We proceed as in Example 8.1.

$$\overline{x^2} = \frac{\displaystyle\int_0^\infty x^2 e^{-x/L}\, dx}{\displaystyle\int_0^\infty e^{-x/L}\, dx}$$

$$= 2L^2$$

For a point source, a relationship between $\overline{r^2}$, the mean square distance from the source to the point of neutron absorption, and L^2 can readily be established by following the procedure of the previous examples in a formal manner.

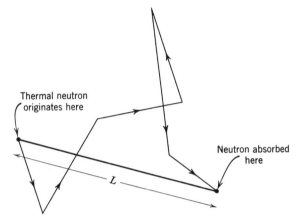

FIG. 8.3. The zigzag path is λ_a, and the straight line labeled L represents the thermal diffusion length.

If $N(r)$ is the number of neutrons per second that penetrate a distance r from the source without being absorbed, but do not get beyond a distance $r + dr$, we can say that $N(r)$ represents the number of neutron absorptions per second within the spherical shell of thickness dr at a distance r from the neutron point source at its center. The total square distance for this group of neutrons is $N(r)r^2$ (Fig. 8.4). Summation over all the neutron groups that are terminated in similar spherical shells as we pass from $r = 0$ to $r = \infty$ and division by the total number of neutrons emitted by the source per second will give us the average value of $\overline{r^2}$. Hence, by applying 4.28, we have for $N(r)$

$$N(r) = \phi \Sigma_a V$$

where $V = 4\pi r^2\, dr$, so that $N(r) = \phi\Sigma_a 4\pi r^2\, dr$. Hence,

$$\overline{r^2} = \frac{1}{Q}\int_0^\infty r^2 \phi\Sigma_a 4\pi r^2\, dr \qquad (8.15)$$

Substituting for ϕ the value as given by 8.10, replacing Σ_a by $1/\lambda_a$ and using 8.8, we get

$$\overline{r^2} = \frac{1}{L^2}\int_0^\infty r^3 e^{-r/L}\, dr$$

$$= 6L^2 \qquad (8.16)$$

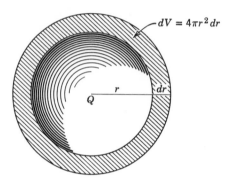

FIG. 8.4. $N(r)$ is the number of neutrons absorbed within a spherical shell of thickness dr, bounded by spheres of radius r and $r + dr$, respectively.

It was stated earlier that L is a measure of the air-line distance traveled by the neutron between the point of its creation as thermal neutron and the point of its absorption. The numerical relation between the rms distance traveled and L is given by 8.16.

The diffusion length can be measured experimentally, and it is often found to differ appreciably from the calculated value. This indicates that the assumptions made in the derivation of the simple diffusion equation are only approximately true in many cases. Reliable numerical values can, therefore, be obtained only from a judicious combination of theoretical calculations and experimental measurements.

Example 8.3. Calculate L for thermal neutrons in graphite using these values: $\sigma_a = 3.2$ mb; $\sigma_s = 4.8$ barns; $\rho = 1.62$ gram/cm³.

$$\Sigma_a = N_0\sigma_a = 6.02 \times 10^{23}\frac{1.62}{12} \times 3.2 \times 10^{-27} = 2.61 \times 10^{-4}\,\text{cm}^{-1}$$

Therefore $\qquad\qquad \lambda_a = 1/\Sigma_a = 3840$ cm

$$\Sigma_s = N_0\sigma_s = 6.02 \times 10^{23} \times \frac{1.62}{12} \times 4.8 \times 10^{-24} = 0.415\,\text{cm}^{-1}$$

Therefore $\qquad\qquad \lambda_s = \dfrac{1}{\Sigma_s} = 2.40$ cm

and $\qquad\qquad \lambda_{tr} = \dfrac{\lambda_s}{1 - 2/3A} = \dfrac{2.40}{1 - \frac{2}{36}} = 2.54$ cm

Therefore $\qquad\qquad L = \left(\dfrac{\lambda_a \lambda_{tr}}{3}\right)^{1/2}$

$$= \left(3840 \times \dfrac{2.54}{3}\right)^{1/2}$$

$$= 57.2 \text{ cm}$$

This is to be compared with an experimentally found value of 52 cm. It should, however, be pointed out that impurities in the graphite will increase the neutron absorption noticeably and thereby shorten the diffusion length (compare section 8.6).

8.5 The Exponential Pile†

The diffusion length L for a moderator can be obtained experimentally from "exponential experiments" using an "exponential pile." This is a rectangular column built from the moderator material with one of its faces containing a neutron source. Either artificial neutron sources or the thermal neutrons from a nuclear reactor can be used as the neutron source.

The neutron flux in such a column falls off exponentially (which explains the nomenclature used for the pile and the experiments performed with it) in a direction perpendicular to the face containing the neutron source, similar to 8.13,

$$\phi \sim e^{-x/L_1} \qquad\qquad (8.17)$$

L_1 is not the diffusion length itself but a constant that is a combination of the diffusion length L for the moderator and the geometry of the column. They are related in this manner.

$$\frac{1}{L_1{}^2} = \frac{1}{L^2} + \frac{\pi^2}{a^2} + \frac{\pi^2}{b^2} \qquad\qquad (8.18)$$

Here, a and b are the linear dimensions of the rectangular base of the column (Fig. 8.5).

We see from Eq. 8.18 that increasing the base dimensions a and b decreases the difference between L and L_1. If we were to allow a and b to increase so as to approach infinity we should again have an infinite planar neutron source, with L_1 then being equal to L. The last two terms of 8.18

† See J. B. Hoag. *Nuclear Reactor Experiments*, Chapter 4.

can, therefore, be considered to represent correction terms that must be applied when we use a noninfinite planar neutron source.

The flux distribution along the x direction is measured by inserting foils of neutron absorbers, usually indium foils, in slots at various distances from the source face and by determining the induced activity in the foil after known periods of irradiation. Details of the calculations are illustrated in a following example.

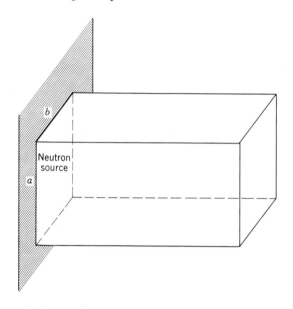

FIG. 8.5. Thermal column. The neutron source is contained within the face a, b.

A logarithmic plot of the experimental values of the neutron flux ϕ against x leads according to 8.17 to a linear graph, the slope of which determines L_1. The diffusion length L can then be computed from L_1 by means of 8.18.

Example 8.4. A manganese foil of 100 mg is placed in an exponential pile and exposed to the thermal neutron flux for 2 hr. After its removal the initial activity of the foil is found to be 200 disintegrations per sec.

If the cross section of manganese for neutrons of 0.025 ev is 13.2 barns and the half-life of the radioactive isotope is 2.58 hr, calculate the thermal neutron flux of the pile at the point of insertion of the manganese foil, assuming that the pile temperature at that location is 50° C.

The nuclear reaction taking place is

$$_{25}Mn^{55} + {}_0n^1 \longrightarrow {}_{25}(Mn^{56})^* \longrightarrow {}_{26}Fe^{56} + e^-$$

The neutron energy corresponding to a pile temperature of $50°$ C or $323°$ K is

$$E = kT = 1.38 \times 10^{-16} \text{ erg/}° \text{ K} \times 323° \text{ K}$$
$$= 4.46 \times 10^{-14} \text{ erg}$$
$$= 4.46 \times 10^{-14} \text{ erg}/1.6 \times 10^{-12} \text{ erg/ev}$$
$$= 0.028 \text{ ev}$$

Hence, for a $1/v$ absorber

$$\sigma_a = \sigma_{a0} \left(\frac{E_0}{E} \right)^{\frac{1}{2}}$$

$$= 13.2 \left(\frac{0.025}{0.028} \right)^{\frac{1}{2}} = 12.5 \text{ barns}$$

The activity A, according to 1.19, is

$$A = R(1 - e^{-\lambda t})$$

where
$$R = \Sigma_a \phi V \qquad \text{by 4.28}$$

Therefore
$$A = \Sigma_a \phi V (1 - e^{-\lambda t})$$

so that

$$\phi = \frac{A}{V N_0 \Sigma_a (1 - e^{-\lambda t})}$$

Here
$$\lambda = \frac{0.693}{T_{\frac{1}{2}}} = \frac{0.693}{2.58 \text{ hr}} = 0.269 \text{ hr}^{-1}$$

Therefore
$$(1 - e^{-\lambda t}) = 1 - e^{-0.538} = 0.416$$

and
$$N = N_0 V = \text{total number of Mn}^{55} \text{ nuclei in foil}$$

$$= \frac{0.1}{55} \times 6.02 \times 10^{23} = 1.094 \times 10^{21}$$

Therefore
$$\phi = \frac{200 \text{ sec}^{-1}}{1.094 \times 10^{21} \times 12.5 \times 10^{-24} \times 0.416 \text{ cm}^2}$$

$$= 3.5 \times 10^4 \text{ neutrons/cm}^2 \text{ sec}$$

Example 8.5. The previous experiment is repeated with the foil inserted at a distance of 16 cm nearer the base of the pile, without changing its position laterally (i.e., in the y-z plane). The neutron flux in the new position is found to be twice as great as the flux in the first position. Calculate the diffusion length L for thermal neutrons for the pile material, if the base is a rectangle of 150 cm by 200 cm.

We denote quantities referring to the first and second positions with subscripts 1 and 2, respectively. Then

$$\frac{\phi_2}{\phi_1} = \frac{\exp{(-x_2/L_1)}}{\exp{(-x_1/L_1)}} \qquad \text{by 8.17}$$

$$= \frac{\exp{(x_1 - x_2)}}{L_1}$$

Therefore
$$\log \frac{\phi_2}{\phi_1} = \frac{x_1 - x_2}{L_1}$$

Therefore $\log 2 = \dfrac{16}{L_1}$ or $\dfrac{1}{L_1} = \dfrac{0.693}{16} = 0.0433$

By 8.18

$$\frac{1}{L^2} = \frac{1}{L_1^2} + \frac{\pi^2}{a^2} + \frac{\pi^2}{b^2}$$

$$= \left(\frac{1}{0.0433}\right)^2 + \left(\frac{\pi}{150}\right)^2 + \left(\frac{\pi}{200}\right)^2$$

$$= 0.00119$$

Therefore $$L = \left(\frac{1}{0.00119}\right)^{\frac{1}{2}}$$

$$= 29 \text{ cm}$$

8.6   The Diffusion Length for a Fuel-Moderator Mixture

So far we have been dealing with the process of thermal neutron diffusion in a pure moderator substance only. In thermal reactors generally we have, however, not a pure moderator but also neutron absorbing fuel (and impurities) present. The natural question now arises: what effect does the presence of the fuel have on the diffusion of the neutrons and on the diffusion length in particular?

The answer to this question can be summed up by saying that the addition of fuel hardly affects the scattering properties of the material but has a marked effect on its absorbing properties. It is found that the diffusion coefficient for a composite assembly is essentially equal to that of the pure moderator. Since the ratio of moderator to fuel in a nuclear reactor is very large, the slowing down and diffusion properties of the mixture are those of the moderator, and hence, the value for λ_{tr} to be used in 8.8 is that for the pure moderator.

Because the neutron absorbing properties, on the other hand, are decisively affected by the presence of the fuel, the λ_a to be used in 8.8 must be that for the mixture as a whole. Thus,

$$\lambda_a = \frac{1}{\Sigma_a} = \frac{1}{\Sigma_{a0} + \Sigma_{am}} \tag{8.19}$$

Introducing this in 8.8, a value for L^2 for the homogeneous mixture is found to be given by

$$L^2 = \frac{\lambda_{tr}\lambda_a}{3} = \frac{\lambda_{tr}}{3\Sigma_a}$$

$$= \frac{\lambda_{tr}}{3} \times \frac{1}{\Sigma_{a0} + \Sigma_{am}} \tag{8.20}$$

It is convenient to use the definition 7.13 of the thermal utilization factor f, in terms of which one can write

$$\frac{\Sigma_{am}}{\Sigma_{a0}} = \frac{1}{f} - 1 \tag{8.21}$$

and to introduce this in 8.20, so that one gets

$$L^2 = \frac{\lambda_{tr}}{3} \times \frac{\lambda_{am}}{1 + (\Sigma_{a0}/\Sigma_{am})}$$

$$= \frac{\lambda_{tr}\lambda_{am}}{3} \times \frac{1}{1/(1-f)}$$

$$= L_m^2(1-f) \tag{8.22}$$

where L_m is the diffusion length of the pure moderator.

This shows that the diffusion length for a fuel-moderator mixture is smaller than that for the pure moderator by a factor of $(1-f)^{1/2}$.

Example 8.6. Calculate the diffusion length for a homogeneous mixture of 1 atom of U^{235} per 10,000 atoms of C^{12} ($L_m = 52$ cm).

$$f = \frac{1}{1 + (\Sigma_{am}/\Sigma_{a0})} = \frac{1}{1 + 10^4(0.003/698)} = 0.958$$

Therefore $L^2 = L_m^2(1-f) = 52^2 \times 0.042$

and $L = 52 \times 0.205 = 10.5$ cm

Expression 8.22 holds also for a heterogeneous combination of fuel and moderator if for f one uses 7.18 and for Σ_a the following average value:

$$\Sigma_a = \frac{V_0\Sigma_{a0}\bar{\phi}_0 + V_m\Sigma_{am}\bar{\phi}_m}{V_0\bar{\phi}_0 + V_m\bar{\phi}_m} \tag{8.23}$$

$$= \Sigma_{am}\frac{1 + (V_0\Sigma_{a0}\bar{\phi}_0/V_m\Sigma_{am}\bar{\phi}_m)}{1 + (V_0\bar{\phi}_0/V_m\bar{\phi}_m)} \tag{8.24}$$

In practice, $V_m \gg V_0$, so that $V_0\bar{\phi}_0/V_m\bar{\phi}_m \ll 1$, and the denominator in 8.24 can be taken as equal to 1. The numerator, by 7.18, is equal to $1/(1-f)$, so that 8.24 becomes simply

$$\Sigma_a = \Sigma_{am}\left(\frac{1}{1-f}\right) \tag{8.25}$$

Introduction of this value for Σ_a in 8.19 gives for L^2

$$L^2 = L_m^2(1-f) \tag{8.22}$$

the same as for the homogeneous mixture.

As, for the same fuel/moderator ratio, f is smaller for a heterogeneous assembly than that for a homogeneous assembly, the diffusion length for the former will be greater than for the latter type of fuel-moderator arrangement.

The preceding result requires some modification in the presence of other materials, for example, coolant or impurities in addition to fuel and moderator. If we use the suffix "1" to denote quantities referring to the additional material, we get instead of 8.22 the following:

$$L^2 = L_m{}^2(1 - f)\frac{1 + (V_1\bar\phi_1/V_m\bar\phi_m) + (V_0\bar\phi_0/V_m\bar\phi_m)}{1 + (V_1\bar\phi_1\Sigma_{a1}/V_m\bar\phi_m\Sigma_{am})} \qquad (8.22a)$$

The derivation of this expression is taken up in Problem 15.

8.7   Fast Neutron Diffusion and the Fermi Age Equation

We must next consider the diffusion of neutrons during the prethermal or slowing-down stage. During this phase the neutrons cannot be treated like a collection of monoenergetic neutrons, as was done for the thermal neutron group since, by virtue of their slowing down, they undergo considerable energy changes while diffusing.

For neutrons still in the slowing-down energy region the neutron density per energy interval, $n(E)$, depends on the difference between the slowing-down density $q(E + \Delta E)$ into the energy interval ΔE and the slowing-down density $q(E)$ out of it.

For thermalized neutrons this difference vanishes because a thermal equilibrium between the neutrons and their surroundings has been established, which is equivalent to saying that, on the average, the rate of neutron flow into an energy interval ΔE is equal to the rate of neutron flow out of it.

It has already been mentioned that, in order to simplify the calculations, one assumes (following Fermi) a continuous loss of energy for a slowing-down neutron instead of working with the actual discontinuous process, whereby a neutron loses its energy in finite amounts after a collision and none in between collisions (Fig. 6.14).

This procedure implies the assumption of a large number of collisions for a neutron between the time of its creation as a fast neutron and the time when it reaches thermal energies. It further implies the assumption of a mean free path between collisions, λ_s, which is essentially constant and varies only slightly with the neutron energy.

The continuous energy loss approximation and its underlying assumptions are valid for most moderators, except for the very lightest, such as hydrogen and deuterium.

Let us investigate the neutron balance in the slowing-down energy region for a moderator material in which there is no neutron absorption ($\Sigma_a = 0$), and in which there are no neutrons being created, i.e., neutron source $Q = 0$.

If we start with a unit volume of moderator in which initially there are n neutrons with energies between E and $E + \Delta E$, the only physical processes that can cause n to change are assumed to be (1) diffusion of neutrons into or out of the unit volume, and (2) slowing down of neutrons into the energy interval ΔE and out of it.

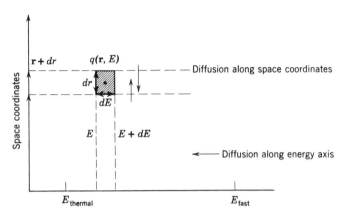

FIG. 8.6. Neutron flow representation in a space-energy coordinate system.

If a steady state is to prevail so that the number of neutrons in the given unit volume and energy interval is to remain constant, the number of neutrons diffusing out of the volume must be compensated by an equal number of neutrons slowing down into and remaining in the energy interval ΔE.

Figure 8.6 illustrates the neutron flow and neutron balance in a space-energy diagram. Neutron leakage by diffusion along the space coordinate is compensated by a neutron excess flowing into the energy interval ΔE along the energy coordinate.

By 8.1 the rate of neutron diffusion is

$$-D\nabla^2 n = -\frac{\lambda_{tr} v}{3} \nabla^2 n \qquad (8.26)$$

The number of neutrons slowing down into the energy interval ΔE and remaining is given by the excess of neutrons flowing into ΔE over the number of neutrons leaving it.

$$q(E + \Delta E) - q(E) = \frac{\partial q}{\partial E} \Delta E \qquad (8.27)$$

influx   outflow

Hence, equating 8.26 and 8.27

$$\frac{\partial q}{\partial E} \Delta E = -\frac{\lambda_{tr} v}{3} \nabla^2 n \tag{8.28}$$

It follows from 6.60 by successive differentiation that

$$\nabla^2 q = E v \xi \Sigma_s \nabla^2 n \tag{8.29}$$

Therefore
$$\nabla^2 n = \frac{\nabla^2 q}{E v \xi \Sigma_s} \tag{8.30}$$

Substituting this value for $\nabla^2 n$ in 8.28 we are led to

$$\frac{\partial q}{\partial E} = -\frac{\lambda_s \lambda_{tr}}{3 \xi E} \nabla^2 q$$

or,

$$\nabla^2 q = \frac{\partial q}{-\dfrac{\lambda_s \lambda_{tr}}{3 \xi E} \partial E} \tag{8.31}$$

This result suggests the introduction of a new variable, τ, such that

$$d\tau = -\frac{\lambda_{tr} \lambda_s}{3 \xi} \frac{dE}{E} \tag{8.32}$$

with the subsidiary condition that

$$\tau = \int_E^{E_0} d\tau; \qquad \tau(E_0) = 0 \tag{8.33}$$

Substitution of this new variable in 8.31 results in the equation

$$\nabla^2 q - \frac{\partial q}{\partial \tau} = 0 \tag{8.34}$$

This equation is known as the **Fermi age equation** and the variable τ as the **Fermi age**, or as the **neutron age**.

It is apparent from 8.32 that the dimensions of τ are those of a (length)^2. The variable τ is formally analogous to the time variable in the nonsteady state heat conduction equation, with q taking the place of temperature, and thus solutions of the Fermi age equation are identical with solutions of the heat equation for corresponding boundary conditions.

It should, however, be remembered that the Fermi age equation does not contain the time variable explicitly and that it is, therefore, a time-independent or steady-state equation. Its derivation was, in fact, based on this assumption. It contains a complete description of the neutron density distribution in both energy and space coordinates for neutrons undergoing moderation.

Returning to 8.32 and 8.33 we see that if λ_s and λ_{tr} can be taken as constant over the slowing-down energy range or, alternatively, if they are replaced by suitable average values over the energy range, integration of 8.32 gives:

$$\int_E^{E_0} d\tau = \tau(E_0) - \tau(E) = -\frac{\lambda_{tr}\lambda_s}{3\xi}\int_E^{E_0} d(\log E) = -\frac{\lambda_{tr}\lambda_s}{3}\frac{\log (E_0/E)}{\xi} \quad (8.35)$$

But, by 6.51, $(1/\xi) \log (E_0/E)$ is the average number of collisions a neutron undergoes with the moderator nuclei in the process of having its energy reduced from E_0 to E. If we use C to signify this number, 8.35 becomes

$$\tau(E) = \frac{\lambda_{tr}\lambda_s}{3} C \quad (8.36)$$

In this expression $C\lambda_s$ represents the total zig-zag path-length of a neutron between the moment of its creation or the beginning of its slowing down and the moment of its arrival at energy E, usually taken at the moment of its arrival as a thermal neutron at the end of its slowing-down career. If we set

$$\Lambda_s = C\lambda_s \quad (8.37)$$

we see that Λ_s is quite analogous to λ_a in 8.8. We can, therefore, in pursuance of this analogy, define a quantity τ_0 such that

$$\tau_0 = \frac{\lambda_{tr}\Lambda_s}{3} = L_f^{\,2} \quad (8.38)$$

The quantity L_f defined in this manner is called the **fast diffusion length**.

It is a measure of the distance a fission neutron has traveled away from its point of creation by the time it reaches thermal energies.

The analogy can be extended to a corresponding relation between L_f^2 and the mean squared distance $\bar{r^2}$ for a neutron during the slowing-down period.

If we solve the Fermi equation 8.34 for the particular case of a point source emitting fast neutrons at a constant rate inside a moderator medium, we get a solution for q in terms of r which is†

$$q(r) \propto \frac{e^{-r^2/4\tau}}{\tau^{3/2}} \quad (8.39)$$

This is the neutron distribution for a given τ. The form of this distribution is well known to scientists as the familiar Gaussian distribution. It has its maximum value at the origin ($r = 0$), and for different choices of the parameter τ, the maximum is higher the smaller the value of τ (Fig. 8.7).

The physical significance of a particular value of τ can be seen from 8.35 and 8.36, from which it appears clearly that the value of a particular τ is

† See Glasstone and Edlund, *op. cit.*, p. 179.

determined by the choice of the lower limit for the energy in the integral. The more advanced the degree of moderation of the neutron, the lower its energy and the greater the corresponding value of τ. The neutron age is, therefore, a direct measure of the degree of moderation of the neutrons. The neutron age that corresponds to the termination of the process of moderation and the attainment of thermal energies by the neutron has been denoted by τ_0.

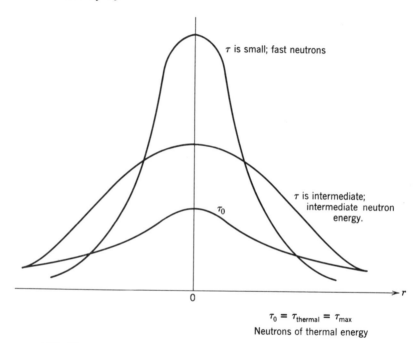

FIG. 8.7. The slowing-down density distribution (Gaussian distribution).

The root mean square distance for a given neutron age can be obtained by following the identical procedure that led to the result of 8.16 for thermal neutrons. Thus,

$$\overline{r^2} = \frac{\int_0^\infty r^2 q(r) 4\pi r^2 \, dr}{\int_0^\infty q(r) 4\pi r^2 \, dr}$$

$$= \frac{\int_0^\infty r^2 e^{-r^2/4\tau} \, dr}{\int_0^\infty r^2 e^{-r^2/4\tau} \, dr} = 6\tau \qquad (8.40)$$

In particular, if $\tau = \tau_0$,

$$\overline{r^2} = 6\tau_0$$
$$= 6L_f^2 \tag{8.41}$$

Thus, the neutron age τ is equal to one-sixth of the mean square distance from the point of creation to the point where their energy has been reduced to a value E which corresponds to that τ. The role of the neutron age is, therefore, quite analogous to that of L^2 in thermal diffusion. For the respective processes of fast diffusion and thermal diffusion, τ_0 and L^2 are each one-sixth of the mean square distance traveled by a neutron from the point of its origin to the point of its termination. The sum of τ_0 and L^2 is called the **migration area** (see section 9.26).

These considerations of a neutron point source and the diffusion away from it are very pertinent because a thermal reactor can be looked upon as a superposition of neutron point sources of varying strengths which are imbedded in a large amount of moderating material to which the above conclusions apply.

It is instructive to transform the neutron age τ from an integral in "energy space" to a time integral by means of expression 6.63.

$$\Delta t = -\frac{\Delta E}{\Sigma_s \xi v E}$$

We then get,

$$\tau = -\int_E^{E_0} \frac{\lambda_{tr}\lambda_s}{3\xi} \frac{dE}{E}$$

$$= -\int_E^{E_0} \frac{\lambda_{tr}\lambda_s v}{3v\xi E} dE$$

$$= -\int_E^{E_0} \frac{\lambda_{tr} v}{3} \frac{dE}{v\Sigma_s \xi E}$$

$$= -\int_E^{E_0} \frac{\lambda_{tr} v}{3} dt \qquad \text{by 6.63} \tag{8.42}$$

$$= -\int_t^{t_0} D \, dt \qquad \text{by 8.1} \tag{8.43}$$

This expresses the neutron age as the time integral of the diffusion coefficient.

By the mean value theorem $\bar{D} = \dfrac{1}{t_0 - t}\displaystyle\int_t^{t_0} D \, dt$ so that

$$\tau = -\int_t^{t_0} D \, dt = \bar{D}(t - t_0) \tag{8.44}$$

This establishes that the neutron age is equal to the product of the slowing-down time $(t - t_0)$ and the average diffusion coefficient over this time interval.

8.8   Correction for Neutron Capture

In the derivation of the age equation we had excluded neutron absorption by the moderator. If the moderator has, however, a measurable but relatively weak capture cross section for neutrons above thermal energies, the form of the solution of the age equation is not affected and only a slight modification is necessary.

The differential equation 8.34, in the case of nonzero absorption, will contain an additional absorption term which is linear in q. If q is the solution of the age equation with zero absorption, and q' is the solution of the modified equation with absorption, it can be shown that

$$q' = pq \qquad (8.45)$$

where p is the resonance escape probability for the medium in which the slowing down is taking place.

Example 8.7. Calculate the neutron age and slowing-down length for fission neutrons of 2 Mev average energy to thermal energy $\frac{1}{40}$ ev in graphite and beryllium.

We start with 8.38 and substitute for λ_{tr}, ξ, and Λ. Then

$$\tau_0 = \frac{\lambda_{tr}\Lambda_s}{3}$$

$$= \frac{\lambda_s}{1 - (2/3A)}\frac{\lambda_s}{3}\frac{\log{(E_0/E)}}{\dfrac{2}{A + \frac{2}{3}}}$$

$$= \frac{\lambda_s{}^2}{6}\frac{A + \frac{2}{3}}{1 - (2/3A)}\log{(E_0/E)}$$

Here, $\log{(E_0/E)} = \log{(8 \times 10^7)} = 2.3 \times 7.9 = 18.2$

Therefore $\tau_0 = \dfrac{3.03}{\Sigma_s{}^2}\dfrac{A + \frac{2}{3}}{1 - (2/3A)}$

For graphite, $A = 12$, $\Sigma_s = 0.335$.

Therefore $\tau_0 = 365 \text{ cm}^2$ and $L_f = 19.2 \text{ cm}$

For beryllium, $A = 9$, $\Sigma_s = 0.57$.

Therefore $\tau_0 = 97 \text{ cm}^2$ and $L_f = 9.8 \text{ cm}$

The diffusion constants of some common moderators are listed in Table 8.1.

TABLE 8.1[†]

	L (cm)	λ_{tr} (cm)	τ_0 (cm^2)
H$_2$O	2.76	0.45	31.4[‡]
D$_2$O	170[§]	2.40	125
Be	20.8	1.43	97.2
BeO	28.6	2.23	105
C	50.8	2.75	364

† Based on ANL-5800; H. Etherington, *Nuclear Engineering Handbook; The Reactor Handbook*, AECD-3645.

‡ More recent experiments indicate a value closer to the theoretical value of $\sim$26 cm^2. See review article by W. C. Redman in *Trans. of Amer. Nucl. Soc.*, **2**, 1 (June 1959).

§ Σ_a and L^2 for D$_2$O are very sensitive to light water contamination (see page 161). If x is the weight percentage of the H$_2$O admixture,

$$L^2 = 28,900(1 - 0.05x)/(1 + 6.56x)$$

(H. Etherington, Ed., *Nuclear Engineering Handbook*, 1.19.)

PROBLEMS

(1) Calculate the thermal diffusion length for neutrons in an aqueous solution of a natural uranium salt if the weight composition is 5% of uranium and 95% of light water.

(2) What is the diffusion length for thermal neutrons in heavy water in which 0.5% (by weight) of U^{235} has been dissolved?

(3) Calculate the migration area for fission neutrons of 2 Mev average energy to thermal energy in (a) graphite, (b) beryllium, (c) light water, and (d) heavy water.

(4) Plot a graph of λ_{tr}/λ_s as a function of the atomic mass number A for $A = 1$ to $A = 16$, with the aid of Eq. 6.44. Compare the values cited in Table 8.1 for Be and C with your graphical values. What values of A on your graph lead to the numerical values cited for H$_2$O, D$_2$O, BeO in Table 8.1?

(5) Calculate the percentage error in the thermal diffusion length in Be^9 and in U^{238} if the scattering mean free path is used instead of the transport mean free-path in Eq. 8.8.

(6) Obtain the general solution of Eq. 8.9 for a point source of thermal neutrons of strength Q. Determine the values of the integration constants by using the conditions (a) that the flux must be finite everywhere and (b) that the total number of absorptions in the material must add up to Q.

(7) Verify that 8.14 is a solution of 8.12.

(8) Evaluate the integrals in Examples 8.1 and 8.2.

(9)   Calculate $\bar{r}$ for a point source of thermal neutrons in an infinite moderator medium $(\bar{r} = 2L)$.

(10)   Calculate the thermal diffusion length for pure D_2O and compare your result with the measured value of 170 cm for D_2O containing 0.16% H_2O.

(11)   A fuel-moderator mixture is found to have a thermal diffusion length which is 15% smaller than the diffusion length in the pure moderator. Calculate the thermal utilization for the material.

(12)   Calculate the age difference for neutrons slowing down in graphite between neutrons that have reached the indium resonance energy of 1.44 ev and neutrons that have reached thermal energies $\frac{1}{40}$ ev.

(13)   Evaluate the integral in 8.40.

(14)   Show that the average distance traveled by a neutron from a point source in a moderator before it becomes thermal is given by $\bar{r} = 4(\tau_0/\pi)^{1/2} = 4L_f/(\pi)^{1/2}$.

Note:
$$\int_0^\infty e^{-au^2} u^{2k} \, du = \frac{1.3 \cdots (2k-1)}{2^{k+1}} \left(\frac{\pi}{a^{2k+1}} \right)^{1/2}$$

$$\int_0^\infty e^{-au^2} u^{2k+1} \, du = \frac{k}{2a^{k+1}}$$

(15)   Derive expression 8.22a for a heterogeneous assembly of fuel, moderator, and coolant materials. By making reasonable assumptions show that it can be reduced to

$$L^2 \simeq L_m^2 (1-f) \frac{V_m + V_1}{V_m} \times \frac{1}{1 + (V_1/V_m)(\Sigma_{a1}/\Sigma_{am})}$$

BIBLIOGRAPHY

Bonilla, C. F. (Ed.): *Nuclear Engineering*, McGraw-Hill, 1957.

Geneva Conference on the Peaceful Uses of Atomic Energy—1955:

P/611: Cohen, E. R.: "A Survey of Neutron Thermalization Theory," vol. 5, 268.

P/603: Chernick, J.: "The Theory of Uranium-Water Lattices," vol. 5, 215.

P/358: Duggal, V. P., and J. Martelly: "A Study of the Slowing Down of Neutrons in Graphite," vol. 5, 28.

Glasstone, S., and M. C. Edlund: *The Elements of Nuclear Reactor Theory*, van Nostrand, 1952.

Goodman, C. (Ed.): *Science and Engineering of Nuclear Power*, Addison-Wesley, 1952.

Littler, D. J., and J. F. Raffle: *An Introduction to Reactor Physics*, Pergamon Press, 1957.

Murray, R. L.: *Nuclear Reactor Physics*, Prentice-Hall, 1957.

Soodak, H., and E. C. Campbell: *Elementary Pile Theory*, Wiley, 1950.

Stephenson, R.: *Introduction to Nuclear Engineering*, McGraw-Hill, 1958.

Syrett, J. J.: *Nuclear Reactor Theory*, Temple Press, 1958.

Weinberg, A. M., and E. P. Wigner: *The Physical Theory of Neutron Chain Reactors*, University of Chicago Press, 1958.

chapter 9

The Critical Equation

9.1 Introduction

We are now in a position to examine the effect of neutron diffusion on the neutron multiplication characteristics of a nuclear reactor of finite size.

We know that the thermal neutron flux is a maximum near the center of the nuclear reactor and that it decreases as one approaches the boundaries of the assembly (Fig. 7.21). The fast neutron flux shows a similar falling off toward the edges because the diminished thermal neutron flux there leads to a reduced fission rate and, consequently, to a reduced production rate of fast neutrons.

There will, therefore, be a steady diffusion of neutrons, both fast and thermal, from the center of the reactor toward its boundaries where they will escape and be lost to the nuclear assembly. The loss of neutrons due to this cause was mentioned earlier and was termed neutron **leakage.**

The effect of neutron leakage can be reduced by the employment of a neutron **reflector** which surrounds the active core of the reactor and which reflects or scatters the escaped neutrons back into the reactor core. The qualifications for an efficient reflector are very much the same as those for a good moderator. The efficiency of a reflector is described by its **albedo**—a term borrowed from astronomy—which is the fraction of neutrons reflected back into the reactor out of all the neutrons incident on the reflector, i.e., the ratio of reflected to incident neutrons.

In the following we want to examine quantitatively the steady-state conditions for a finite reactor without a reflector—generally called a **bare reactor**—where a steady rate of neutron fissions supplies a steady source of thermal neutrons to balance exactly neutron losses due to (1) neutron absorption in the reactor, and (2) neutron leakage from the reactor.

We may recall that the size of a reactor that operates under these conditions of exact balance between neutron production and neutron loss is its critical size; the reactor itself is said to be critical.

For a critical reactor a relation between its geometric properties and the material properties of the assembly can be shown to hold; this is known as the **critical equation**, which we shall now derive.

We shall, in the first instance, assume a homogeneous assembly, but our reasoning will also be applicable to a heterogeneous assembly if its unit cell—i.e., the representative unit from which the whole lattice can be imagined to have been built up—is very much smaller than the critical dimensions of the reactor.

By treating such a heterogeneous system as a homogeneous assembly we neglect the local depressions in the flux density that occur at the location of the fuel lumps and we consider only the large-scale variation of the flux across the linear extension of the reactor (Fig. 7.21).

9.2   Diffusion Equation Applied to a Thermal Reactor

Within the limitations just described the critical equation now to be derived will be applicable to all types of reactors, both homogeneous and heterogeneous.

We start with Eq. 8.6.

$$\nabla^2 \phi - \frac{3}{\lambda_{tr}\lambda_a} \phi + \frac{3q}{\lambda_{tr}} = 0 \qquad (8.6)$$

where the source of thermal neutrons is represented by the slowing-down density q. It is a function of the space coordinates $\mathbf{r}$ and the neutron age τ, so that the rate of supply of thermal neutrons at a given location in the reactor is determined by the value of q for a neutron age $\tau = \tau_{(\text{thermal})} = \tau_0$.

Our first step, therefore, must be to find the value of $q_{(\text{thermal})}$ to be used in 8.6; in other words, q must first be found for thermal energies. This is done by solving the age equation 8.34 as it is outlined in the following.

9.3.   Thermal Neutron Source as Obtained from the Fermi Age Equation

Assume that the desired solution can be written in the form of a product of two functions $R(\mathbf{r})$ and $T(\tau)$, where the function R depends on the space coordinates $\mathbf{r}$ only, but not on τ, and the function T depends on τ only, but not on $\mathbf{r}$. If this is the case, the variables $\mathbf{r}$ and τ are said to be separable and we can then set

$$q(\mathbf{r}, \tau) = R(\mathbf{r})T(\tau) \qquad (9.1)$$

This being so, it follows, by taking the second derivatives with respect to the space coordinates only, that

$$\nabla^2 q = T(\tau)\nabla^2 R \tag{9.2}$$

and by taking the derivative with respect to τ only, that

$$\frac{\partial q}{\partial \tau} = R(\mathbf{r})\frac{\partial T}{\partial \tau} \tag{9.3}$$

Substitution of Eqs. 9.2 and 9.3 in the age equation 8.34 gives

$$T(\tau)\nabla^2 R = R(\mathbf{r})\frac{\partial T}{\partial \tau}$$

Therefore

$$\frac{\nabla^2 R}{R} = \frac{1}{T}\frac{\partial T}{\partial \tau} \tag{9.4}$$

Each side of Eq. 9.4 is independent of the variables of the other side and, since they are equal, each side must be equal to the same constant. Let this constant be $-B^2$, so that

$$\frac{1}{T}\frac{\partial T}{\partial \tau} = -B^2 \tag{9.5}$$

and

$$\frac{\nabla^2 R}{R} = -B^2 \tag{9.6}$$

or,

$$\nabla^2 R + B^2 R = 0 \tag{9.7}$$

The solution of Eq. 9.5 is

$$T = T_0 \exp\left(-B^2\tau\right) \tag{9.8}$$

where T_0 is the value of T initially, when $\tau = 0$. Since q decreases with increasing age because of neutron losses, $T < T_0$, so that B^2 must be a real and positive number.

The slowing-down density at the beginning of the slowing-down process, q_0, is then by 9.1

$$q_0 = R(\mathbf{r})T(0)$$
$$= R(\mathbf{r})T_0 \tag{9.9}$$

We can also express the same quantity q_0 in terms of the physical properties of the assembly since the mathematical symbols are related to and represent definite and specific physical events that are taking place in the reactor.

The number of neutrons per cubic centimeter per second that become available for slowing down is given by the rate of production of fission neutrons. This rate is equal to $\varepsilon f \eta$ per thermal neutron absorbed (omitting for the moment resonance absorption).

The rate of thermal neutron absorption per cubic centimeter of the reactor is $\phi \Sigma_a$, so that the rate of production of fission neutrons per cubic centimeter is

$$(\varepsilon f \eta)(\phi \Sigma_a)$$

This is also the rate per cubic centimeter at which fast neutrons become available for slowing down, which is the same as the initial slowing-down density q_0. Hence

$$q_0 = \phi(\mathbf{r})\Sigma_a \varepsilon f \eta \tag{9.10}$$

Since

$$\begin{aligned}
q &= T(\tau)R(\mathbf{r}) \\
&= T_0 e^{-B^2 \tau} R(\mathbf{r}) \qquad \text{by 9.8} \\
&= q_0 e^{-B^2 \tau} \qquad \text{by 9.9}
\end{aligned}$$

we find, by substituting here for q_0 the expression 9.10, that

$$q = e^{-B^2 \tau} \phi \Sigma_a \varepsilon f \eta \tag{9.11}$$

This is the desired solution of the Fermi age equation, neglecting any neutron absorption during the prethermal stage. However, since we have a certain amount of neutron absorption during slowing down if we use uranium, we must allow for this absorption in our calculation. We know that according to 8.45 the necessary correction is made by multiplying the solution 9.11 by p. Hence, the required solution for the age equation in the presence of absorption during slowing down is

$$\begin{aligned}
q' = qp &= pe^{-B^2 \tau} \phi \Sigma_a f \varepsilon \eta \\
&= k_\infty \Sigma_a \phi e^{-B^2 \tau} \tag{9.12}
\end{aligned}$$

This is the appropriate source term to be used in the steady-state equation 8.6 for the thermal neutron source q, so that with this substitution in 8.6, we now get

$$\nabla^2 \phi - \frac{3}{\lambda_{tr}\lambda_a} \phi + \frac{3k_\infty e^{-B^2 \tau}}{\lambda_{tr}\lambda_a} \phi = 0 \tag{9.13}$$

or, using $L^2 = \frac{1}{3}\lambda_{tr}\lambda_a$

$$\nabla^2 \phi + \phi \frac{k_\infty e^{-B^2 \tau} - 1}{L^2} = 0 \tag{9.14}$$

9.4   Critical Equation and Reactor Buckling

Returning once more to the age equation 8.34, we can show that the numerical value of the constant B^2 depends on and is determined by the neutron flux distribution ϕ inside the reactor. For this purpose we evaluate $\nabla^2 q'$ and $\partial q'/\partial \tau$ for the slowing-down density q' as given by 9.12.

$$\nabla^2 q' = k_\infty \Sigma_a e^{-B^2\tau} \nabla^2 \phi \tag{9.15}$$

$$\frac{\partial q'}{\partial \tau} = k_\infty \Sigma_a \phi(-B^2) e^{-B^2\tau} \tag{9.15a}$$

Therefore $\nabla^2 q' - \dfrac{\partial q'}{\partial \tau} = k_\infty \Sigma_a e^{-B^2\tau}(\nabla^2 \phi + B^2 \phi) = 0$

or,

$$\nabla^2 \phi + B^2 \phi = 0 \tag{9.16}$$

Since the thermal flux distribution $\phi(\mathbf{r})$ across the reactor depends on the size, shape, and the general geometry of the assembly, the value of B^2, similarly, is determined by the geometry of the reactor. In fact, it is given by 9.16 as

$$B^2 = -\frac{\nabla^2 \phi}{\phi} \tag{9.17}$$

Because of its intimate connection with the geometry of the nuclear assembly, B^2 as determined by 9.16 or 9.17 is called the **geometrical buckling**, and is usually denoted, more specifically, by $B_g{}^2$.

The term "buckling" is explained by the fact that $-\nabla^2\phi/\phi$ is essentially the second derivative of ϕ divided by the function ϕ itself, which describes the curvature or bending of ϕ or the buckling of its physical counterpart, the neutron flux.

Combining now 9.16 with 9.14 we get the important result

$$\frac{k_\infty e^{-B^2\tau}}{1 + L^2 B^2} = 1 \tag{9.18}$$

This is the **critical equation** and the left-hand side expression is what we had previously denoted by k_{eff}, or the **criticality**.

$$k_{\text{eff}} \equiv \frac{k_\infty e^{-B^2\tau}}{1 + L^2 B^2} \tag{9.19}$$

Equation 9.18 is a transcendental equation for B^2; it determines B^2 in terms of the physical properties of the reactor materials which are involved through k_∞, τ, and L^2. The numerical value of B^2 as determined from this equation is, therefore, called the **material buckling** of the reactor, and is designated more specifically by $B_m{}^2$.

When the reactor is critical, as has been assumed in our current discussion, the geometrical buckling $B_g{}^2$ as determined by 9.16 is equal to the material buckling $B_m{}^2$ as obtained from 9.18. This assumption was made when we combined 9.14 with 9.16.

The numerical value of B^2 in 9.16 for different specific reactor shapes is found by expressing ∇^2, the Laplacian, in the most suitable and appropriate coordinates, depending on the reactor shape, and then solving the resultant differential equation, subject to the boundary conditions that apply in the particular case. We shall return to this problem in the next section where the procedure described here very cursorily will be applied to particular reactor shapes in more detail. In general, the choice of B^2 that satisfies the mathematical requirements of 9.16 is not unique, but the smallest numerical value for B^2 that satisfies the equation 9.16 is the one that has physical significance for our problem, and it is this numerical value which we shall be interested in obtaining.†

It is clear from the combination in which B^2 appears in 9.19 that it has the dimensions of a reciprocal area, cm^{-2}, since $B^2\tau$ and L^2B^2 must be pure numbers.

It will also be shown presently that increasing the geometrical dimensions of a critical reactor causes the numerical value for the geometrical buckling B_g^2 to decrease. But, increasing the size of a reactor beyond its critical size results in a k_{eff} greater than unity. On the other hand, the material buckling B_m^2 as given by 9.18 depends only on the material properties of the assembly and does not change with the reactor size. Hence, we can conclude that for a supercritical reactor ($k_{eff} > 1$), B_m^2 must be greater than B_g^2.

Similarly, a reduction in size which makes the reactor subcritical ($k_{eff} < 1$), causes B_g^2 to increase without causing a similar change in B_m^2, so that we then have B_g^2 greater than B_m^2.

We can then summarize the critical conditions for a thermal reactor for which the neutron slowing-down density is determined by the Fermi age equation by these three relations:

$$\nabla^2\phi + B^2\phi = 0 \tag{9.16}$$

$$k_{eff} \equiv k_\infty \frac{e^{-B^2\tau}}{1 + L^2B^2} \tag{9.19}$$

$$= 1 \tag{9.18}$$

$$B_g^2 = B_m^2 \tag{9.20}$$

9.5 The Nonleakage Factors

In our preliminary discussion of neutron leakage in section 7.4 the nonleakage factors l_f and l_{th} were introduced by expression 7.11. These

---

† The solutions corresponding to higher values of B^2 are transient solutions which are rapidly attenuated (Glasstone and Edlund, *op. cit.*, Chapter 7).

factors can be related to the material properties of the assembly in a straightforward manner.

To do this we return to the steady-state equation in the form of Eq. 9.13. When we multiply each term of that equation by $-\lambda_{tr}$ and, replacing λ_a by $1/\Sigma_a$, it becomes

$$-\frac{\lambda_{tr}}{3}\nabla^2\phi + \Sigma_a\phi = k_\infty\Sigma_a\phi e^{-B^2\tau} \qquad (9.21)$$

diffusion rate + absorption rate = production rate

where the physical meaning of each term is as indicated previously.

In the production term, $\Sigma_a\phi$ is the rate of thermal neutron absorption per cm³, and if this is multiplied by k_∞, we obtain the rate of fission neutrons produced per cm³. For a reactor of infinite size, all these neutrons would survive through the slowing-down stage and reach thermal energies. Since our reactor is finite, we do not expect all these neutrons to remain inside the assembly because some of them will reach the boundaries of the system and leak to the outside. The nonleakage probability will be given by the ratio of the actual production rate of thermal neutrons, $k_\infty\Sigma_a\phi e^{-B\tau^2}$, over the maximum possible for a reactor of infinite size, $k_\infty\Sigma_a\phi$. Hence,

$$\text{Nonleakage factor} = \frac{\text{actual neutron production rate per cm}^3}{\text{maximum rate for infinite reactor per cm}^3}$$

$$= \frac{k_\infty\Sigma_a\phi e^{-B^2\tau}}{k_\infty\Sigma_a\phi}$$

$$= e^{-B^2\tau}$$

This, then, is the fraction of fast neutrons that does not leak out of the assembly during slowing down and reaches thermal energies. Therefore

$$l_f = e^{-B^2\tau} \qquad (9.22)$$

The left-hand side of 9.21 represents the rate at which thermal neutrons disappear from the reactor. Thus, the fraction of thermal neutrons that disappears each second per centimeter³ through diffusion as compared to all causes of thermal neutron destruction is the thermal leakage factor. Therefore

$$\text{Thermal leakage factor} = \frac{\text{thermal diffusion rate}}{\text{thermal diffusion rate + thermal absorption rate}}$$

$$= \frac{-\frac{1}{3}\lambda_{tr}\nabla^2\phi}{-\frac{1}{3}\lambda_{tr}\nabla^2\phi + \Sigma_a\phi}$$

Therefore

$$\text{Thermal nonleakage factor} = 1 - \text{thermal leakage factor}$$

That is,
$$l_{th} = 1 - \frac{-\frac{1}{3}\lambda_{tr}\nabla^2\phi}{-\frac{1}{3}\lambda_{tr}\nabla^2\phi + \Sigma_a\phi}$$

$$= \frac{\Sigma_a\phi}{-\frac{1}{3}\lambda_{tr}\nabla^2\phi + \Sigma_a\phi}$$

If we now use 9.16 to replace $\nabla^2\phi$, and also replace Σ_a by $1/\lambda_a$, we get

$$l_{th} = \frac{1}{1 + \frac{\lambda_{tr}\lambda_a}{3}B^2}$$

$$= \frac{1}{1 + B^2L^2} \tag{9.23}$$

The factors 9.22 and 9.23 appear in the criticality equation 9.19 in the same form, so that we can equate 7.11 and 9.19 and obtain

$$k_{\text{eff}} = k_\infty l_f l_{th} = \frac{k_\infty e^{-B^2\tau}}{1 + L^2B^2} \tag{9.24}$$

Example 9.1. Estimate the relative neutron loss due to leakage for a critical thermal reactor employing U^{235} and graphite in an atom ratio of $1:10^5$, using these constants: For graphite, $\sigma_a = 0.003$ barn; $L_m = 54$ cm; $\tau_0 = 364$ cm²; for uranium, $\eta = 2.08$. Assume $p = 1$, $\varepsilon = 1$.

Since $p = 1$, $\varepsilon = 1$, $k_\infty = \eta f$
$$f = \frac{1}{1 + \frac{N_{0(C)}\sigma_{a(C)}}{N_{0(235)}\sigma_{a(235)}}}$$

$$= \frac{1}{1 + 300/698} = 0.699$$

Therefore $k_\infty = 2.08 \times 0.699 = 1.45$

The thermal diffusion length L for the mixture is given by

$$L^2 = L_m^2(1 - f) = 54^2 \times 0.301 = 878 \text{ cm}^2$$

The total nonleakage factor by 9.24 is

$$l_f l_{th} = \frac{k_{\text{eff}}}{k_\infty} = \frac{1}{1.45} = 0.69$$

Therefore total leakage $= 1 - 0.69 = 0.31 = 31\%$.

To find B^2 we solve 9.24 by trial and error, substituting for L and τ_0

$$1 = \frac{1.45 \times e^{-364B^2}}{1 + 878B^2}$$

Therefore $B^2 = 0.000325$

Hence $l_f = e^{-B^2\tau} = e^{-364 \times 0.000325} = 0.888$

Therefore fast leakage probability $= 1 - 0.888 = 0.112 = 11.2\%$.

$$l_{th} = \frac{1}{1 + L^2B^2} = \frac{1}{1 + 878 \times 0.000325} = 0.778$$

Therefore thermal leakage probability $= 1 - 0.778 = 0.222$.

This fraction of the surviving neutrons after having been slowed down leak away as thermal neutrons. Since only a fraction of 0.888 of the original number have reached thermal energies, however, the fraction of the original number that are lost by thermal leakage is given by

$$0.222 \times 0.888 = 0.197 = 19.7\%$$

The total leakage is therefore

Fast leakage + thermal leakage $= 11.2\% + 19.7\% = 30.9\%$

which is in agreement with our previous result within the limits of computational error.

Out of an original number of, say, 1000 neutrons

Number lost by fast diffusion	112 neutrons
Number lost by thermal diffusion	197 neutrons
Therefore total number lost by diffusion	309 neutrons

9.6 Criticality of Large Thermal Reactors

As has been mentioned earlier, B^2 is related reciprocally to the dimensions of the reactor, so that for large reactors B^2 becomes small enough (compare the value of 0.000325 for B^2 in the last example) to permit an expansion of the exponential term and, if τ is not too large, to omit terms containing higher orders of B^2 with negligible error. Thus

$$k_{\text{eff}} = k_\infty \frac{e^{-B^2\tau}}{1 + L^2B^2}$$

$$= k_\infty \frac{1}{e^{B^2\tau}(1 + L^2B^2)}$$

$$\doteq \frac{k_\infty}{(1 + B^2\tau)(1 + L^2B^2)}$$

$$\doteq \frac{k_\infty}{1 + B^2(L^2 + \tau)} \tag{9.25}$$

The quantity $L^2 + \tau$ is usually denoted by M^2 and is known as the **migration area** and M as the **migration length**. Therefore

$$M^2 = L^2 + \tau \tag{9.26}$$

Hence, one can write for a large thermal critical reactor

$$k_{\text{eff}} = \frac{k_\infty}{1 + B^2 M^2} = 1 \tag{9.27}$$

Example 9.2. Calculate the material buckling of a large critical homogeneous reactor employing U^{235} and beryllium in an atomic ratio of 1:30,000. For Be, $L_m = 21$ cm;. $\tau_0 = 98$ cm^2; $\sigma_a = 0.01$ barn.

$$k_\infty = \eta f \quad \text{since} \quad p = 1; \quad \varepsilon = 1$$

$$f = \cfrac{1}{1 + \cfrac{N_{0(\text{Be})}\sigma_{a(\text{Be})}}{N_{0(\text{U})}\sigma_{a(\text{U})}}} = \cfrac{1}{1 + 30{,}000 \times \cfrac{0.01}{698}}$$

$$= \frac{1}{1.430} = 0.700$$

Therefore
$$k_\infty = 2.08 \times 0.70 = 1.456$$
$$L^2 = L_m{}^2(1 - f) = 21^2(1 - 0.70) = 132 \text{ cm}^2$$

Therefore
$$M^2 = L^2 + \tau = 132 + 98 = 230 \text{ cm}^2$$

$$k_{\text{eff}} = \frac{k_\infty}{1 + M^2 B^2} = 1$$

Therefore
$$B^2 = \frac{k_\infty - 1}{M^2}$$

$$= \frac{0.456}{230} \text{ cm}^{-2}$$

$$= 0.00198 \text{ cm}^{-2}$$

9.7 The Critical Equation for Reactors with Hydrogenous Moderators

It has already been mentioned that the Fermi age equation is not satisfactory for hydrogen or deuterium moderators because the assumption of a large number of collisions preceding the attainment of thermal energies is not valid. On the contrary, the probability of thermalization by single neutron-moderator collisions is high.

If Σ^0 is the cross section for this type of collision, the factor for non-leakage probability during slowing down to be used, which has been found to be more satisfactory, is[†]

$$l_{f(\text{hydrogen})} = \frac{\tan^{-1}(B/\Sigma^0)}{B/\Sigma^0} \tag{9.28}$$

† Weinberg and Wigner, *op. cit.*, p. 403; A. M. Weinberg, *Am. Journ. Phys.*, **20**, 7, 401 (1952).

This expression replaces the factor $e^{-B^2\tau}$ in the criticality equation, which then becomes

$$k_{\text{eff}} = k_\infty \frac{\dfrac{\tan^{-1}(B/\Sigma^0)}{B/\Sigma^0}}{1 + L^2B^2} \tag{9.29}$$

This is a better approximation than the result of age theory.

The cross section Σ^0 can be determined experimentally from a measurement of τ_0, because it can be shown that the two quantities are related by the expression

$$\Sigma^0 = \frac{1}{(3\tau_0)^{\frac{1}{2}}} \tag{9.30}$$

The critical equation 9.29 should be used in the case of thermal reactors moderated with water, hydrocarbons, or other materials in which hydrogenous components predominate.

Example 9.3. Calculate the material buckling for a reactor of the LOPO-type, for which we had found in Example 7.4 that $k_\infty = 1.50$ and $f = 0.754$, assuming no reflector.

Compare the results for B^2 on the basis of age theory and on the basis of criticality equation 9.29 for a hydrogenous moderator.

Also, compare the fast nonleakage factors according to these results. For water, $\tau_0 = 31.4$ cm^2; $L_m = 2.76$ cm.

The "single collision cross section" Σ^0 and L, the thermal diffusion length in the presence of the neutron absorber, will be needed and shall be calculated first.

$$\Sigma^0 = (3\tau_0)^{-\frac{1}{2}} = (3 \times 31.4)^{-\frac{1}{2}} = 0.103 \text{ cm}^{-1}$$
$$L^2 = L_m^2(1 - f) = 7.62 \times 0.246 = 1.87 \text{ cm}^2$$

1. From the age theory expression 9.24 we get

$$k_\infty = e^{B^2\tau}(1 + B^2L^2)$$

so that by taking the logarithm, we have

$$\log k_\infty = B^2\tau + \log(1 + B^2L^2)$$

By expanding $\log(1 + B^2L^2)$ and neglecting higher powers of B^2, which introduces a negligible error if $B^2L^2 \ll 1$, we get:

$$\log k_\infty = B^2\tau + B^2L^2$$

so that

$$B^2 = \frac{\log k_\infty}{L^2 + \tau}$$

Using this approximation we get

$$B^2 = \frac{0.406}{33.3 \text{ cm}^2} = 0.0122 \text{ cm}^{-2}$$

which agrees well with the computed value by trial and error of 0.01223.

The fast nonleakage factor is, therefore,

$$l_f = e^{-0.0122 \times 31.4} = 0.682$$

2. Using the large reactor approximation 9.27 we get

$$B^2 = \frac{k_\infty - 1}{L^2 + \tau}$$

$$= \frac{0.50}{33.3 \text{ cm}^2} = 0.015 \text{ cm}^{-2}$$

This gives for the nonleakage factor,

$$l_f = e^{-0.015 \times 31.4} = 0.624$$

3. Finally, from the criticality equation 9.29 we get by trial and error

$$B^2 = 0.019 \text{ cm}^{-2} \quad \text{and} \quad B = 0.138 \text{ cm}^{-1}$$

The fast nonleakage factor is therefore

$$l_f = \frac{\tan^{-1}(0.138/0.103)}{0.138/0.103} = \frac{\tan^{-1}(1.34)}{1.34} \equiv 0.694$$

This result shows that with a hydrogenous moderator, age theory leads to a neutron leakage loss which is in excess of the fast leakage loss obtained by the expression 9.29.

9.8 Critical Size and Geometrical Buckling

The geometrical buckling was defined in section 9.4 as the smallest number B^2 which satisfies Eq. 9.16 for the neutron flux in a critical reactor. This differential equation is familiar from other branches of physics and is generally known as the wave equation.

Solutions of the wave equation are obtained by first expressing the Laplacian ∇^2 in the variables that are best suited to the particular physical situation and then selecting a solution in conformity with the boundary conditions that apply in a particular case. An obvious and natural boundary condition for the case of a bare nuclear reactor would be the requirement that the neutron flux ϕ should become zero at the boundary of the reactor. This boundary condition is assumed here, although it requires a correction which will be taken up in the next section.

The shapes of nuclear reactors are almost exclusively either a rectangular parallelepiped (most frequently a cube), a sphere, or a cylinder; and the most suitable coordinate systems are Cartesian coordinates for the first, spherical coordinates for the second, and cylindrical coordinates for the last.

Equation 9.16 and the appropriate solutions for the three coordinate systems are summarized here, and the flux distribution for these three geometries is shown in Fig. 9.1.

Parallelepiped of Sides a, b, c
Cartesian coordinates (Fig. 9.2):

$$\nabla^2\phi + B^2\phi \rightarrow \frac{\partial^2\phi}{\partial x^2} + \frac{\partial^2\phi}{\partial y^2} + \frac{\partial^2\phi}{\partial z^2} + B^2\phi = 0 \qquad (9.31)$$

Solution

$$\phi = A\cos\left(\pi\frac{x}{a}\right)\cos\left(\pi\frac{y}{b}\right)\cos\left(\pi\frac{z}{c}\right) \qquad (9.32)$$

Sphere of Radius R
Spherical coordinates (Fig. 9.3) and spherical symmetry:

$$\nabla^2\phi + B^2\phi \rightarrow \frac{d^2\phi}{dr^2} + \frac{2}{r}\frac{d\phi}{dr} + B^2\phi = 0 \qquad (9.33)$$

Solution

$$\phi = \frac{A}{r}\sin\left(\pi\frac{r}{R}\right) \qquad (9.34)$$

Cylinder of Height H and Base Radius R
Cylindrical coordinates (Fig. 9.4) and cylindrical symmetry:

$$\nabla^2\phi + B^2\phi \rightarrow \frac{\partial^2\phi}{\partial r^2} + \frac{1}{r}\frac{\partial\phi}{\partial r} + \frac{\partial^2\phi}{\partial z^2} + B^2\phi = 0 \qquad (9.35)$$

Solution

$$\phi = A\cos\left(\pi\frac{z}{H}\right)J_0\left(\frac{\alpha r}{R}\right) \qquad (9.36)$$

where J_0 is the zero order Bessel function and α is its smallest root, $\alpha = 2.405$.

By substituting the relevant solution back into the differential equation 9.16 we can find the geometrical buckling B^2 for a reactor of given shape and dimensions.

Let us do this, for example, for a spherical reactor by substituting Eq. 9.34 in 9.33. Thus

$$\phi = \frac{A}{r}\sin\left(\pi\frac{r}{R}\right)$$

$$\frac{d\phi}{dr} = -\frac{A}{r^2}\sin\left(\pi\frac{r}{R}\right) + \frac{\pi A}{Rr}\cos\left(\pi\frac{r}{R}\right)$$

$$\frac{d^2\phi}{dr^2} = \frac{2A}{r^3}\sin\left(\pi\frac{r}{R}\right) - \frac{2A}{Rr^2}\cos\left(\pi\frac{r}{R}\right) - \frac{A\pi^2}{R^2r}\sin\left(\pi\frac{r}{R}\right)$$

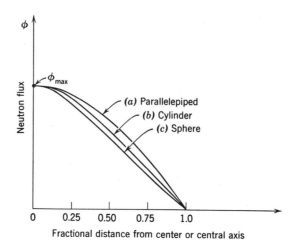

FIG. 9.1. The flux distribution along a line through the center of a bare reactor and parallel to one side for the parallelepiped, and in a radial direction for the cylinder and the sphere.

$$(a) \quad \phi = \phi_{max} \cos \frac{\pi x}{a}$$

$$(b) \quad \phi = \phi_{max} J_0\left(\frac{\alpha r}{R}\right)$$

$$(c) \quad \phi = \phi_{max} \frac{\sin\left(\pi \frac{r}{R}\right)}{\pi \left(r/R\right)}$$

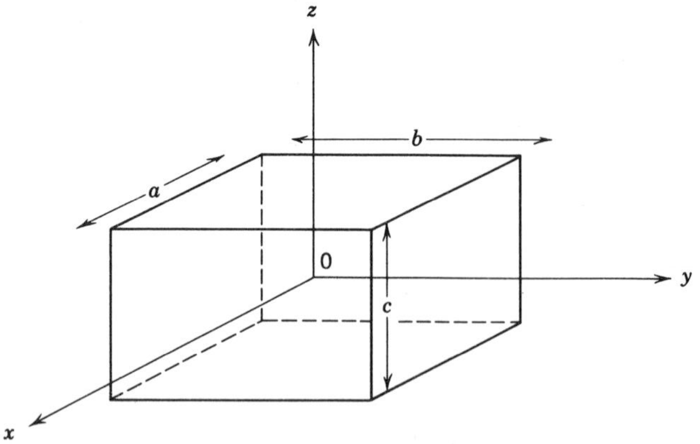

FIG. 9.2. Coordinate system suitable for parallelepiped. The coordinate system is a Cartesian coordinate system parallel to the sides of the configuration.

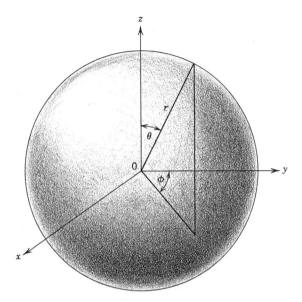

FIG. 9.3. Coordinate system suitable for a spherically shaped reactor assembly. The system is a spherical coordinate system with r, θ, ϕ as the coordinates. No angular dependence of the neutron flux is assumed in the text.

Therefore

$$\frac{d^2\phi}{dr^2} + \frac{2}{r}\frac{d\phi}{dr} + B^2\phi = -\frac{A\pi^2}{R^2 r}\sin\left(\pi\frac{r}{R}\right) + \frac{B^2 A}{r}\sin\left(\pi\frac{r}{R}\right)$$

$$= 0$$

Therefore

$$B^2 = \frac{\pi^2}{R^2} \tag{9.37}$$

This relates the critical radius R to the geometrical buckling and it also confirms our previous statement that B^2 is related inversely to the dimensions of the system.

The critical radius follows from 9.37, as given by

$$R = \frac{\pi}{B} \tag{9.38}$$

and the critical volume V,

$$V = \frac{4\pi}{3}R^3$$

$$= \frac{4\pi^4}{3B^3} = \frac{130}{B^3} \tag{9.39}$$

In the case of a parallelepiped or cylinder, where one has more than one parameter determining the volume—three sides for the former, and base radius and height for the latter—a multiplicity of choices is possible for a given value of B^2.

The particular set of parameters which is of special significance, however, is that which gives the minimum critical volume, as this choice of parameters, will at the same time determine the minimum amount of reactor

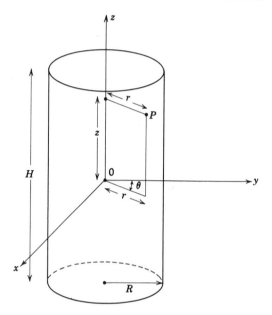

FIG. 9.4. Coordinate system suitable for a cylindrical assembly. The coordinates are the cylinder coordinates r, z, θ, as shown in the figure. No angular dependence of the neutron flux is assumed in the text.

material required to become critical. In order to demonstrate the general method of procedure let us determine the minimum critical volume for a cylinder.

First, we have to find the buckling B^2 in terms of the cylinder parameters R and H in a way similar to the one we followed for the spherical reactor. Thus

$$\phi = A \cos\left(\pi \frac{z}{H}\right) J_0(kr) \quad \text{where } k = \frac{\alpha}{R} \quad (\alpha = 2.405)$$

Therefore

$$\frac{\partial \phi}{\partial r} = kA \cos\left(\pi \frac{z}{H}\right) J_0'(kr)$$

Therefore

$$\frac{\partial^2 \phi}{\partial r^2} = k^2 A \cos\left(\pi \frac{z}{H}\right) J_0''(kr)$$

and

$$\frac{\partial^2 \phi}{\partial z^2} = -A \frac{\pi^2}{H^2} \cos\left(\pi \frac{z}{H}\right) J_0(kr)$$

Therefore $\frac{\partial^2 \phi}{\partial r^2} + \frac{1}{r}\frac{\partial \phi}{\partial r} + \frac{\partial^2 \phi}{\partial z^2} + B^2\phi = A \cos\left(\pi \frac{z}{H}\right) k^2 J_0''(kr)$

$$+ \frac{k}{r} J_0'(kr) - \frac{\pi^2}{H^2} J_0(kr) + B^2 J_0(kr) = 0$$

Therefore $\qquad B^2 = \frac{\pi^2}{H^2} - \frac{k^2}{J_0(kr)}\left[J_0''(kr) + \frac{J_0'(kr)}{kr}\right]$

It can be shown that for the Bessel function $J_0(kr)$, the expression in the brackets is equal to $-J_0(kr)$, so that finally we get that the geometrical buckling of a cylindrical reactor is given by

$$B^2 = \frac{\pi^2}{H^2} + k^2$$

$$= \frac{\pi^2}{H^2} + \frac{(2.405)^2}{R^2} \qquad (9.40)$$

To find the smallest critical volume of the cylinder we must minimize its volume $V = \pi R^2 H$. Thus, by substituting for R^2 in this formula the value for R^2 as obtained from 9.40, we get

$$V = \frac{H^3(2.405)^2}{B^2 H^2 - \pi^2} \qquad (9.41)$$

and, hence,

$$\frac{dV}{dH} = \pi(2.405)^2 \frac{3H^2(B^2 H^2 - \pi^2) - 2B^2 H^4}{B^2 H^2 - \pi^2} = 0$$

Therefore $\qquad B^2 = \frac{3\pi^2}{H^2} \qquad (9.42)$

Substitution of this value for B^2 in 9.41 leads to a minimum critical volume of

$$V_{min} = \frac{3^{3/2}}{2} \frac{(2.405)^2 \pi^2}{B^3}$$

$$= \frac{148}{B^3} \qquad (9.43)$$

An analogous procedure for the parallelepiped shows that the minimum critical volume is a cube, $(a = b = c)$, for which

$$B^2 = 3\left(\frac{\pi^2}{a^2}\right) \tag{9.44}$$

so that the minimum critical volume is equal to

$$V_{min} = a^3 = 3^{3/2}\left(\frac{\pi^3}{B^3}\right)$$

$$= \frac{161}{B^3} \tag{9.45}$$

The geometrical buckling for a parallelepiped of sides a, b, c is given by

$$B^2 = \frac{\pi^2}{a^2} + \frac{\pi^2}{b^2} + \frac{\pi^2}{c^2} \tag{9.46}$$

as can be shown by following a procedure similar to that in the two previous cases.

Comparing 9.39, 9.43, and 9.45, it is apparent that for a given buckling B^2, the least critical volume is that of a sphere, and that the least critical volume for a cylindrical reactor is smaller than that for a reactor of cubical shape. Also, if the reactor is to have a rectangular shape a cube will have the least critical volume.

Example 9.4. Calculate the critical radius for the spherical reactor of Example 9.3, using the value $B^2 = 0.019$.
From 9.37 we have

$$R = \frac{\pi}{B} = \frac{3.14}{0.138} = 22.8 \text{ cm}$$

Example 9.5. Obtain the ratio of average to maximum neutron flux $\bar{\phi}/\phi_0$ for a critical reactor core of (1) cubic shape, (2) spherical shape, (3) cylindrical shape.
The average flux $\bar{\phi}$ for a reactor is found by averaging ϕ over the reactor volume V.

$$\bar{\phi} = \frac{1}{V}\int^V \phi \, dV \tag{9.47}$$

1. It follows from 9.32 that the flux is a maximum for $x = y = z = 0$, i.e., at the center of the cube, so that we can set $\phi_0 = A$ and therefore

$$\frac{\bar{\phi}}{\phi_0} = \frac{1}{V}\int \cos\left(\pi\frac{x}{a}\right)\cos\left(\pi\frac{y}{b}\right)\cos\left(\pi\frac{z}{c}\right) dV$$

$$= \frac{1}{a^3}\int_{-a/2}^{+a/2}\cos\left(\pi\frac{x}{a}\right) dx \int_{-a/2}^{+a/2}\cos\left(\pi\frac{y}{a}\right) dy \int_{-a/2}^{+a/2}\cos\left(\pi\frac{z}{a}\right) dz$$

since $dV = dx \, dy \, dz$ and $a = b = c$.

Each of the integrals is equal to $2a/\pi$, so that we have

$$\frac{\bar{\phi}}{\phi_0} = \frac{1}{a^3}\left(\frac{2a}{\pi}\right)^3 = \frac{8}{\pi^3} = 0.256$$

2. By 9.34 we have,

$$\bar{\phi} = \frac{1}{\frac{4}{3}\pi R^3}\int \frac{A}{r}\sin\left(\pi\frac{r}{R}\right)dV$$

with $dV = 4\pi r^2\,dr$, so that

$$\bar{\phi} = \frac{3A}{R^3}\int_0^R r\sin\left(\pi\frac{r}{R}\right)dr$$

$$= \frac{3A}{R^3}\left[-r\frac{R}{\pi}\cos\left(\pi\frac{r}{R}\right)\Big|_0^R + \frac{R}{\pi}\int_0^R\cos\left(\pi\frac{r}{R}\right)dr\right]$$

$$= \frac{3A}{\pi R}$$

$$\phi_0 = A\lim_{r\to 0}\frac{\sin[\pi(r/R)]}{r}$$

$$= A\lim_{r\to 0}\frac{\pi}{R}\cos\left(\pi\frac{r}{R}\right)$$

$$= A\frac{\pi}{R}$$

Therefore $\dfrac{\bar{\phi}}{\phi_0} = \dfrac{3}{\pi^2} = 0.304$

3. Since $\cos 0 = 1$ and $J_0(0) = 1$, the flux as given by 9.36 is equal to A at the center of the cylinder. Thus, $\phi_0 = A$ and

$$\frac{\bar{\phi}}{\phi_0} = \frac{1}{V}\int\cos\left(\pi\frac{z}{H}\right)J_0\left(\alpha\frac{r}{R}\right)dV \qquad \text{with } dV = 2\pi r\,dr\,dz$$

$$= \frac{2}{R^2 H}\int_{-H/2}^{+H/2}\cos\left(\pi\frac{z}{H}\right)dz\int_0^R rJ_0\left(\alpha\frac{r}{R}\right)dr$$

$$= \frac{4}{\pi R^2}\int_0^R rJ_0\left(\alpha\frac{r}{R}\right)dr$$

$$= \frac{4}{\pi R^2}\frac{R^2}{\alpha^2}\int_0^\alpha xJ_0(x)\,dx, \quad \text{if we set } x = \frac{\alpha}{R}r$$

By using a recurrence formula for Bessel functions, the integral can be evaluated and shown to be equal to $J_1(\alpha)$, where J_1 is the Bessel function for the first order and $\alpha = 2.405$. The value of $J_1(2.405)$ can be obtained from tables and is 0.333, so that

$$\frac{\bar{\phi}}{\phi_0} = \frac{4}{\pi\alpha}J_1(\alpha)$$

$$= \frac{4\times 0.333}{3.142\times 2.405} = 0.176$$

Example 9.6. An aqueous solution of a U^{235} salt is to be stored in a cylindrical container. If the base radius of the container does not exceed a certain value, the liquid cannot become critical whatever the height of the cylinder may be. Calculate this maximum safe base radius.

We use the criticality equation in the form 9.27, and obtain for the material buckling $B_m{}^2$

$$B_m{}^2 = \frac{k_\infty - 1}{L^2 + \tau}$$

$$= \frac{\eta f - 1}{\tau + L_m{}^2(1 - f)}$$

since, with $\varepsilon = 1$ and $p = 1$, $k_\infty = \eta f$.

The geometrical buckling for a cylinder, by 9.40, is

$$B_g{}^2 = \frac{\pi^2}{H^2} + \frac{\alpha^2}{R^2} \quad \text{with } \alpha = 2.405$$

For criticality $B_m{}^2 = B_g{}^2$, so that we can set

$$\frac{\eta f - 1}{\tau + L_m{}^2(1 - f)} = \frac{\pi^2}{H^2} + \frac{\alpha^2}{R^2}$$

The largest possible value for H is $H = \infty$, and in that case, the last equation simplifies to

$$\frac{\eta f - 1}{\tau + L_m{}^2(1 - f)} = \frac{\alpha^2}{R^2}$$

Therefore $$R^2 = \frac{\tau + L_m{}^2(1 - f)}{\eta f - 1} \alpha^2$$

If the numerical value of f is known, R can be obtained from this expression.

If the denominator vanishes, the assembly cannot become critical for finite values of R. The physical reason for this is that for $\eta f = k_\infty$ just equal to 1, any neutron leakage will reduce the value of k_{eff} to below 1.

In any case, f cannot exceed unity, so that by setting $f = 1$, we can calculate a value for R which will be safe for any concentration of U^{235} that may be used. Thus, for $f = 1$

$$R^2 = \frac{\tau}{\eta - 1} \alpha^2$$

$$= \frac{31.4 \text{ cm}^2 \times (2.405)^2}{2.08 - 1}$$

Therefore $R = 16.8$ cm

A cylindrical container with base radius not exceeding this value cannot become critical, whatever its height and whatever the concentration of U^{235} may be.

9.9   Extrapolation Length Correction

The neutron flux distributions as given by expressions 9.32, 9.34, and 9.36 for the various reactor shapes considered lead to a vanishing of the neutron flux at the reactor boundaries in accordance with the boundary conditions that had been postulated to apply in each case.

In actual fact, the assumption of zero flux at the boundary is only approximately true for a nuclear reactor. Indeed, the neutron flux at a boundary between a moderator where neutron diffusion is taking place and a vacuum (or air) cannot be strictly zero, because there is always some neutron leakage flow from the moderator across the boundary into the vacuum or air.

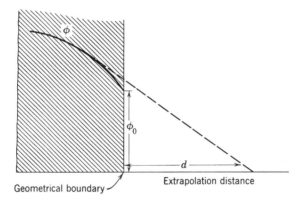

FIG. 9.5. Extrapolation distance correction.

When solving the differential equation 9.16 for a given reactor shape, it would therefore be more correct to use as the boundary condition for the neutron flux the condition that $\phi = \phi_0$, where ϕ_0 is the small but non-vanishing neutron flux at the boundary (Fig. 9.5). The value of ϕ_0 will depend on the reactor shape and, in general, will be different in each case.

Instead of working with ϕ_0 it is, however, more convenient to use a boundary condition for which the neutron flux does vanish nevertheless, and to reconcile the experimental fact of nonzero flux at the boundary with the mathematically desirable and convenient assumption of zero flux in the following manner. We use a hypothetical boundary at a distance d beyond the actual physical boundary, where d is determined by a linear extrapolation of the neutron flux from a point near the reactor boundary (Fig. 9.5).

This distance d beyond the physical boundary where the mathematical neutron flux vanishes is called the **extrapolation** or **augmentation distance.**

Transport theory leads to a numerical value for this distance given by the expression,

$$d = 0.71\lambda_{tr}$$

$$= 0.71\frac{\lambda_s}{1 - (2/3A)} \tag{9.48}$$

This extrapolation does not correspond to a physical condition of the system, but is merely a mathematical device to obtain a convenient boundary condition for the solution of the diffusion equation.†

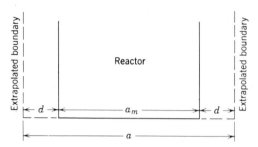

FIG. 9.6. Extrapolated and material boundary.

As a consequence of the introduction of the extrapolated distance, the critical dimensions which were obtained in our critical size calculations are not the physical dimensions of the material but include the augmentation

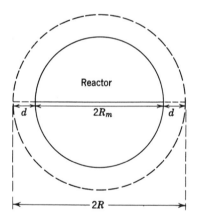

FIG. 9.7. Extrapolated boundary for a spherical bare reactor.

distances. To obtain the physical dimensions, the extrapolated distance d must be subtracted from each moderator vacuum boundary, as is shown in Fig. 9.6 and Fig. 9.7.

† The extrapolation distance increases with increasing curvature of the boundary to a maximum value of $\frac{4}{3}\lambda_{tr}$ for infinite curvature. The value of $0.71\lambda_{tr}$ as given by 9.48 is, however, sufficiently accurate in most practical cases. A slight increase occurs also if neutron absorption in the moderating medium is taken into account.

If R and a are the critical distances as obtained from the diffusion equation, and R_m and a_m are the corrected material distances, then

$$2R_m = 2R - 2d$$

Therefore
$$R_m = R - 0.71\lambda_{tr}$$

$$= R - 0.71 \frac{\lambda_s}{1 - (2/3A)} \tag{9.49}$$

and

$$a_m = a - 2d$$

$$= a - 1.42 \frac{\lambda_s}{1 - (2/3A)} \tag{9.50}$$

Example 9.7. Calculate the critical size and critical mass of U^{235} for the reactor of Example 9.1, assuming a cubical reactor shape. For graphite, $\lambda_s = 2.60$ cm; $\rho_m = 1.62$ gram per cm^3.

By 9.44

$$a = (3)^{\frac{1}{2}} \frac{\pi}{B} \qquad \text{with } B = 0.018$$

$$= 300 \text{ cm}$$

The extrapolation length correction is by 9.50

$$d = \frac{1.42 \times 2.60}{1 - (\frac{2}{3} \times 12)} = 4 \text{ cm}$$

Therefore
$$a_m = 300 \text{ cm} - 4 \text{ cm} = 296 \text{ cm}$$

If M_u and M_m are the masses of U^{235} and moderator, respectively, then

$$\frac{M_u}{M_m} = \frac{N_u}{N_m} \times \frac{235}{12} \qquad \text{with } \frac{N_u}{N_m} = 10^{-5}$$

and

$$\frac{M_u}{\rho_u} + \frac{M_m}{\rho_m} = V = a_m{}^3 \qquad \text{with } \rho_u = 18.7 \text{ grams/cm}^3$$

Combining these two relations, we get, solving for M_u

$$M_u = \frac{\rho_u a_m{}^3}{1 + \dfrac{N_m}{N_u} \times \dfrac{12}{235} \times \dfrac{\rho_u}{\rho_m}}$$

$$= \rho_m a_m{}^3 \left(\frac{N_u}{N_m}\right) \times \frac{235}{12}$$

if we neglect the 1 in the denominator, which reflects the physical condition that the volume of U^{235} can be neglected as compared to the volume of graphite present. Hence,

$$M_u = 1.62 \times 296^3 \times 10^{-5} \times \frac{235}{12}$$

$$= 8250 \text{ grams}$$

$$= 8.25 \text{ kg}$$

The volume of U^{235} is therefore

$$V_u = \frac{8250}{18.7} \text{ cm}^3$$

$$= 440 \text{ cm}^3$$

as compared to a total volume of $260 \times 10^5 \text{ cm}^3$.

9.10   Effect of Reflector

Surrounding a reactor with a reflector (often called a **tamper**)—which is a medium of high scattering cross section and low absorption cross section—has certain distinct advantages over the bare reactor which are briefly stated as follows: (1) improved neutron economy, (2) possibility of fuel savings, and (3) improved reactor power utilization.

1. The reflector reduces neutron leakage from the core by reflecting or scattering many of the escaping neutrons back into the core region of the reactor and also acts as a moderator for the fast neutrons that have entered it from the core. In a way, the moderation of the fast neutrons in the reflector will be more efficient than in the core itself, since the absence of neutron absorbing material in the reflector will reduce neutron loss due to resonance absorption, so that a larger fraction of the fast neutrons in the reflector can reach thermal energies than is possible in the fuel-containing region of a moderator.

2. The improvement in the neutron economy reduces the amount of fuel or, for constant core size, the fuel concentration required to achieve criticality. This means that fuel saving can be achieved if a reflector is incorporated in the design of a nuclear reactor. It is possible with proper design to reduce the size of the nuclear reactor including the reflector to below the size of a similar bare reactor with the same fuel concentration.

3. The improvement in the power utilization is a consequence of the **flux flattening** across the reactor core that occurs when a reflector is employed (Fig. 9.8). The neutron flux will be markedly greater at the core-reflector interface than its value there, i.e., at the boundary of the bare reactor, in the absence of the reflector. Thus, the average neutron flux $\bar{\phi}$ is greater for a reflected reactor than for a bare reactor with the same maximum neutron flux ϕ_0.

Since the power production rate is proportional to the average neutron flux, the reactor can be operated at a higher total power output for the same maximum neutron flux. By virtue of the flux-flattening effect the power production rate will also be more uniform over the core volume, which is highly desirable from the operational point of view, especially with large power reactors.

Theoretically, a critical reactor could be run at any power level, as can be deduced from the fact that the solutions for the neutron flux as given by 9.32, 9.34, or 9.36 contain an arbitrary constant A. The actual power output of a reactor is, however, limited by the practical consideration of the need for the efficient removal of the heat produced in the core in order not to exceed the permissible thermal tolerances of the materials which are incorporated in the structural parts of the fuel elements, the fuel cooling system, etc.

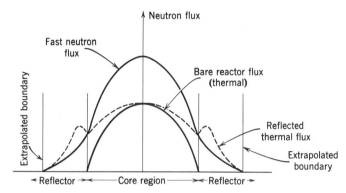

FIG. 9.8. The figure shows the flux-flattering effect of the reflector on the thermal neutron flux in the core. The peaks in the thermal neutron flux that appear in the reflector are caused by the reduced neutron absorption in that region as compared to the core, while the production of slow neutrons through the slowing down of fast neutrons in the reflector continues.

A flux flattening is, therefore, desirable as it permits a higher power-level operation without, at the same time, overheating the central portions of the core.

The effectiveness of a reflector as a flux-flattening agent decreases with increasing size of the reactor core. A common method that is employed with large reactors in order to improve further the evening out of the neutron flux is the nonuniform loading of the core. This can be done by reducing the amount of fuel in the central portions of the reactor, or by using fuel elements of lower degrees of enrichment in the center and building up the fuel concentration in the noncentral part of the core. Alternately, the neutron flux can be depressed and a degree of flux flattening achieved by introducing neutron absorbing materials in the high flux regions of the reactor.

The theoretical treatment of the reflected reactor in terms of the Fermi age theory is generally very complicated, and recourse is usually had to what is known as the **group diffusion method**. In this approach the total neutron spectrum is subdivided into a finite number of energy groups, and the diffusion equation is solved for each energy group which can be treated as a monoenergetic neutron group. The disappearance of neutrons from a group of higher energy through moderating collisions is represented in the diffusion equation by the inclusion of a "pseudo-absorption" term so as to take account of this "scattering absorption."

The approach most often used is the **two-group** method, which can be applied to the bare reactor as well as to the reflected reactor. For a spherical reflected reactor, solutions to the diffusion equation can be found, whereas numerical methods of solution must be used for more complicated systems.

For reflected reactors of large size the **one-group** calculations give satisfactory results and the neutron flux distribution deviates markedly from the calculated values only near the core boundary where theoretical predictions fall below the experimental values.

One-group calculations for two simple geometries are presented in Appendix C.

PROBLEMS

(1) Draw suitable graphs to show the variation of the nonleakage factors l_f and l_{th} for H_2O, D_2O, and C with the geometrical buckling.

(2) Find the geometrical buckling for a cylindrical reactor assembly of 66 cm diameter and 90 cm height.

(3) What would be the length of the side of a cubical reactor having the same geometrical buckling as the reactor in Problem 2?

(4) Find the material buckling of the reactor in Example 9.3 by solving the critical equation 9.24 graphically. Find the intersection of the two graphs $y_1 = \exp(-B^2\tau)$ and $y_2 = (1/k_\infty) + B^2(L^2/k_\infty)$ and show that this intersection gives the desired value of B^2.

In order to be able to choose a suitable scale along the B^2-axis, solve the large reactor approximation equation 9.27 first and use that solution as a guide.

(5) Calculate the critical volume of a spherical thermal reactor that uses U^{235} as fuel and heavy water as moderator in a molecular ratio of $1:10^5$.

(6) A critical reactor of cubical shape uses U^{235} and ordinary water in a molar ratio of $1:400$. Calculate the critical mass of U^{235} for this reactor.

(7) Calculate the fraction of neutrons that are lost (a) through fast leakage, and (b) through thermal leakage for the reactors in Problems 5 and 6.

(8) Plot a graph to show the nonleakage probability during the slowing-down stage, L_f, as a function of $B(\tau)^{1/2}$ for (a) the Fermi expression $\exp(-B^2\tau)$, (b) the large reactor approximation $(1 + B^2\tau)^{-1}$, and (c) the hydrogen collision formula $\tan^{-1}(3B^2\tau)^{1/2}/(3B^2\tau)^{1/2}$.

(9) At what distance from the center of a spherical reactor will the neutron flux be equal to the average flux?

(10) Calculate and compare the neutron flux for (a) cylindrical, (b) cubical, and (c) spherical reactors at a distance half-way between the center and the outer edges of the reactor.

(11) In order to reduce neutron leakage it is desired to design a cylindrical reactor with minimum surface area for a given volume. Calculate the necessary geometrical condition that will insure this result.

(12) Calculate the material buckling for the reactor of Example 7.4 and find the critical size for this reactor, assuming its shape to be (a) a sphere, and (b) a cylinder with height equal to its base diameter.

(13) A fuel-moderator solution is to be stored in a rectangular tank of square base area with sides 100 cm long. If the material buckling of the solution is 0.04, calculate the maximum permissible height to insure subcriticality.

(14) For the fuel-moderator solution of Problem 13, calculate the always safe dimensions of a rectangular tank with square base area.

BIBLIOGRAPHY

Bonilla, C. F. (Ed.): *Nuclear Engineering*, McGraw-Hill, 1957.

Dopchie. H., et al.: "Conducting an Exponential Experiment with a Natural Uranium Graphite Lattice," *Nucleonics*, **14**, No. 3 (March 1953).

Duret, M. F., and W. J. Henderson: "Effect of Flux Flattening on Pile Power," AECL-347 (1956).

Geneva Conference on the Peaceful Uses of Atomic Energy—1955:

P/605: Cohen, E. R.: "Exponential Experiments on D_2O—Uranium Lattices," vol. 5, 605.

P/834: Callihan, A. D., et al.: "Small Thermal Homogeneous Critical Assemblies," vol. 5, 145.

P/600: Kouts, H., et al.: "Exponential Experiments with Slightly Enriched Uranium Rods in Ordinary Water," vol. 5, 183.

P/601: Krasik, S., and A. Radkowsky: "PWR Critical Experiments," vol. 5, 203.

Glasstone, S.: *Principles of Nuclear Reactor Engineering*, van Nostrand, 1955.

Glasstone, S., and M. C. Edlund: *The Elements of Nuclear Reactor Theory*, van Nostrand, 1952.

Hoag, J. B.: *Nuclear Reactor Experiments*, van Nostrand, 1958.

Littler, D. J., and J. F. Raffle: *An Introduction to Reactor Physics*, Pergamon Press, 1957.

Miles, F. T., and H. Soodak: "Nomogram for the Critical Equation," *Nucleonics*, **11**, No. 1 (January 1953).

Murray, R. L.: *Nuclear Reactor Physics*, Prentice-Hall, 1957.

Persson, R., et al.: "Exponential Pile Experiments with Natural Uranium and Heavy Water," *Journ. Nucl. Energy*, **3**, 188 (1956).

Soodak, H. and E. C. Campbell: *Elementary Pile Theory*, Wiley, 1950.

Stephenson, R.: *Introduction to Nuclear Engineering*, McGraw-Hill, 1957.

Syrett, J. J.: *Nuclear Reactor Theory*, Temple Press, 1958.

Weinberg, A. M., and E. P. Wigner: *The Physical Theory of Neutron Chain Reactors*, University of Chicago Press, 1958.

chapter 10

The Nonsteady Nuclear Reactor

10.1 Introduction

In our discussion so far we have been dealing with the behavior of a reactor in a steady state ($k_{eff} = 1$), when neutron loss through leakage and absorption was exactly balanced by neutron production through fission, (compare 9.21), so that neutron flux and power output remained constant during the reactor operation.

We shall now consider the case when this exact balance is disturbed by some outside factor—say the experimenter—which can be done, for example, by changing the position of control rods that are incorporated in the design of most nuclear reactors. Such a change in control rod position will cause the neutron production rate either to exceed or to fall short of the combined leakage and absorption rates. The neutron flux will then no longer be constant, but instead will show a variation with time which we shall next proceed to obtain.

10.2 Thermal Lifetime and Generation Time

To simplify matters, let us assume that all neutrons are produced at thermal energies and let us also, for the present, ignore the slowing-down part of their history. This omission is feasible with thermal reactors, as the average slowing-down time is quite small as compared to the average thermal diffusion time, or thermal lifetime of the neutrons (Table 10.1).

The thermal lifetime t can be calculated from the relation

$$t = \frac{\lambda_a}{v}$$

$$= \frac{1}{v\Sigma_a} \tag{10.1}$$

where v is the average thermal neutron speed of 2200 meters per sec at 293.6° K.

It should be noted that the thermal lifetime of the neutrons will be shorter in an assembly which contains a neutron absorber (i.e., fuel) than in a pure moderator because of the increase in Σ_a as a result of the presence of the absorber.

Furthermore, the average lifetime in a finite assembly will be shorter than the lifetime in a similar but infinite assembly because of the thermal neutron leakage from the system that occurs with the former. The effective shortening of the average neutron lifetime due to thermal leakage in a finite reactor will be determined by the thermal nonleakage factor l_{th}.

If t_0 is the thermal lifetime in the presence of thermal neutron leakage, we have

$$t_0 = t l_{th}$$

$$= \frac{t}{1 + L^2 B^2} \tag{10.2}$$

For large reactors where $L^2 B^2 \ll 1$, it is obvious that t and t_0 differ only very slightly, so that we can set $t = t_0$. Combination of Eqs. 10.1 and 10.2 gives for the thermal lifetime of reactor neutrons

$$t_0 = \frac{1}{v \Sigma_a (1 + L^2 B^2)} \tag{10.3}$$

In the light of the preceding assumptions, and to the approximation which these assumptions imply, the average time that elapses between two successive generations of thermal neutrons which is called the **generation time** is then essentially equal to the **thermal diffusion time**.

The slowing-down time and the thermal diffusion time for some common moderators are given in Table 10.1.

Example 10.1. Calculate the thermal diffusion time for graphite and compare the result with the slowing-down time for this moderator.

$$\Sigma_a = N_0 \sigma_a$$

$$= 6.03 \times 10^{23} \times \frac{1.62}{12} \times 0.003 \times 10^{-24} \text{ cm}^{-1}$$

$$= 24.4 \times 10^{-5} \text{ cm}^{-1}$$

Therefore
$$t = \frac{1}{24.4 \times 10^{-5} \times 2.2 \times 10^5} \text{ sec}$$

$$= 1.8 \times 10^{-2} \text{ sec}$$

This is about 120 times the slowing-down time in graphite (compare Example 6.14).

Example 10.2. Calculate the generation time for neutrons in the critical reactor of Example 9.1.

$$\Sigma_a = \Sigma_{am} + \Sigma_{au} = N_{om}\left(\sigma_{am} + \frac{N_{ou}}{N_{om}}\sigma_{au}\right)$$

$$= 6.03 \times 10^{23} \times \frac{1.62}{12}(0.003 + 10^{-5} \times 683) \times 10^{-24}$$

$$= 0.0008 \text{ cm}^{-1}$$

Using the previously calculated values of $B^2 = 0.000325$ and $L^2 = 878$ cm^2 we get

$$t_0 = \frac{1}{0.0008 \times 22 \times 10^4(1 + 0.000325 \times 878)} \text{ sec}$$

$$= 4.4 \times 10^{-3} \text{ sec}$$

This is only about one-fourth of the time found in the previous example and it shows the effect on the generation time of the increased neutron absorption, and also the effect, although less marked, of the thermal diffusion.

TABLE 10.1

Moderator	Slowing-Down Time (sec)	Diffusion Time (sec)
H_2O	5.6×10^{-6}	2.1×10^{-4}
D_2O	4.3×10^{-5}	1.4×10^{-1}
Be	5.7×10^{-5}	3.7×10^{-3}
BeO	7.6×10^{-5}	6.2×10^{-3}
C	1.5×10^{-4}	1.8×10^{-2}

10.3   Time-Dependent Reactor Equation

We return once more to the time-dependent equation 8.2 for the neutron density n.

$$\frac{\partial n}{\partial t} = \text{production} - \text{leakage} - \text{absorption}$$

which, in view of the relation $\phi = nv$, can also be stated in terms of the neutron flux in this equivalent form.

$$\frac{1}{v}\frac{\partial \phi}{\partial t} = \text{production} - \text{leakage} - \text{absorption} \qquad (10.4)$$

Here, the production rate of thermal neutrons is given by 9.12

$$\text{Production rate } Q = k_\infty \phi \Sigma_a e^{-B^2\tau}$$

and the leakage and absorption rates as they appear in 8.3

$$\text{Leakage rate} = -\frac{\lambda_{tr}}{3}\nabla^2\phi$$

$$\text{(10.5)}$$

$$\text{Absorption rate} = \phi\Sigma_a$$

With these expressions substituted in 10.4, the nonsteady-state equation becomes

$$\frac{1}{v}\frac{\partial\phi}{\partial t} = k_\infty \phi \Sigma_a e^{-B^2\tau} + \frac{\lambda_{tr}}{3}\nabla^2\phi - \phi\Sigma_a \tag{10.6}$$

By means of 8.8 and 10.1 this can be further transformed to

$$\frac{t}{L^2}\frac{\partial\phi}{\partial t} = \nabla^2\phi + \frac{k_\infty e^{-B^2\tau} - 1}{L^2}\phi \tag{10.7}$$

For $\partial\phi/\partial t = 0$, this reduces to the steady-state equation 9.14 as it should.

If we limit ourselves to disturbances of the steady state that are very slight, which means that the reactor is operating very close to criticality, the spatial flux distribution ϕ will be very nearly the same as the flux distribution for the critical reactor.

Under this condition we can apply 9.17 and, with the introduction of $-B^2\phi$ for $\nabla^2\phi$ in 10.7, we get

$$\frac{t}{1 + B^2L^2}\frac{1}{\phi}\frac{\partial\phi}{\partial t} = \frac{k_\infty e^{-B^2\tau}}{1 + B^2L^2} - 1$$

$$= k_{\text{eff}} - 1 \tag{10.8}$$

If we define the **excess reactivity** Δk by

$$\Delta k \equiv k_{\text{eff}} - 1 \tag{10.9}$$

and use Eq. 10.2, Eq. 10.8 can be written in the simple form

$$\frac{\partial\phi}{\partial t} = \frac{\Delta k}{t_0}\phi \tag{10.10}$$

10.4 Excess Reactivity and Reactor Period

Integration of Eq. 10.10 leads to a time-dependent solution for the neutron flux which is

$$\phi(t) = \phi(0)e^{(\Delta k/t_0)t} \tag{10.11}$$

If we define the **reactor period** T as the generation time t_0 divided by the excess reactivity Δk,

$$T = \frac{t_0}{\Delta k} \qquad (10.12)$$

and introduce this in 10.11, we can write the time-dependent reactor flux in this form

$$\phi(t) = \phi(0)e^{t/T} \qquad (10.13)$$

This shows that the reactor period T represents the time interval required for the neutron flux to change by the factor e and, hence, is sometimes referred to as the *e-folding period*.

If we use an average neutron lifetime of $\sim 10^{-3}$ sec for a typical reactor,[†] an excess reactivity of only 0.005, for example, would lead to a 20,000 fold increase of the neutron flux in about 2 sec. In Fig. 10.1 the increase in the relative neutron flux is shown for three values of Δk, assuming an average neutron lifetime of 10^{-3} sec.

Such a rapid multiplication of the neutron flux as a result of a small increase in the multiplication factor of the reactor, with the accompanying sharp increase in the reactor power could cause serious damage to the reactor assembly. It would be virtually impossible to control such rapid snowballing of neutron flux and power build-up.

The saving feature which, nevertheless, permits an effective control to be exerted on the neutron multiplication in a nuclear reactor is the presence of the delayed neutrons which we have so far omitted from our considerations. Their effect on the neutron multiplication is now described.

Example 10.3. Calculate the increase in neutron flux in 1 sec for a H_2O-moderated nuclear reactor when the multiplication factor is suddenly increased by 0.1%.

From 10.12

$$T = \frac{t_0}{\Delta k} \qquad \text{(where } t_0 = 2 \times 10^{-4} \text{ sec for } H_2O\text{)}$$

$$= \frac{2 \times 10^{-4}}{0.001}$$

$$= 0.2 \text{ sec}$$

Therefore
$$\frac{\phi(1)}{\phi(0)} = e^{t/T} = e^{1/0.2} = 150$$

The flux, therefore, increases by a factor of 150.

† The mean prompt neutron generation time τ can vary within rather wide limits for different reactor types. A representative value for a thermal reactor is $\tau = 10^{-3}$ sec, whereas for a fast reactor $\tau = 10^{-8}$ sec.

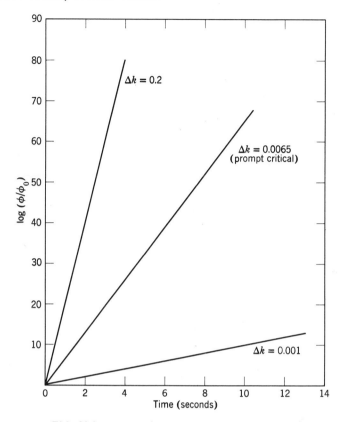

FIG. 10.1. Neutron flux multiplication for different Δk's.

10.5 Effect of Delayed Neutrons

The delayed neutrons have an important and very marked effect on the controllability and on the ease with which such control can be exerted in the case of a nuclear reactor. This is because a delay (of up to a considerable number of seconds after the creation of the main body of the fission neutrons) in the appearance of only a small fraction of them results in a very considerable lengthening of the average lifetime for the neutrons of one generation.

The prompt neutrons which make up over 99% of all fission neutrons are emitted within $\sim 10^{-13}$ sec after initiation of the fission process. U^{235} yields the largest fraction of delayed fission neutrons (0.645%), U^{233} yields less than half as many (0.266%), and Pu^{239} about one-third as many

(0.209%). There are very slight differences in these yields for fast and thermal neutron fissions.†

The delayed neutrons originate from unstable nuclides, commonly known as **precursors**, which in turn are the result of radioactive disintegrations of some primary fission products. The rate at which these primary radioactive fission fragments decay will determine the time lag between the original fission process and the appearance of the delayed neutron groups. Thus, although the delayed neutrons give the superficial appearance of radioactive decay products, they are known to be emitted as a secondary process, subsequent to a β^--decay as was described in section 5.7.

(In reactors where Be^9 and H^2 are employed as moderator or reflector an additional "delayed neutron group" arises from the contribution of the (γ, n) reactions with these nuclei.‡)

The results of Keepin, Wimett, and Zeigler (LA-2118, 1957 or *Journ. Nucl. Energy*, **6**, No. 1, 1 (1957)) for the delayed neutrons from U^{235} are shown in Table 10.2.

TABLE 10.2

Delayed Neutron Group	Yield (%)	Mean Life (sec)	Yield × Mean Life (% × sec)
i	n_i	τ_i	$n_i \times \tau_i$
1	0.0267	0.33	0.009
2	0.0737	0.88	0.065
3	0.2526	3.31	0.836
4	0.1255	8.97	1.125
5	0.1401	32.78	4.592
6	0.0211	80.39	1.688

$$\sum_{i=1}^{6} n_i = 0.64 \qquad \sum_{i=1}^{6} n_i \tau_i = 8.315$$

Presumably, the more recent data of Keepin et al. quoted in Table 10.2 are more accurate than the traditional data of Hughes et al. (*Phys. Rev.*, **73**, 111 (1948)), although they have not yet found universal acceptance in reactor calculations. The reason for the adherence to and the continuing use of the value of 0.00755 (as obtained by Hughes for the delayed neutron fraction for U^{235} thermal neutron fissioning) instead of the smaller but more recent value of 0.0064 is the enhanced effectiveness of the delayed

† G. R. Keepin, T. F. Wimett, and R. K. Zeigler, *Phys. Rev.*, **107**, 1044 (1957).

‡ Proceedings of Second U. N. Conference on Peaceful Uses of Atomic Energy, A. K. Krasin et al., P/2146, vol. 12, 571 (1958).

neutrons in the neutron economy of a reactor as compared to the prompt neutron effectiveness. This increased effectiveness results from the much lower initial energy of the delayed neutrons, which is approximately 0.5 Mev as compared to an average energy of 2 Mev for the prompt neutrons.[†] The smaller energy reduces the chance of the delayed neutrons leaking out of the thermal reactor before being absorbed, and therefore increases their relative contribution to the neutron economy. The correction factor which is usually chosen to take account of the greater weight of the delayed neutron contribution has been assumed to be given by the ratio of the two values, i.e., $0.00755/0.0064 = 1.18$. It is claimed that this procedure makes reactivity measurements more realistic (see K. V. Moore, IDO-16485, September 1958). Because neutron leakage conditions depend on the reactor design and, therefore, vary from one reactor to another, the effectiveness factor, similarly, will vary for different reactors. In the presentation that follows, we shall use the more recent values of Table 10.2.

To find the average life $\bar{\tau}$ for a generation of fission neutrons, considering all different neutron groups of both prompt and delayed neutrons, we use the standard method of finding the average and have thus

$$\bar{\tau} = \frac{\sum_{i=0}^{i=6} n_i \tau_i}{\sum_{i=0}^{i=6} n_i} \tag{10.14}$$

where the suffix 0 refers to the prompt neutrons. For these we have $n_0 = 99.36\%$ and $\tau_0 = 10^{-3}$ sec.

With these values and those from Table 10.2 for the delayed neutrons we get from 10.14

$$\bar{\tau} = \frac{8.315 + 99.36 \times 10^{-3}}{100}$$

$$= 0.084 \text{ or about } 10^{-1} \text{ sec}$$

This result shows that the presence of delayed fission neutrons has lengthened the average lifetime of a neutron generation by a factor of nearly 100. Instead of a mean life for the prompt neutrons alone of 10^{-3} sec, the lifetime of a neutron generation has been increased to $\sim 10^{-1}$ sec by the delay in the emission of only a minute fraction of the fission neutrons.

Since it is the generation time that determines the period of the reactor, this means that the delayed neutrons have effectively lengthened the reactor period by a factor of 100, thus making reactor control much more manageable and elastic.

† R. Batchelor and H. R. McK. Hyder, "The Energy of Delayed Neutrons from Fission," *Journ. Nucl. Energy*, **3**, 7 (1956).

10.6   Delayed Neutrons and Reactor Period

The presence of delayed fission neutrons was not taken into account in the formulation of the nonsteady state equation 10.6. It is clear that the production term Q will be more complicated if the delayed creation of a portion of the fission neutrons is taken into consideration.

Detailed calculations show that the groups of delayed neutrons contribute what are called **transient** effects, which introduce additional reactor periods.† These transients disappear, however, after a very short time and, for $k_{eff} > 1$, the power-level build-up after this initial period is determined by the **stable reactor period** alone.

This is the reactor period that was previously introduced by 10.12 and 10.13. The transient periods for $\Delta k > 0$ are negative and have no direct physical significance.

A quantity which enters, however, significantly in the calculation of the reactor period and which is important in nuclear reactor physics in general is the **reactivity**, usually denoted by ρ. It is defined as the excess multiplication Δk divided by the multiplication factor k_{eff}.

$$\rho \equiv \frac{\Delta k}{k_{eff}}$$

$$= \frac{k_{eff} - 1}{k_{eff}}$$

$$= 1 - \frac{1 + L^2 B^2}{k_\infty e^{-B^2 \tau}} \tag{10.15}$$

It is apparent from this definition of ρ that, for reactors operating close to criticality,

$$\rho \doteq \Delta k \tag{10.16}$$

When a reactor is operated so that it is critical on the prompt neutron contribution alone, it is said to be **prompt critical** and it can be shown that in this case ρ is numerically equal to the fraction of delayed neutrons. If we use β to signify this fraction, then

$$\rho = \beta \tag{10.17}$$

In the case of U^{235} fuel, $\beta = 0.0064$, so that a reactor using this fuel becomes prompt critical for $\rho = 0.0064$, or, by 10.16, for $\Delta k = 0.0064$.

If $\Delta k > 0.0064$, the delayed neutrons will not be able to make their decisive contribution to the lengthening of the reactor period, because the neutron flux will rise at a rate which is determined by the prompt neutrons alone. Since these multiply at a much faster rate than the delayed neutrons

† See, e.g., S. Glasstone, *Principles of Nuclear Reactor Engineering*, Chapter 4.

the initial rate of increase in the neutron flux will also be much greater for a prompt critical reactor (Figure 10.2).

If, however, $0 < \Delta k < 0.0064$, the rate of rise of neutron flux and reactor power will be much slower because now it is dependent upon the contribution from the delayed neutrons. The reactor, when operating in this manner, is said to be **delayed critical**.

The flux multiplication for various values of Δk is shown in Fig. 10.1.

For safe operation when the power is to be increased, the reactor should be kept in the delayed critical operating condition because the reactor period is then sufficiently long to allow adequate control of the reactor to be exercised by the operator or by mechanical means.

Figure 10.2 shows, qualitatively, the variation of the relative neutron flux ϕ/ϕ_0 with time upon the introduction of a small sudden step change, $\Delta k > 0$, in the multiplication factor of the reactor. Initially, within a very short time after the original disturbance, the flux increase will be determined by the prompt neutron lifetime. However, after a very short time interval has elapsed, the delayed neutrons will become effective and will cause the build-up rate of neutron flux to diminish considerably. The nature of a step-function and its effect on k is illustrated in Fig. 10.3.

For a negative step change, $\Delta k < 0$, the flux will show an initial decrease and, within the very short time interval after the disturbance before the delayed neutron contribution becomes effective, the flux behavior will be the mirror image of its behavior for a positive Δk. After a very short time, however, the flux change will flatten out. As the precursors of the shorter lived delayed neutron groups rapidly disappear, the flux will eventually fall off exponentially in a manner determined by the longest lived delayed neutron group.

This is essentially what happens when the reactor is shut down. As the control rods are inserted into the core, k_{eff} is reduced to below unity. This negative change in reactivity causes an initial steep exponential decrease of neutron flux. After a short time interval (of the order of minutes) the neutron flux and the power level decrease with a period of 80.4 sec, corresponding to the average lifetime of the longest delayed neutron group.

10.7 The Inhour Equation

The general relation between the reactivity ρ and the reactor period T, which is known as the **inhour equation**, is stated here for reference.

$$\rho = \frac{t}{T k_{\text{eff}}} + \sum_i \frac{n_i \tau_i}{T + \tau_i} \tag{10.18}$$

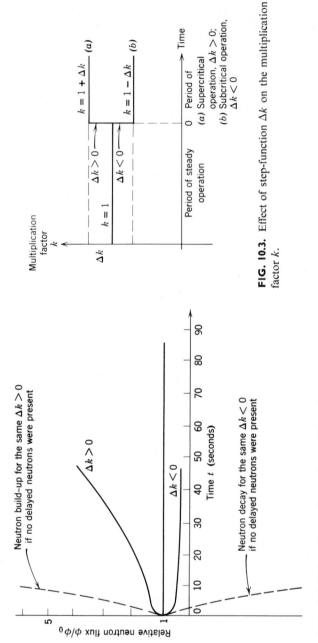

FIG. 10.3. Effect of step-function Δk on the multiplication factor k.

FIG. 10.2. Effect of a small step change Δk on the neutron flux of a critical reactor.

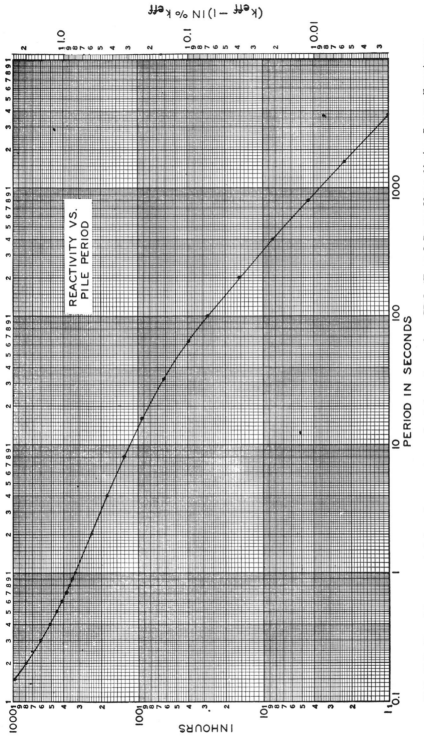

FIG. 10.5. Reactivity *vs.* period for a heavy-water-moderated reactor such as CP-5. (From J. Barton Hoag, *Nuclear Reactor Experiments,* Copyright 1958, D. van Nostrand Company, Princeton, N. J.)

Example 10.4. Calculate the reactivity of a graphite-uranium reactor when its initially steady power operation is suddenly increased by changing the position of a control rod, with the result that its stable reactor period is 10.5 min.

From 10.21

$$\rho = \frac{10^{-3}}{10.5 \times 60} + \frac{0.0064 \times 13}{10.5 \times 60 + 13}$$

$$= 13.0 \times 10^{-5}$$

Therefore

$$\rho = \frac{13 \times 10^{-5}}{2.30 \times 10^{-5}} \text{ inhr}$$

$$= 5.65 \text{ inhr}$$

$$\delta = \frac{\rho}{\beta}$$

$$= \frac{13.0 \times 10^{-5}}{0.0064}$$

$$= 0.02 \text{ dollars}$$

$$= 2 \text{ cents}$$

PROBLEMS

(1)   Calculate the average lifetime of 0.25 Mev neutrons in U^{235} and in Pu^{239}, ignoring leakage.

(2)   What is the stable reactor period for a generation time of 1.2×10^{-3} sec and an excess reactivity of 0.001 %?

(3)   The sudden withdrawal of a neutron absorber from a uranium fueled research reactor operating at criticality causes a slight increase in the reactivity corresponding to a stable reactor period of 25 min. Assuming a prompt neutron lifetime of 2×10^{-4} sec, calculate the reactivity that results from this action.

(4)   In practice Δk is kept below 0.005. Calculate the corresponding shortest safe operating reactor period for a typical thermal reactor.

(5)   Considering only the stable negative period due to the longest delayed neutron group, estimate the minimum time required to shut down a reactor from an average neutron flux of 10^{14} to 10^3 neutrons/cm² sec.

(6)   Calculate the fraction of thermal neutrons that survive at a given instant out of the total number of thermal neutrons produced per second in a thermal reactor, and show that this fraction is equal to the thermal lifetime as given by 10.3.

(7)   Starting with an initial number of 1000 neutrons, how many neutrons will there be present after ten generations, assuming $k = 1.0025$?

(8)   Calculate the generation time for neutrons in a thermal nuclear reactor core in the shape of a sphere of 30 cm diameter, using a fuel solution as in the LOPO reactor of Example 7.4.

(9) When enriched uranium is used as fuel, the generation time for prompt neutrons is $\sim 10^{-4}$ sec. How will this affect the time behavior of a reactor when it operates (a) above prompt criticality, and (b) below prompt criticality?

(10) A reactor has an excess reactivity of 0.025. After how many generations will the neutron flux be doubled?

(11) Using the data in Table 10.3, calculate the mean lives $\bar{\tau}$ for delayed neutrons from U^{233} and Pu^{239}.

TABLE 10.3

Group (i)	Half-Life (sec)		Relative Yield (β_i/β)	
	U^{233}	Pu^{239}	U^{233}	Pu^{239}
1	55.00	54.28	0.086	0.035
2	20.57	23.04	0.299	0.298
3	5.00	5.60	0.252	0.211
4	2.13	2.13	0.278	0.326
5	0.615	0.618	0.051	0.086
6	0.277	0.257	0.034	0.044
Total yield			0.266%	0.209%

From data of Keepin, Wimett, and Zeigler.

(12) Starting with the definition of k_{eff} as the number of neutrons present in each generation per neutron present in the previous generation, derive Eq. 10.11.

(13) What will be the total number of thermal neutrons produced per neutron present initially during each second of a reactor in operation, if the reactor has a prompt k of 1.002 and the generation time of thermal neutrons in the reactor is 10^{-3} sec?

(14) Derive the following alternative expression for the reactivity:

$$\rho = \frac{\beta + t_0\lambda}{1 + \lambda T} \quad \text{with} \quad \frac{1}{\lambda} = \frac{1}{\beta}\sum_i \frac{\beta_i}{\lambda_i}$$

where λ is the average decay constant for the delayed neutrons.

(15) What modifications are necessary to adapt the inhour equation to reactors using U^{233} or Pu^{239} as fuel?

BIBLIOGRAPHY

Allred, J. C., and D. S. Carter: "Kinetics of Homogeneous Power Reactors of the LAPRE Type," *Nucl. Sci. and Engin.*, **3**, 482 (1958).

Bonilla, F. C. (Ed.): *Nuclear Engineering*, McGraw-Hill, 1957.

Brunson, G. S., et al.: "Measuring the Prompt Period of a Reactor," *Nucleonics*, **15**, 132 (November 1957).

Etherington, H. (Ed.): *Nuclear Engineering Handbook*, McGraw-Hill, 1958.

Forbes, S. G., et al.: "Instability in SPERT-1," *Nucleonics*, **15**, No. 1 (January 1957).

Geneva Conference on the Peaceful Uses of Atomic Energy—1955:
    P/834: Callihan, A. D., et al.: "Small Thermal Homogeneous Critical Assemblies," vol. 5, 145.

Glasstone, S.: *Principles of Nuclear Reactor Engineering*, van Nostrand, 1955.

Glasstone, S., and M. C. Edlund: *The Elements of Nuclear Reactor Theory*, van Nostrand, 1952.

Harrer, J. M.: "Controlling a Power Producing Nuclear Reactor," *Nucleonics*, **6**, No. 3 (March 1948).

Hoag, J. B.: *Nuclear Reactor Experiments*, van Nostrand, 1958.

Isbin, H. S., and J. W. Gorman: "Applications of Pile Kinetic Equations," *Nucleonics*, **8**, No. 11 (November 1950).

Keepin, G. R., and T. F. Wimett: "Reactor Kinetic Equations: A New Evaluation," *Nucleonics*, **16**, No. 10 (October 1958).

Littler, D. J., and J. F. Raffle: *An Introduction to Reactor Physics*, Pergamon Press, 1957.

Lundby, A., and N. Holt: "Kinetic Behavior of a Thermal Heavy Water Reactor," *Nucleonics*, **12**, No. 1 (January 1954).

Murray, R. L.: *Nuclear Reactor Physics*, Prentice-Hall, 1957.

Schultz, M. A.: *Control of Nuclear Reactors and Power Plants*, McGraw-Hill, 1955.

Stephenson, R.: *Introduction to Nuclear Engineering*, McGraw-Hill, 1957.

Thie, J. A.: "Boiling Water Reactor Instability," *Nucleonics*, **16**, No. 3 (March 1958).

"Special Report on Reactor Control," *Nucleonics*, **16**, No. 5 (May 1958).

Weinberg, A. M., and E. P. Wigner: *The Physical Theory of Neutron Chain Reactors*, University of Chicago Press, 1958.

chapter **11**

Conditions Affecting
the Reactivity

11.1 Introduction

The reactivity of a nuclear reactor will change not only as a consequence of extraneous changes in the operating conditions that can be brought about, for example, by altering the position of control rods, by modifying the arrangement of reflectors, by inserting neutron sources or neutron absorbers, or by modifications required to satisfy experimental arrangements. But, every reactor has also inherent factors which, sooner or later, and also from time to time, will cause changes in the reactivity even when the reactor initially has been set to run at constant power level.

In the case of Boiling Water Reactors, for example, the formation of steam bubbles or voids in the core will effect the reactivity by causing a reduction of parasitic neutron absorption by the water and an increase of neutron leakage from the active core.

The most important contributory causes to the slow changes in the reactivity are (1) temperature changes; (2) increased concentrations of poisonous fission products; and (3) depletion and, in the case of a breeder reactor, increase of fuel in the reactor core.

In order to be able to compensate for the drop in reactivity that takes place during the continuous operation of a reactor because of some of these factors a large amount of **excess reactivity** $\Delta\rho$ must be built into the reactor initially. This is done by adding to the core more fissile material than that needed for criticality. For example, the smallest critical load of the MTR core is 1.81 kg, but a core load of 4.66 kg is used for full power operation.

At the beginning of the reactor operation the control rods are inserted deeply into the core to balance out the initial overproduction of neutrons. As the reactivity drops during the operation of the reactor the control rods are gradually withdrawn just enough to counteract the decrease in the reactivity.

11.2   Effect of Temperature Changes on the Reactivity

The continuous power output of a nuclear reactor in operation if not fully drawn upon will lead to a rise in the temperature of the reactor materials which will affect the reactivity of the reactor.

The change in the reactivity per degree temperature increase, $d\rho/dT$, is called the **temperature coefficient** of the reactor.

The temperature coefficient of a reactor, in order to increase its safety of operation, should be negative, since an increase in temperature will then lead to a decrease in the reactivity with consequent reduction of its power because of the reduced fission rate. The fall in the fission rate will result in a diminished heat release and this will counteract the original rise in the temperature so that the reactor will thus be brought back to a lower operating temperature.

A negative temperature coefficient thus acts as a self-regulatory device, so that a reactor having this characteristic would be stable with respect to small temperature changes.

If the temperature coefficient were positive, a rise in the temperature would increase the reactivity, and with it the fission rate. An increased fission rate would cause a further rise in the temperature of the reactor and so create a runaway condition. A reactor with a positive temperature coefficient is very unsafe to operate because of this inherent instability.

The temperature coefficient can conveniently be considered to consist of the three following partial contributions: (1) a **nuclear temperature coefficient,** which represents the partial change in the reactivity due to changes in the nuclear cross sections, (2) a **density temperature coefficient** which takes account of that part of the change in reactivity which is due to the change in the densities of the materials, and (3) a **volume temperature coefficient** which arises from the thermal expansion of the over-all reactor volume, so causing a change in the buckling B^2 of the reactor. We can therefore write the temperature coefficient as the sum of three terms

$$\frac{d\rho(\sigma, B^2, d)}{dT} = \left(\frac{\partial\rho}{\partial T}\right)_{B^2,d} + \left(\frac{\partial\rho}{\partial T}\right)_{\sigma,B^2} + \left(\frac{\partial\rho}{\partial T}\right)_{\sigma,d} \qquad (11.1)$$

with

$\left(\dfrac{\partial\rho}{\partial T}\right)_{B^2,d}$ the nuclear temperature coefficient due to the temperature dependence of the cross sections (B^2 and density d being kept constant),

$\left(\dfrac{\partial\rho}{\partial T}\right)_{\sigma,B^2}$ the density temperature coefficient due to the temperature dependence of the number of nuclei per cm³, N_0 (σ, B^2 being kept constant), and

$\left(\dfrac{\partial \rho}{\partial T}\right)_{\sigma,d}$ the volume temperature coefficient due to the temperature dependence of the dimensions of the reactor (σ, d being kept constant).

The nuclear temperature coefficient portion of the change in the reactivity takes account of the change in the neutron absorption cross sections due to the increased mean thermal energy of the neutrons. The absorption cross sections are energy dependent and will, therefore, change as the temperature of the reactor rises.

The density coefficient takes account of the fact that an increase in temperature causes an expansion of the reactor materials which results in a decreased density of the materials. The change in densities alters the macroscopic cross sections and mean free paths which involve the number of nuclei per unit volume, N_0. The nonleakage probabilities, similarly, are functions of the density and they will, therefore, also be affected by any density changes brought about by a rise in the temperature.

The volume coefficient takes account of the fact that, as the system as a whole changes in size through thermal expansion, this will cause the buckling of the reactor to be altered.

Let us now examine the temperature variation of the reactivity ρ as given by 10.15 for a large reactor, which contains the three temperature-dependent quantities, k_∞, τ_0, and L^2 explicitly.

$$\rho = 1 - \frac{1 + (L^2 + \tau_0)B^2}{k_\infty} \tag{11.2}$$

Starting with the four factors of k_∞, we can see that the fast fission factor ε is not expected to be influenced by small temperature changes since it is determined by the behavior of the fast neutrons.

It is also reasonable to expect that the number of neutrons released per fission, v, is not temperature dependent and, if σ_f and σ_a follow the $1/v$ law, the number of neutrons released per capture, η, will also be independent of temperature as is apparent from 5.3.

By similar reasoning and under the same assumption that the thermal cross sections are $1/v$ dependent, it follows from 7.13 that for a homogeneous reactor, the thermal utilization, f, will be independent of the temperature.

For a heterogeneous assembly, however, an increase in the temperature will lower the numerical value of the thermal disadvantage factor because the decreased uranium absorption cross section will be less effective in reducing the neutron flux entering the fuel rods, so that a more even distribution of the neutron flux across the lattice cells ensues. A smaller thermal disadvantage factor means an increased value of f, as is apparent from 7.18.

The resonance escape probability p decreases somewhat with rising temperature because of an increase in the resonance absorption with higher temperature. This increase is caused by the broadening of the resonance absorption lines of U^{235} for higher thermal kinetic energies of neutrons.†

On the whole, the effect of a rise in temperature on k_∞ is, however, less significant than its effect on the remaining reactor parameters, so that one can reasonably assume that k_∞ is constant for small temperature changes.

Of the remaining quantities, the neutron age τ will be affected by a change in temperature to the extent that the fast leakage probability and the slowing-down properties of the assembly are temperature dependent.

From the definition of the Fermi age, equation 8.32, it is clear that $\tau \propto 1/\Sigma_s^2$, so that it will vary with the temperature to the degree that $1/\Sigma_s^2$ is temperature dependent. This means that if we can ignore the temperature dependence of the scattering cross sections (which, in any case, is negligible) the variation of τ is determined by the temperature dependence of the density.

The variation of the neutron age with temperature, however, is generally much less pronounced than the variation of the thermal diffusion length L with temperature. From the definition 8.8 it is apparent that L^2, too, is inversely proportional to the square of the density and, in addition, to the absorption cross section σ_a.

The change in the thermal diffusion length is more significant than the change in τ with temperature, so that a rise in temperature will lead to an increased diffusion length and, consequently, to increased thermal leakage. Indeed, the variation of L^2 with temperature is the primary contribution to the nuclear temperature coefficient. Through their dependence on the density, L^2 and τ will also make a contribution to the density temperature coefficient.

An increase in temperature will increase the size of the reactor core, which causes a decrease in the buckling B^2. This effect accounts for the volume coefficient of reactivity.

A detailed numerical analysis of all the factors involved shows that, as far as the nuclear cross sections are concerned, a rise in temperature leads to a decrease in the reactivity so that the nuclear temperature coefficient turns out to be negative.

Similarly, the density temperature coefficient, too, turns out to be negative, so that only the volume temperature coefficient makes a positive

† See Weinberg and Wigner, op. cit. p. 69.

contribution to the over-all temperature coefficient of the reactivity. Since this latter contribution is, however, much smaller than the first two, the net effect is a decrease in the reactivity with an increase in the reactor temperature.

For a natural uranium and graphite assembly, as well as for many other types of reactor assemblies, a representative numerical value for $d\rho/dT$ is one lying between 10^{-4} per $C°$ and 10^{-5} per $C°$ (Table 11.1).

Reactors that use ordinary or heavy water as moderators as a rule have larger negative temperature coefficients than graphite-moderated reactors and possess, therefore, more inherent stability than the latter. (Under certain special circumstances, for particular moderator to fuel ratios the water-moderated assemblies can actually have positive temperature coefficients for certain operating temperature ranges.)

Example 11.1. By performing the differentiation as indicated by 11.1 on 11.2, obtain the nuclear temperature coefficient and estimate its value for the reactor of Example 9.1.

$$\left(\frac{\partial\rho}{\partial T}\right)_{B^2,d} = -\frac{B^2}{k_\infty}\frac{\partial(L^2)}{\partial T}$$

From (8.8)

$$\frac{\partial(L^2)}{\partial T} = \frac{\lambda_{tr}}{3N_0}\frac{\partial(1/\sigma_a)}{\partial T}$$

$$= -\frac{\lambda_{tr}}{3N_0\sigma_a{}^2}\frac{\partial\sigma_a}{\partial T}$$

$$= -\frac{L^2}{\sigma_a}\frac{\partial\sigma_a}{\partial T}$$

By 4.38 and 6.6

$$\sigma_a = \sigma_0\left(\frac{T_0}{T}\right)^{\frac{1}{2}}$$

Hence,

$$\frac{\partial\sigma_a}{\partial T} = -\frac{1}{2T}\sigma_a$$

Therefore $\quad\left(\dfrac{\partial\rho}{\partial T}\right)_{B^2,d} = -\dfrac{B^2}{k_\infty}\dfrac{L^2}{2T}$

$$= -\frac{0.000325 \times 878}{1.45 \times 2 \times 500} \qquad \begin{array}{l}\text{(assuming an operating}\\\text{temperature of } 500°\text{ K)}\end{array}$$

$$= -19.7 \times 10^{-5}\,\text{per }°\text{C}$$

11.3   Effect of Fission Products Accumulation

When a reactor is being run at power, a gradual build-up of fission products takes place in the reactor core and in the fuel elements which

TABLE II.I

Reactor Name and Type	Temperature Coefficient $\Delta k/k$ per °C
Graphite	
X-10	-2.86×10^{-5}
BNL	$-3.9 \ \times 10^{-5}$
GLEEP	$-2.5 \ \times 10^{-5}$
BEPO	$-1 \ \ \times 10^{-5}$
Homogeneous	
LOPO	-6.2×10^{-3}
HYPO	$-2 \ \ \times 10^{-4}$
SUPO	-2.9×10^{-4}
HRE	$-6 \ \ \times 10^{-4}$
WBNS	-2.9×10^{-4}
NCSR	-8.2×10^{-4}
ARMOUR R.R.	$-3 \ \ \times 10^{-4}$
HRT-1	$-2 \ \ \times 10^{-3}$
LAPRE-1	$-7 \ \ \times 10^{-4}$
LAPRE-2	$-4 \ \ \times 10^{-4}$
Pressurized H_2O	
APPR	$-2 \ \ \times 10^{-4}$
PWR	-3.6×10^{-4}
Boiling H_2O	
BORAX-III	-5.2×10^{-5}
EBWR	$-1 \ \ \times 10^{-4}$
Swimming pool	
BSR	$-8 \ \ \times 10^{-5}$
PENN. STATE R.	$-8 \ \ \times 10^{-5}$
FORD (Univ. of Mich.)	-1.1×10^{-4}
NRL	$-6 \ \ \times 10^{-5}$
ORR	-1.1×10^{-4}
LIVERMORE	$-6 \ \ \times 10^{-5}$

TABLE II.I (*continued*)

Reactor Name and Type	Temperature Coefficient $\Delta k/k$ per °C
Tank type	
LITR	-1.7×10^{-2}
MTR	-1.7×10^{-2}
OMEGA WEST	-3.9×10^{-5}
ETR	-3.5×10^{-4}
Heavy water	
CP-2	$-1 \quad \times 10^{-4}$
CP-3′	$-5 \quad \times 10^{-4}$
CP-5	$-4 \quad \times 10^{-4}$
JEEP	-2.5×10^{-4}
EL-2	-1.25×10^{-5}
R-1	-1.5×10^{-4}
Miscellaneous	
SRE	-1.25×10^{-5}
LMFRE	$-2 \quad \times 10^{-4}$
OMRE	-1.3×10^{-4}
ARGONAUT	-1.5×10^{-4}

must affect the neutron multiplication and, hence, the reactivity of the reactor. The most important fission products from the point of view of their influence on the reactor reactivity are Xe^{135} and Sm^{149}. The parasitic neutron absorption of these two isotopes is very pronounced because of their large thermal absorption cross sections, $\sim 3 \times 10^6$ barns for Xe^{135}, and $\sim 5 \times 10^4$ barns for Sm^{149} (Table 4.1 and Fig. 11.1).

By 7.13 such an increase in the nonproductive absorption of thermal neutrons must result in a reduction of the thermal utilization f and, therefore, of k_{eff} and hence, the reactivity.

Xe^{135} is an intermediate product of the fission product chain

$$Te^{135} \xrightarrow[\text{2 min}]{} I^{135} \xrightarrow[\text{6.7 hr}]{} Xe^{135} \xrightarrow[\text{9.2 hr}]{} Cs^{135} \xrightarrow[\text{2} \times 10^4 \text{ years}]{} Ba^{135}$$

which terminates with Ba^{135} as the stable end-product, and Sm^{149} is the stable end-product of the fission chain,

$$Nd^{149} \xrightarrow[\substack{\text{1.7 hr} \\ \text{2.9}}]{} Pm^{149} \xrightarrow[\substack{\text{47 hr} \\ \text{2.5}}]{} Sm^{149}$$

An inspection of Fig. 5.1 shows that Te[135] and Nd[149], the progenitors of these two fission product chains, occur as fission products with a frequency of 5.6% and 1.4%, respectively, which are relatively high incidences for primary fission nuclei.

A state of secular equilibrium for the Xe[135] will be reached when the reactor has been running for some time at a steady power level, and the rate of formation of Xe[135] from I[135] will then have become equal to the

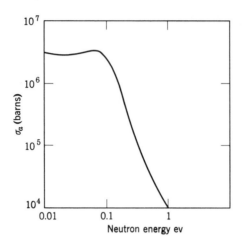

FIG. 11.1. Neutron absorption cross section of Xe[135] for low-energy neutrons.

rate of its destruction through radioactive decay into Cs[135] and through neutron absorption.

If c is the fission yield of Xe[135] (which we shall equate to the fission yield of the short-lived progenitor of the chain, Te[135]) and ϕ the average neutron flux, then the rate of its production is $c\phi\Sigma_f$. The rate of its destruction by radioactive decay is $\lambda_{Xe}N_{Xe}$, and the rate of its disappearance through thermal neutron capture is $\phi\Sigma_{aXe}$, so that the condition for balance and equilibrium between these processes becomes

$$\underset{\substack{\text{production}\\\text{rate}}}{c\phi\Sigma_f} = \underset{\substack{\text{absorption}\\\text{rate}}}{\phi N_{Xe}\sigma_{aXe}} + \underset{\substack{\text{decay}\\\text{rate}}}{\lambda_{Xe}N_{Xe}} \qquad (11.3)$$

The number of Xe nuclei per cubic centimeter, or the equilibrium concentration of Xe, as obtained from 11.3 is therefore (Fig. 11.2)

$$N_{Xe} = \frac{c\phi\Sigma_f}{\phi\sigma_{aXe} + \lambda_{Xe}} \qquad (11.4)$$

In the case of the stable Sm^{149}, the concentration reached after a long enough time has been allowed to elapse is given by

$$N_{Sm} = \frac{\Sigma_f c}{\sigma_{aSm}} \qquad (11.5)$$

Expressions 11.4 and 11.5 represent the poisonous fission nuclei concentrations, and we are now in a position to calculate the change in

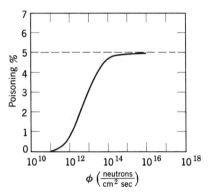

FIG. 11.2. Equilibrium values of Xe^{135} poisoning during reactor operation shown as a function of thermal neutron flux.

reactivity, $\Delta\rho$, due to their accumulation by referring to 11.2. Differentiation of that expression gives for $\Delta\rho$

$$\Delta\rho = \frac{1 + (L^2 + \tau_0)B^2}{k_\infty} \frac{\Delta k_\infty}{k_\infty} \qquad (11.6)$$

where we have assumed that the increased neutron absorption due to the poisonous nuclei does not noticeably affect the value of L^2. That L^2 undergoes some change as a consequence of the poisoning is evident from 8.8 and 8.22, but for large reactors $B^2 L^2 \ll 1$, so that a slight change in L^2 will not significantly affect the numerator of 11.6.

As explained earlier, the change in k_∞ due to the poisonous nuclei is mainly attributable to a change in f, so that we can write

$$\Delta k_\infty = \varepsilon\eta p \Delta f$$

$$= k_\infty \left(\frac{\Delta f}{f}\right) \qquad (11.7)$$

Therefore $\qquad\qquad \dfrac{\Delta k_\infty}{k_\infty} = \dfrac{\Delta f}{f}$

$$= -f\Delta\left(\frac{1}{f}\right) \qquad (11.8)$$

Since

$$f = \frac{\Sigma_{a(\text{fuel})}}{\Sigma_{a(\text{fuel})} + \Sigma_a''}$$

where Σ_a'' refers now to the neutron absorption due to all nonfuel components of the assembly, such as moderator, coolant, structural components, etc.; hence

$$\frac{1}{f} = 1 + \frac{\Sigma_a''}{\Sigma_{a(\text{fuel})}} \tag{11.9}$$

Therefore

$$\Delta\left(\frac{1}{f}\right) = \frac{\Delta\Sigma_a''}{\Sigma_{a(\text{fuel})}} \tag{11.10}$$

Hence, substituting 11.10 in 11.8, we have

$$\frac{\Delta k_\infty}{k_\infty} = -f\left(\frac{\Delta\Sigma_a''}{\Sigma_{a(\text{fuel})}}\right) \tag{11.11}$$

If we now identify the change in the macroscopic cross section of the nonfuel components $\Delta\Sigma_a''$ with the increase of the neutron absorption cross section of the assembly due to the accumulation of the poisonous nuclei, we can set

$$\Delta\Sigma_a'' \equiv \Sigma_{a(\text{poison})} \tag{11.12}$$

so that 11.11 becomes now

$$\frac{\Delta k_\infty}{k_\infty} = -f\left(\frac{\Sigma_{a(\text{poison})}}{\Sigma_{a(\text{fuel})}}\right) \tag{11.13}$$

Substitution of this expression in 11.6 leads to the result

$$\Delta\rho = -\frac{1 + (L^2 + \tau_0)B^2}{k_\infty}f\left(\frac{\Sigma_{a(\text{poison})}}{\Sigma_{a(\text{fuel})}}\right)$$

$$= -\frac{f}{k_{\text{eff}}} \times \frac{\Sigma_{a(\text{poison})}}{\Sigma_{a(\text{fuel})}} \tag{11.14}$$

If we now wish to calculate the reactivity change introduced by the accumulation of Xe^{135} we only have to set, using 11.4,

$$\Sigma_{a(\text{poison})} = N_{Xe}\sigma_{aXe}$$

$$= \frac{\phi\Sigma_f\sigma_{aXe}c_{Xe}}{\phi\sigma_{aXe} + \lambda_{Xe}} \tag{11.15}$$

and substitute this value in 11.14. This gives finally for the drop in reactivity due to Xe poisoning

$$\Delta\rho_{Xe} = -f\left(\frac{\Sigma_f}{\Sigma_{a(\text{fuel})}}\right) \times \frac{c_{Xe}}{1 + \dfrac{\lambda_{Xe}}{\phi\sigma_{aXe}}} \tag{11.16}$$

where we have, in addition, used a value of 1 for k_{eff}, since the reactor had been assumed to be running at a steady power level.

For Sm poisoning, we get a somewhat simpler expression, because of the simpler form of 11.5 as compared to 11.4 for the case of Xe by repeating the same argument as was done for Xe. This simpler expression is:

$$\Delta\rho_{Sm} = -f\left(\frac{\Sigma_f}{\Sigma_{a(\text{fuel})}}\right)c_{Sm} \qquad (11.17)$$

When the reactor is shut down, the production of poisonous Xe nuclei will not stop immediately, but will continue and eventually the concentration will build up to reach a maximum which, for high flux thermal reactors, can be many times the equilibrium value for steady operation (Figs. 11.3a and b).

The high build-up of poisonous Xe nuclei concentration after shut down is caused by the continuing decay of the parent I^{135} (6.7 hr half-life) into Xe^{135} (9.2 hr half-life) without the compensating poison-consuming neutron absorption reactions that would occur if the reactor were still operating at power. These neutron reactions are no longer taking place at a significant rate after shut down because of the rapid decay of the neutron flux that follows a reactor shut down.

The build-up of Xe^{135} after shut down proceeds along the lines of parent-daughter decay which were described in section 1.12 and Fig. 1.6 for $\lambda_{parent} > \lambda_{daughter}$ (case 3).

It is evident from Fig. 11.3a and Fig. 11.3b that the maximum Xe poisoning after shut down becomes increasingly important for reactors operating at high thermal neutron fluxes ($>10^{14}$), whereas for a neutron flux of 10^{13} the build-up after shut down is not markedly greater than the saturation value before shut down.

For a reactor operating at a steady power level with the relatively high neutron flux of about 2×10^{14} neutrons/cm^2 sec prior to shut down the maximum Xe^{135} concentration occurs in about 11 hr after shut down and results in a reactivity loss of about 40% (Fig. 11.4). This means that an appreciable amount of excess reactivity must be on hand and kept in reserve in the form of extra fuel inventory in the core in order to "override" the Xe poisoning if one wants to be able to restart the reactor within a few hours after shut down.

This consideration is of particular importance for thermal reactors designed, for example, to operate a ship or submarine. Unless a sufficiently large excess reactivity were provided for in the design of the reactor to override Xe poisoning after shut down, the reactor could not again be brought up to criticality before enough time (many hours!) had been allowed to elapse in order to permit a large enough number of Xe nuclei to

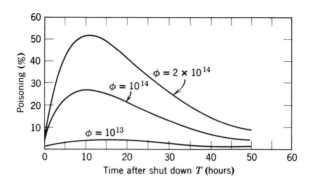

FIG. 11.3a. Xe poisoning after shut down.

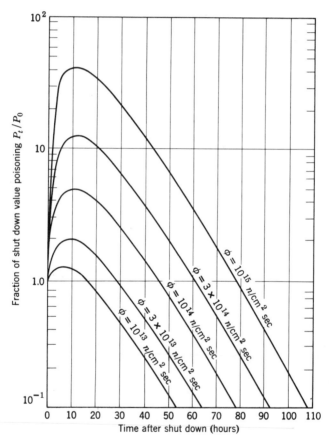

(*b*) Value of Xe[135] poisoning after shut down in a U[235] reactor, assuming equilibrium conditions prior to shut down. (From J. O. Blomeke and Mary F. Todd, *ORNL*-2127 August 1957.)

decay in the interim. Alternately, the reactor would have to be restarted soon after shut down, before the Xe poisoning has built up to a point where it would exceed the amount of excess-reactivity provided for by the fuel reserve in the core.

Intermediate reactors do not have to contend with Xe poisoning effects to this degree (the neutron cross sections of Xe^{135} at epithermal energies are

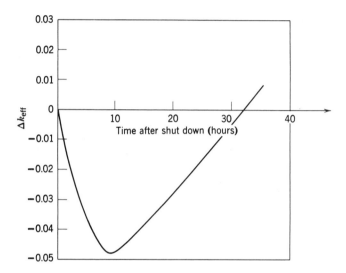

FIG. 11.4. Reactivity drop after reactor shut down, due to Xe and Sm poisoning for a typical reactor.

not exceptionally large) and, therefore, do not require large amounts of built-in excess reactivity to override Xe poisoning;† nor are they limited operationally in the same way as thermal reactors are by virtue of reactivity loss due to Xe build-up after shut down.

Only one type of intermediate reactor has so far been designed, however, and a reactor of this design has been installed in the submarine Seawolf. It employs beryllium as partial moderator and liquid sodium as coolant.

Example 11.2. Estimate the change in reactivity due to Xe poisoning for a large natural uranium reactor that has been operating at a steady power level long enough to allow the Xe poison to have reached its equilibrium value, assuming a neutron flux of 10^{14} neutrons per cm^2 per sec and an initial value for f of 0.9.

† See, however, H. B. Steward, et al., P/2381, PUAE Geneva Conference 1958, vol. 12, p. 149.

For natural uranium: $\sigma_f = 4.18$ barns; $\sigma_a = 7.68$ barns; for Xe^{135}: $c = 5.6\%$; $\lambda = 2.1 \times 10^{-5}\,sec^{-1}$; $\sigma_a = 3.5 \times 10^6$ barns.

By 11.16

$$\Delta\rho = -0.9 \times \frac{4.18}{7.68} \times \frac{0.056}{1 + \dfrac{2.1 \times 10^{-5}}{10^{14} \times 3.5 \times 10^{-18}}}$$

$$= -\frac{(0.9 \times 0.545 \times 0.056)}{1.06}$$

$$= -0.026 = 2.6\%$$

11.4 Fuel Depletion and Fuel Production

Another long-range factor that influences the reactivity of a reactor—and the last one we shall consider—is the gradual depletion, or, in some cases, the increase of the active nuclear fission component. Depending on the length of time that it is desired to keep the reactor in continuous operation before a recharge of fuel is considered necessary, a sufficient amount of excess reactivity must be built into the assembly to compensate for fuel depletion.

For highly enriched uranium reactors the decrease in reactivity is proportional to the fraction of U^{235} burnt up. For nuclear reactors which employ natural uranium as fuel the depletion of U^{235} is partly compensated through the production of Pu^{239} from U^{238} by neutron absorption.

In a breeder reactor the amount of Pu^{239} produced exceeds the amount of U^{235} burnt up, which would cause the reactivity to increase unless proper means of control were provided.

The number of new fissionable nuclei produced for each U^{235} nucleus destroyed in the reactor is termed the **conversion factor** and denoted by C.

Since a U^{235} nucleus upon fission releases, on the average, η fast neutrons per neutron absorbed (i.e., including fission and nonfission absorptions), of which one neutron is required to continue the chain reaction, the maximum conversion factor possible is

$$C_{max} = \eta - 1 \qquad (11.18)$$

If we make allowances for the fact that neutrons are lost through leakage from the assembly and through poison nuclei absorptions, the conversion factor will be less than the maximum by a certain amount which takes account of these additional neutron losses and which we shall denote by A. Hence

$$C = \eta - 1 - A \qquad (11.19)$$

The **breeding gain** G is defined as the excess of fissionable nuclei produced over the number of fissionable nuclei consumed per nucleus of U^{235} fuel consumed.

Therefore
$$G = C - 1 = \eta - 2 - A \qquad (11.20)$$

When the reactor has been in steady operation for a time t, the number of U^{235} nuclei consumed during that time, ΔN^{235}, is

$$\Delta N^{235} = \text{(number of absorptions per sec)} \times \text{time}$$
$$= \Sigma_{a(235)} \phi t V \qquad (11.21)$$

Hence, the total net gain in new fissionable nuclei (Pu^{239}), ΔN^{Pu}, is

$$\Delta N^{Pu} = \Delta N^{235} G$$
$$= \Delta N^{235}(\eta - 2 - A) \qquad (11.22)$$
$$= \Sigma_{a(235)}(\eta - 2 - A)\phi t V$$

The **doubling time** T_d, in connection with breeders, is defined as the time required for the number of fissionable nuclei (i.e., fuel) to increase to twice their original number, so that the total net gain equals the original number of fissionable nuclei present.

Therefore
$$\Delta N^{Pu} = N \sigma_{a(235)} \phi t (\eta - 2 - A)$$
$$= N \qquad \text{when } t = T_d,$$

Therefore
$$T_d = \frac{1}{\phi \sigma_{a(235)}(\eta - 2 - A)} \qquad (11.23)$$

The conversion factor C can also be derived by comparing the number of U^{235} nuclei used up in the reactor during one neutron cycle with the number of U^{238} nuclei that absorb a neutron during the cycle.

Neutron absorptions by U^{238} occur (1) during the resonance absorption stage of the cycle, and (2) during the thermal neutron absorption stage.

The number of neutrons that enter the resonance region is $N\eta\varepsilon$, where N is the number of U^{235} nuclei that underwent neutron reactions (both fission and nonfission) at the beginning of the cycle, giving rise to $N\eta$ fast neutrons. The constant η is, as before, the number of neutrons released per neutron absorbed by a U^{235} nucleus.

$$\eta = \frac{\Sigma_{f(235)}}{\Sigma_{a(235)}} \nu$$
$$= \frac{\Sigma_{a(238)} + \Sigma_{a(235)}}{\Sigma_{a(235)}} \eta_U \qquad (11.24)$$

Here η_U is the constant "η" as used in the derivation of the four-factor formula and refers to the uranium as a whole, according to the definition 7.4.

Of the neutrons entering the resonance absorption region, the fraction that is absorbed by U^{238} in that region is

$$N\eta\varepsilon(1 - p)e^{-B^2\tau} \qquad (11.25)$$

where p is the resonance escape probability, so that $(1 - p)$ is the absorption probability in that region and $e^{-B^2\tau}$ is the fast nonleakage probability. These absorptions lead to the formation of Pu^{239} nuclei, so that the production ratio so far is obtained by dividing 11.25 by the number N:

$$\eta\varepsilon(1 - p)e^{-B^2\tau} \qquad (11.26)$$

A further loss of U^{235} nuclei takes place after the neutrons have become thermalized. The fraction of neutrons absorbed by the U^{238} nuclei as compared to the total number of thermal neutron absorptions by U^{235} will give us the number of Pu^{239} nuclei produced as compared to the number of U^{235} nuclei burnt up during this stage of the neutron cycle. This fraction is

$$\frac{\Sigma_{a(238)}}{\Sigma_{a(235)}} \qquad (11.27)$$

The conversion factor C is obtained by adding 11.26 and 11.27, so that one gets for the complete cycle

$$C = \eta\varepsilon(1 - p)e^{-B^2\tau} + \frac{\Sigma_{a(238)}}{\Sigma_{a(235)}} \qquad (11.28)$$

The effect the fuel conversion has on the reactivity of the reactor can now be seen quite readily by considering its effect on the neutron economy of the reactor. The neutron yield by a Pu^{239} nucleus as compared to that of a U^{235} nucleus in the reactor will be in the same ratio as their absorption cross sections multiplied by their neutron yields per absorption. Hence, by replacing a U^{235} nucleus by a Pu^{239} nucleus the neutron multiplication will be altered in the ratio

$$\frac{\sigma_{a(Pu)}}{\sigma_{a(235)}} \times \frac{\eta_{(Pu)}}{\eta_{(235)}} = \frac{1028}{683} \times \frac{2.08}{2.07} = 1.51$$

A Pu^{239} nucleus is, therefore, seen to be about $1\frac{1}{2}$ times as neutron-productive as a U^{235} nucleus. This would indicate that a conversion factor of $\sim\frac{2}{3}$ would leave the reactivity unchanged. For a greater conversion factor the reactivity would increase during a continuous operation of the reactor. Because of various other additional factors involved, some of which have been cited before, the actual increase in the reactivity, however, will be much less than the maximal possible change.

The use of Th^{232} as fertile material offers some advantage over that of U^{238} because of its higher thermal neutron absorption cross section which is 7.45 barns as compared to that of 2.75 barns for U^{238}. Hence, it is possible to achieve a given conversion ratio with thorium using a lower fuel to moderator ratio than would be possible with U^{238}. Alternately, for a given fuel to moderator ratio the conversion ratio will be higher with Th^{232} than with U^{238}.*

PROBLEMS

(1) By referring to Table 5.2 obtain the maximum permissible neutron loss (in percent) for each nuclear fuel if it is to be used successfully in a breeding reactor.
Which of the fuels cited appears to be the most promising for breeding purposes?

(2) Calculate the breeding gain per day with U^{233} as fuel in a thermal reactor of average neutron flux 10^{12} neutrons/cm^2 sec, assuming a neutron loss of 15% due to leakage and parasitic absorption, and using Th^{232} as the fertile material.

(3) Find the doubling time for the process described in Problem 2.

(4) A breeder reactor having a conversion factor of 1.10 for the production of Pu^{239} operates at a constant power level of 200,000 kw. Calculate the amount of Pu^{239} produced per day.

(5) A nuclear reactor is in continuous operation for one year at an average power level of 150,000 kw. How many grams of Ba^{135} would accumulate in the fuel rods during this time?

(6) Calculate the maximum possible change in the reactivity of a reactor in constant operation due to the accumulation of Sm^{149}.

(7) Derive explicit expressions for $(\partial\rho/\partial T)_{\sigma, B^2}$ and $(\partial\rho/\partial T)_{\sigma, d}$ for ρ given by 11.2.

(8) Calculate the temperature coefficient of reactivity for a natural uranium-graphite-moderated reactor, operating at an average temperature of 100° C, using the data of Example 7.8, and a linear temperature coefficient of expansion of 10^{-5} per °C for the reactor material.

(9) A nuclear reactor which is so designed that a rise in temperature will cause a small amount of the fuel to be expelled from the active core will show a negative partial contribution to the total temperature coefficient of reactivity due to this effect. If dm/dT is the change in the fuel mass per °C temperature change, calculate $d\rho/dm$.

(10) When water is used as coolant circulating through the reactor core with some other substance being used as moderator, a rise in temperature will cause a decrease in the parasitic neutron absorption by the coolant. This will make a positive contribution to the temperature coefficient of the reactivity. Derive an expression for this contribution and estimate its magnitude, using a value of 2×10^{-4} per °C for the temperature coefficient of expansion of water and a value of 0.85 for the thermal utilization factor.

* L. I. Katzin and B. I. Spinrad, "U^{233} Breeder–U^{235} Converter Reactor," *Nucl. Sci. and Engin.*, **1**, 343 (1956).

(11) Calculate the initial conversion ratio for the replacement of U^{235} by Pu^{239} for the critical reactor of Example 7.8.

BIBLIOGRAPHY

Bogaardt, M., and M. Bustraan: "Producing Plutonium in U-D$_2$O Reactors," *Nucleonics*, vol. 12, No. 12 (December 1954).

Caillet, C. P., and J. Carpentier: *Journ. of Nucl. Energy*, vol. 3, 49 (1956).

Deutsch, R. W.: "Fission Product Buildup in Enriched Thermal Reactors," *Nucleonics*, vol. 14, No. 9 (September 1956).

Etherington, H. (Ed.): *Nuclear Reactor Handbook*, McGraw-Hill, 1958.

Geneva Conference on the Peaceful Uses of Atomic Energy—1955:

P/5; P/6: Hurst, D. G., and Ward, A. G.: "Experiments on Some Characteristics of the NRX Reactor," vol. 5, 111–124.

P/432: Littler, D. J.: "Long Term Reactivity Changes in Natural Uranium Reactors," vol. 5, 141.

P/835: Spinrad, B. I., et al.: "Reactivity Changes and Reactivity Lifetimes of Fixed Fuel Elements in Thermal Reactors," vol. 5, 125.

Second Geneva Conference on the Peaceful Uses of Atomic Energy—1958:

P/596: Levine, S. H., et al.: "Temperature Coefficient Measurements of Light-Water Moderated Homogeneous Critical Assemblies," vol. 12, 483.

Glasstone, S.: *Principles of Nuclear Reactor Engineering*, van Nostrand, 1955.

Glasstone, S., and M. C. Edlund: *The Elements of Nuclear Reactor Theory*, van Nostrand, 1952.

Littler, D. J., and J. F. Raffle: *An Introduction to Reactor Physics*, Pergamon Press, 1957.

Lundby, A., and N. Holt: "Kinetic Behavior of a Thermal Heavy Water Reactor," *Nucleonics*, vol. 12, No. 1 (January 1954).

Murray, R. L.: *Nuclear Reactor Physics*, Prentice-Hall, 1957.

Robb, W. L., et al.: "Fission Product Buildup in Long-Burning Thermal Reactors," *Nucleonics*, vol. 13, No. 12 (December 1955).

Stephenson, R.: *Introduction to Nuclear Engineering*, McGraw-Hill, 1957.

Syrett, J. J.: *Nuclear Reactor Theory*, Temple Press, 1958.

Weinberg, A. M., and E. P. Wigner: *The Physical Theory of Neutron Chain Reactors*, University of Chicago Press, 1958.

chapter **12**

Nuclear Radiations and Their Interactions with Matter

12.1 Introduction

A nuclear reactor is a prolific source of nuclear radiations† that consist of or can give rise to almost all varieties of radiation known to the nuclear scientist. Most abundant are neutrons and electromagnetic or γ-radiation. For the purpose of experimental and theoretical study of nuclear radiations it is convenient to divide these into three broad categories: (1) primary ionizing radiation, i.e., charged particle radiation, (2) electromagnetic radiation, i.e., γ-radiation, and (3) neutron radiation.

The charged particle, or ionizing radiation, interacts primarily with the atoms of matter as a whole, or with the atomic electrons, and only very infrequently with the nuclei of the atoms themselves. Nuclear collisions are rare and the probability of their occurrence is very small for the charged particles. Neutrons, on the other hand, cannot interact electrically with atoms, since they are electrically neutral and, therefore, can lose energy only through interactions with atomic nuclei. The interaction of neutrons with matter was described extensively in previous chapters, so that in this chapter we shall be able to concentrate mainly on the interaction of charged particles and γ-radiation with matter.

The group of charged particles consists of heavy, positively charged particles, like α-particles, protons, deuterons, and the fission fragments, and the much lighter electrons and β-particles. We shall consider the heavy and light particles separately. In what follows we shall generally

† The total amount of activity in curies contained within a nuclear reactor can be estimated by multiplying the thermal power (in watts) by the factor 10. Thus, A (curies) $= 10 \times P$ (watts).

329

illustrate the properties of heavy charged particles by special reference to α-particles, but it is to be understood that conclusions similar to those for α-particles apply also to the other heavy charged particles. We are using the α-particle merely as a representative of the whole class.

The presence of α-particles in nuclear reactors arises from the radioactive decay of the fuel which, as we have seen, consists of naturally radioactive materials. Protons and deuterons are present in negligible numbers only, generally as the result of neutron reactions with the nuclei of the moderator, coolant, and the surrounding air as, for example, from the (n, p) reaction with N^{14}.

The β-particles originate from the decay of the radioactive fission fragments which undergo a series of consecutive β-transformations (Chapter 5), and from the radioisotopes that are formed in the reactor as a result of neutron captures. Electrons are also liberated through the interaction of electromagnetic radiation with atoms and nuclei, as we shall see later in this chapter.

12.2 Absorption of Heavy Charged Particles in Matter

The characteristic property of heavy charged particles passing through matter and one which has been used extensively as a convenient method for their detection and for measuring their energy is the ionization they produce along their paths. In an ionization process the charged nuclear particle transfers some of its kinetic energy to the atomic electrons it encounters, which are thereby either raised to an excited energy state or completely removed from the atom, thus causing it to become ionized.

As a consequence of the large disparity between the mass of an α-particle and that of an electron, the heavy particle loses its energy in collisions with electrons very gradually by transferring small amounts at a time to the atomic electrons of the absorbing material, until it is finally stopped completely and disappears. This general behavior is common to all heavy, electrically charged particles. They each have a definite **range**, characteristic for the particle type, which depends on and is determined by their initial kinetic energy and the properties of the absorbing material (Fig. 12.1).

Since the masses of the colliding electrons are very much smaller than that of the charged particle passing through the material, they will not be able to deflect it from its initial direction of travel. Occasionally, and generally towards the end of its track when the particle energy has been considerably reduced from its original value, an α-particle may collide with an atomic nucleus and be deflected by a large angle of scattering (Fig. 12.1).

Although the range of an α-particle is quite well defined, determination of the range for a group of α-particles of the same initial energy will show a distribution of their ranges over measurable limits, somewhat like Fig. 12.2. If all particles had exactly the same range, the graph would show a

FIG. 12.1. Schematic representation of α-particle tracks as observed in a cloud-chamber.

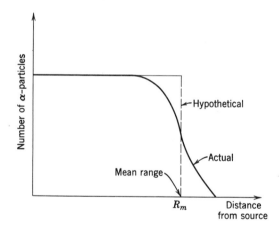

FIG. 12.2. Distribution of α-particle ranges, α-particle straggling, and hypothetical distribution if all had the same range.

sudden drop to zero at a certain definite distance from the origin. However, we do not expect all α-particles to make exactly the same number of collisions along their paths and to lose exactly the same amount of energy in each collision. We can, therefore, anticipate the result that the measured ranges will show a certain spread with small deviations from a mean value in the total length because of the random or statistical nature of the collision processes along their paths. The small variation of the ranges, as a consequence of this, is called "**straggling**," so that, when referring to the range, we generally have in mind an average or **mean range** R_m. The mean range is that distance from the source at which the number of particles has been reduced to one-half the original number (Fig. 12.2).

For α-particles in air at NTP, the mean range R_m and α-particle energy E are related by

$$R_m = 0.318E^{3/2} \tag{12.1}$$

where R_m is in centimeters and E in million electron volts.

If the range in air is known, we can obtain the range in another material by using the empirical approximate formula

$$\frac{R}{R_{\text{air}}} = 1.51 \times 10^{-4} \frac{A}{\rho} \frac{(Z + 10)^{1/2}}{Z} \tag{12.2}$$

where all quantities on the right-hand side refer to the material, with A its atomic mass number, Z its atomic number, and ρ its density.

The range of other heavy, charged particles can be obtained from the α-particle range of the same initial velocity by means of the approximate relation,

$$\frac{R}{R_\alpha} = \frac{M/z^2}{M_\alpha/z_\alpha^2} \tag{12.3}$$

where M, M_α are the respective masses and z, z_α their respective electric charges.

The number of ion pairs that are produced by a heavy, charged particle per centimeter of particle track length defines the **specific ionization** n_i. The total number of ion pairs produced along its entire range determines the **total ionization**. The amount of energy lost by a charged particle per unit track length in a given medium, $-(dE/dx)$, is called the **stopping power** of the material. It is proportional to the specific ionization n_i. If I_m is the average energy loss per ion pair formed in the material, we can set,

$$-\frac{dE}{dx} = n_i I_m \tag{12.4}$$

The average energy loss per ion pair, I_m, is considerably greater than the ionization potential of the material, indicating that other, nonionizing processes of excitation must contribute to the dissipation of the energy of the heavy particle. Some comparative values for the ionizing potential and I_m are shown in Table 12.1.

TABLE 12.1

Absorber	I_m (ev)	Ionizing Potential (ev) (minimum)
H_2	36.3	13.5
N_2	36.6	14.5
O_2	32.5	13.55
Air	35.5	
He	42.7	24.5
Ne	36.8	21.5
A	26.4	15.7
Kr	24.1	14.0
Xe	21.9	12.1

W. P. Jesse and J. Sadauskis, *Phys. Rev.*, **90**, 1120 (1953); S. C. Brown, *Nucleonics*, **2**, 625 (1949).

If the specific ionization is determined experimentally as a function of the distance from the α-emitting source, a graph is obtained of the general shape shown in Fig. 12.3, which is known as a Bragg curve. The graph shows that the specific ionization increases with decreasing velocity of the particle, reaching a maximum very near the end of its path and then dropping rapidly to zero.

An expression for the stopping power was first derived along classical lines by Bohr and later modified quantum mechanically by Bethe and Bloch. According to these authors the stopping power for nonrelativistic speeds is

$$-\frac{dE}{dx} = \left(\frac{4\pi z^2 e^4}{mv^2}\right) N_0 Z \log\left(\frac{2mv^2}{I}\right) \tag{12.5}$$

where N_0 is the number of atoms per centimeter^3 of absorber, Z is the atomic number of the absorber, and I is an empirical constant which depends on and is related to the ionization potential of the stopping material.† The mass m is the electron mass and only z and v refer to the charged ionizing particle, z being its charge and v its initial velocity. Notable by its absence from expression 12.5 is the mass of the charged ionizing particle. It is seen from 12.5 that the stopping power is essentially proportional to z^2/v^2 (since the log term varies only slightly with v), so that the specific ionization—which by 12.2 is proportional to the stopping

† On the basis of the Thomas-Fermi model of the atom Bloch has derived an expression for I which is $I = kZ$ where $k \cong 11.5$ ev (W. A. Aron, B. G. Hoffmann, and F. C. Williams: AECU-663 1951; also E. Segrè, *Experimental Nuclear Physics*, vol. I, p. 204).

power—for an α-particle is four times the specific ionization for a proton of the same velocity, except towards the end of the range.

The **relative stopping power** S of a substance is the ratio of the stopping power of the material, $-(dE/dx)_m$, to the stopping power of air (at NTP), $-(dE/dx)_{air}$, for equal energy loss.

$$S = \frac{(dE/dx)_m}{(dE/dx)_{air}} = \frac{(dx)_{air}}{(dx)_m}$$

$$= \frac{\text{range of } \alpha\text{-particle in air}}{\text{range of } \alpha\text{-particle in material}}$$

$$= \frac{R_{air}}{R_m} \tag{12.6}$$

The **relative atomic stopping power**, i.e., the relative stopping power per atom, S_a as well as the **relative electronic stopping power**, i.e., the relative stopping power per atomic electron, S_e are frequently used, as is also the **relative mass stopping power** S_m. These quantities are defined as follows:

$$S_a = \frac{(1/N)_m(dE/dx)_m}{(1/N)_{air}(dE/dx)_{air}}$$

$$= \frac{Z_m \log(2mv^2/I_m)}{Z_{air} \log(2mv^2/I_{air})} \quad \text{by 12.5} \tag{12.7}$$

$$S_e = \frac{(1/NZ)_m(dE/dx)_m}{(1/NZ)_{air}(dE/dx)_{air}}$$

$$= \frac{\log(2mv^2/I_m)}{\log(2mv^2/I_{air})} \quad \text{by 12.5} \tag{12.8}$$

$$S_m = \frac{(1/\rho)_m(dE/dx)_m}{(1/\rho)_{air}(dE/dx)_{air}}$$

$$= S_a\left(\frac{A_{air}}{A_m}\right) \tag{12.9}$$

since $\rho = (N_0/N_{Avogadro})A$, where A is the atomic weight.

Example 12.1. Calculate the range in aluminum of a 6 Mev α-particle if the relative stopping power of Al is 1700.

From 12.1 the range in air is found to be

$$R_{air} = 0.318 \times 6^{1.5} = 4.66 \text{ cm}$$

Hence, by 12.6,

$$R_{Al} = \frac{R_{air}}{S_{Al}} = \frac{4.66}{1700} = 2.75 \times 10^{-3} \text{ cm}$$

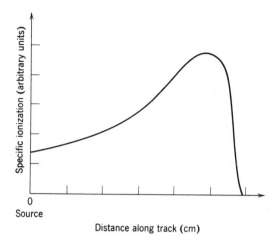

FIG. 12.3. Bragg ionization curve.

Example 12.2. If the range is multiplied by the density we obtain the equivalent thickness in gm/cm². Calculate the thickness of material that is equivalent in stopping power to 1 cm of air.

The equivalent thickness in the medium is

$$R_m \rho_m$$

where $R_m = R_{air}/S$ by 12.6, so that we can write,

$$R_m \rho_m = \frac{R_{air}}{S} \rho_m$$

The thickness equivalent to 1 cm of air, therefore, is

$$R_m \rho_m = \frac{\rho_m}{S} \times 1 \text{ cm}$$

For Al this would be (2.7/1700) gram per cm² $= 1.59 \times 10^{-3}$ gram/cm².

Example 12.3. Derive Eq. 12.3 from the Bethe-Bloch equation 12.5.

The range can be obtained from the stopping power by integration,

$$R = \int_0^{E_0} \frac{dE}{dE/dx}$$

$$= \int_0^v \frac{d(\frac{1}{2}Mv^2)}{(4\pi e^4 NZz^2/mv^2) \log (2mv^2/I)}$$

$$= \text{constant} \times \left(\frac{M}{z^2}\right) f(v) \tag{12.10}$$

where

$$f(v) = \int_0^v \frac{v^3 \, dv}{\log (2mv^2/I)}$$

For another ionizing particle of mass M_0 and charge z_0, the range becomes, similarly,

$$R_0 = \text{constant} \times \left(\frac{M_0}{z_0^2}\right) f(v)$$

with the constant the same in both cases and $f(v)$ the same if both particles have the same initial velocity. Hence, by taking the ratio,

$$\frac{R}{R_0} = \frac{M/z^2}{M_0/z_0^2}$$

which is the same expression as 12.3.

For the heavy, charged fission fragments nuclear collisions occur more frequently than for the faster moving α-particles, and energy losses through nuclear collisions become more important than ionization losses, especially in the final portion of the range. Furthermore, a fission fragment is highly ionized, carrying initially a net charge of twenty or more electron charges,[†] which is gradually being reduced, as the fragment slows down, by picking up electrons from its surroundings. Its state of ionization, therefore, varies along its path as it captures more and more electrons, causing a gradual and steady reduction in the amount of ionization in the material through which it passes. Even for α-particles where charge exchanges with the absorbing medium are much less significant, on the average about 1000 such exchanges take place over its entire range. An α-particle will pick up an electron or two as it moves along and then will quickly lose them again as it meets other atoms on its way. Alpha-particles show an increasing rate of energy loss towards the end of their career. In contrast with this, the fission fragments lose most of their energy at the beginning of the track because of their high state of ionization which gradually tapers off (Fig. 12.4). Thus most of the energy transfer will occur inside the fuel elements which, as a consequence, will heat up considerably.

We saw in Chapter 5 that the total kinetic energy of the fission fragments amounted to ~168 Mev per fission which by 5.1 was shared by the two fragments in a ratio inversely proportional to their masses. If we take a typical mass ratio of 7:5 for the fission fragments, their energies would be ~70 Mev and ~98 Mev, respectively. This would give the lighter fragment an initial velocity corresponding to that of a 4 Mev α-particle. The range in air of an α-particle having this initial velocity is 2.5 cm, which is very nearly the same as the observed range in air for the light fission fragment.

The mass stopping powers for an average fission fragment agree very well with those for α-particles of 4.66 Mev energy as appears from Table 12.2.

[†] N. O. Lassen, *Phys. Rev.*, **69**, 137 (1946).

The total range of an average fission fragment in uranium is $\sim$6 × 10^{-4} cm and about twice this amount in aluminum. The thickness of Al cladding usually employed is 50 to 100 times the range in aluminum, so that no fission fragments can escape from the fuel elements to the outside. All fission fragments are absorbed in the fuel elements or fuel cladding which heat up considerably as a consequence. The range of a fission fragment

FIG. 12.4. Ionization track of fission fragment.

can be estimated in terms of the range of an α-particle of the same initial velocity by means of the approximate relation (v is the fragment velocity and c the velocity of light in vacuo),

$$\frac{R_f}{R_\alpha} = 3.73 \times 10^{-4} \frac{(A/Z^{\frac{2}{3}})}{(v/c)^2} \tag{12.11}$$

TABLE 12.2

Absorbing Material	Al	Cu	Ag	Au
S_m (fission fragments)	1.00	0.66	0.55	0.34
S_m (4.66 Mev α-particles)	1.00	0.69	0.51	0.36

From E. Segrè and C. Wiegand, *Phys. Rev.*, **70**, 808 (1946).

12.3 Absorption of Electrons in Matter

The range of energetic electrons in matter through which they are passing is considerably more intricate to calculate than that of heavy, charged particles for several reasons. First, the path of an electron as it passes through matter is very irregular and not at all as straight as the paths of heavy, charged particles (Fig. 12.5). Because of its much smaller mass the electron will suffer many, often abrupt and considerable deflections, when colliding with the atomic electrons of the absorber, so that it becomes difficult to associate a definite range with an electron's tortuous zigzag path as could be done with α-particles and heavy, charged particles. Second, the nuclear β-particles are not monoenergetic groups as is the case with α-particles, but instead show a continuous energy distribution (Fig. 12.6). Third, a purely quantum mechanical effect, a so-called exchange phenomenon due to the identity in character of the two colliding particles—the β-particle and the atomic electron of the scattering material—must be taken into account in the theoretical investigation of the electron-electron collision. Fourth and last, the high speeds of the β-particles make it necessary generally to employ a relativistic treatment of the collision mechanism.

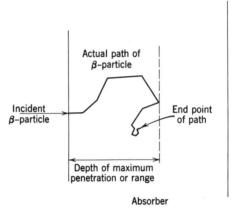

FIG. 12.5. Track of β-particle in absorbing medium.

There are several processes which contribute to the dissipation of the energy of electrons passing through matter. In addition to energy losses through ionization similar to the corresponding effect with heavy, charged particles, high-energy electrons lose energy primarily through a radiation process often referred to as "Bremsstrahlung," which literally translated means "braking radiation." As the electrons are slowed down in the absorbing medium, they radiate away their energy in the form of a continuous X-ray emission as a result of inelastic collisions with the atomic nuclei of the material.

The energy loss through ionization is the most important factor for electron energies below $\sim$1 Mev, whereas energy loss in the form of Bremsstrahlung is predominant for energies above $\sim$1 Mev (Fig. 12.7). The energy loss attributable to each varies approximately as follows:

$$\left(\frac{dE}{dx}\right)_{\text{ion}} \sim \frac{NZ}{v^2}$$

$$\left(\frac{dE}{dx}\right)_{\text{rad}} \sim NZ^2E \tag{12.12}$$

This shows that, since $(dE/dx)_{\text{rad}}$ varies as Z^2, energy loss due to this factor is relatively more important for heavy elements than for light elements.

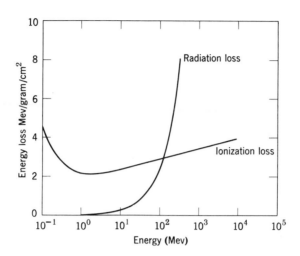

FIG. 12.6. Continuous β-spectrum.

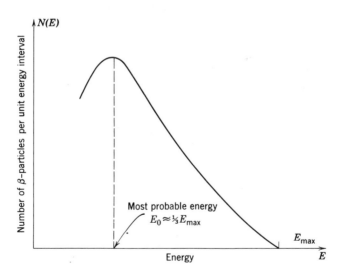

FIG. 12.7. Energy loss in water by high-energy electrons due to ionization and radiation. The radiation loss in water is seen to be zero below 1 Mev.

The ratio of radiative loss to ionization loss is given approximately by

$$\frac{(dE/dx)_{\text{rad}}}{(dE/dx)_{\text{ion}}} = \frac{ZE}{800} \text{ Mev} \tag{12.13}$$

The fraction f of the electron energy which is dissipated by the radiative process can be estimated by means of the empirical expression

$$f = 0.7 \times 10^{-3}ZE \tag{12.14}$$

where E is expressed in Mev. This estimate is fairly reliable for electron energies up to about 2.5 Mev. For 1 Mev electrons in aluminum about 1% would be dissipated by radiation, whereas for lead this fraction would be ~6%. The energy loss in water due to ionization and radiation is shown in Fig. 12.7.

Since the radiative energy loss $(dE/dx)_{\text{rad}}$ is inversely proportional to the square of the mass of the incident charged particle this effect is of small importance with the heavier, charged particles.

We have seen that it is not possible to determine a range for β-particles in the precise way possible with the heavier, charged particles because of their excessive straggling and the large statistical fluctuations in the results of their collisions in the absorber. One can nevertheless obtain a practical range for β-particles, also called **extrapolated range**, if one understands by it that thickness of material required to reduce the observed β-particle intensity to the background counting rate. Suitable extrapolation methods have been devised by Feather and others, and a simplified procedure is indicated schematically in Fig. 12.8. The exact shape of the initial portion of the curve depends on the absorber and also somewhat on the counting method employed. An empirical relation between the range R (expressed in gram/square centimeter) and the electron energy E (expressed in Mev) which gives reliable results for energies up to about 3 Mev is as follows:

$$R(\text{gram/cm}^2) = 0.546E(\text{Mev}) - 0.108 \tag{12.15}$$

Strictly speaking, this relation is valid in the first instance for mono-energetic electrons. Through fortuitous circumstances, however, the same relation also applies to the continuous β-spectrum, Fig. 12.8, if E is identified with E_{max} of the β-spectrum.

If the intensity of transmission from a continuous β-spectrum source is plotted on a logarithmic scale against the absorber thickness, a curve is obtained which has the general shape as shown in Fig. 12.9. This linear relationship indicates that the absorption follows an exponential law, so that one can set

$$I = I_0 \exp\left(-\mu_l x\right) \tag{12.16}$$

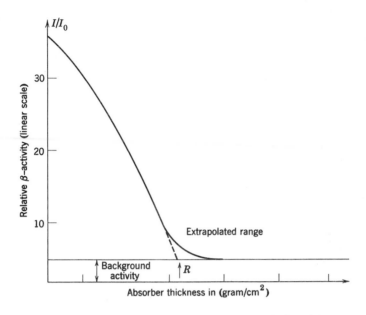

FIG. 12.8*a*. Range determination for monoenergetic β-particles.

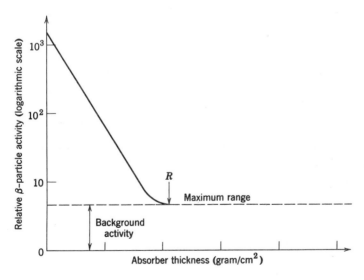

(*b*) Range determination for a continuous β-spectrum.

Here I_0 is the initial ionization produced and I that produced after the β-particles have passed through a thickness of absorber x. The constant μ_l is a characteristic property of the absorber (and of the β-spectrum), known as the **linear absorption coefficient**. Its dimension is seen to be that of a reciprocal length.

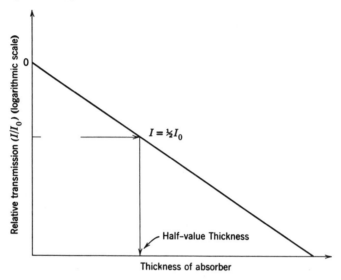

FIG. 12.9. Exponential absorption of β-radiation from a continuous β-spectrum source. (A similar result is also found for γ-radiation absorption.)

If one defines a **mass absorption coefficient** by the relation

$$\mu = \frac{\mu_l}{\rho} \tag{12.17}$$

where ρ is the density of the absorbing material in gram per centimeter^3, experimental evidence shows that μ is very nearly independent of the atomic weight of the absorber, although it increases slightly with Z. It can be calculated if E_{max} is known, by means of the empirical relation

$$\mu = \frac{22}{E_{max}^{1.33}} \; cm^2/gram \tag{12.18}$$

The mass absorption coefficient for β-radiation from various β-emitters is shown as a function of E_{max} in Fig. 12.10.

Example 12.4. Calculate the half-value thickness for β-absorption in Al for the β-spectrum from Ra-E (Bi^{210}), with $E_{max} = 1.17$ Mev for this spectrum.

The **half-value thickness** is that thickness of absorber that reduces the intensity to one-half its original value.

Therefore
$$\frac{I}{I_0} = \exp\left(-\mu_l x_{\frac{1}{2}}\right) = \tfrac{1}{2}$$

Therefore
$$x_{\frac{1}{2}} = \frac{(\log 2)}{\mu_l} = \frac{(\log 2)}{\mu\rho}$$

where μ is given by 12.18,

$$\mu = \frac{22}{(1.17)^{1.33}} = 17.8 \text{ cm}^2/\text{gram}$$

Therefore
$$x_{\frac{1}{2}} = \frac{0.693}{17.8} \times 2.7 = 0.014 \text{ cm}$$

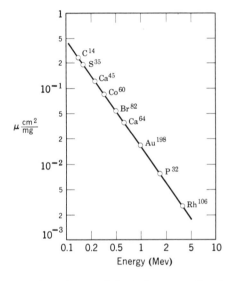

FIG. 12.10. The mass-absorption coefficients shown as a function of E_{max} for various β-emitters. (From G. I. Gleason, D. L. Tabern, I. D. Taylor, *Nucleonics*, **8**, 5 (1951), 12.)

12.4   Interaction of Electromagnetic Radiation with Matter

Nuclear reactors are also profuse sources of very energetic electro-magnetic radiation, usually called γ-rays when they originate in nuclear processes. We saw in section 5.5 that the fissioning of a U^{235} nucleus is accompanied by the emission of γ-radiation of 10 Mev energy in all, on the average, either as prompt γ-rays or as fission product γ-rays. A further source of γ-radiation is the various radiative neutron capture processes in the fuel, moderator, coolant, and structural materials of the reactor assembly. In addition, the electron absorption processes described in the preceding section give rise to γ-radiation in the form of Bremsstrahlung.

The most important mode of interaction between γ-radiation and matter which leads to a reduction of the γ-ray energy is that between γ-radiation and the electrons of the absorbing material. Although interactions between γ-radiation and nuclei occur sometimes, the frequency of this occurrence or the cross sections for these processes are relatively small compared to those for the electron interactions, generally of the order of millibarns or less. Such γ-induced nuclear reactions have quite high thresholds, of about 8 Mev or more, except for the photodisintegration of Be^9 and of H^2 which have Q-values of -1.67 Mev and -2.21 Mev respectively.

Experiment shows that the attenuation of γ-radiation as it penetrates matter follows the exponential law 4.16. This relation can be derived for γ-radiation in the same manner as was done for neutrons in section 4.6, assuming that a γ-ray or photon is removed from the incident beam in a single scattering event. That this assumption is valid is borne out by experiment which shows that the fractional decrease of γ-radiation intensity per unit thickness of absorber is constant, i.e., that

$$-\frac{1}{\Delta x}\frac{\Delta I}{I} = \mu_l \qquad (12.19)$$

or

$$-\frac{\Delta(\log I)}{\Delta x} = \mu_l \qquad (12.20)$$

This result is shown in Fig. 12.9.

The previous result can also be written in an integrated form, leading to an expression very similar to 4.16.

$$I = I_0 \exp(-\mu_l x) \qquad (12.21)$$

The coefficient μ_l is the **linear absorption coefficient** which can be related to an absorption cross section for the γ-radiation in matter, as was done in the case of a neutron beam passing through matter, by setting

$$\mu_l \equiv \Sigma = N_0 \sigma \qquad (12.22)$$

The experimental arrangement that leads to an attenuation as given by 12.21 is sketched in Fig. 12.11a, which is a "good geometry" arrangement. The beam of radiation is collimated and the detector is so placed that no scattered radiation can reach it. A photon which is either absorbed or scattered, even if only by a very small angle, is considered as having been

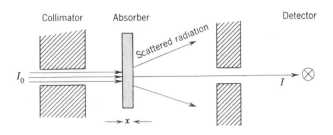

FIG. 12.11a. "Good geometry" or "narrow beam" experiment $I = I_0 e^{-\mu x}$.

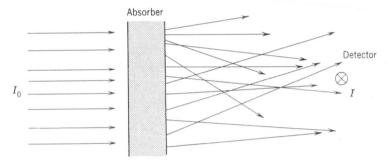

(*b*) "Broad beam" or "poor geometry" experiment. Intensity measured by detector contains also components of scattered radiation. Attenuation is less than for "good geometry" experiment and measured intensity is greater than that given by $I_0 e^{-\mu x}$.

removed from the original beam. The absorption coefficient μ_l in 12.19 is so defined that it refers to the measured intensity of the uncollided or virgin flux of radiation. It is, therefore, not a pure absorption coefficient as it also includes the attenuating contribution of scattering collisions to the total resultant attenuation of the photon flux.

If the experimental setup is a "poor geometry" arrangement, Fig. 12.11*b*, the measured radiation intensity will be greater than in the previous case through the additional contribution from some of the scattered components which can now reach the detector. This addition to the registered intensity from the scattered radiation will have the effect of reducing the attenuation and will thereby increase the intensity to a value which is greater than that as given by 12.21. This fact is of importance in the design of protective shielding and it will be taken up again when we consider that topic in Chapter 14.

The absorption of γ-radiation can be attributed to three separate physical processes of interaction with matter, with each of the three types of interaction contributing, in general, to the total absorption. The relative importance of each varies with the energy of the γ-radiation and depends on the properties of the absorbing material. The three processes are known as (1) the Compton effect, (2) the photoelectric effect, and (3) pair production.

The Compton effect is an inelastic scattering collision between a photon and an electron, during which part of the photon energy is transferred to the electron and the original photon energy is reduced by an equal amount.

The photoelectric effect results in the total destruction of the photon, with the entire γ-ray energy being used up in the process of detaching an atomic electron from its parent atom and endowing it with kinetic energy.

A pair production, similarly, results in the complete absorption of the γ-radiation quantum, which is converted entirely into rest energy of an electron pair (a positron and a negative electron) plus a certain amount of kinetic energy.

Accordingly, one can subdivide the linear absorption coefficient μ_l into three partial coefficients, associating a corresponding partial absorption coefficient with each of the preceding absorption processes. Thus

$$\mu_l = \mu_{\text{Compton}} + \mu_{\text{photo}} + \mu_{pp} \tag{12.23}$$

$$= N_0 Z \sigma_C + N_0 \sigma_p + N_0 \sigma_{pp} \tag{12.24}$$

Here, N_0, is the number of atoms or nuclei per centimeter^3 of absorber and Z its atomic number.

Since the photoelectric effect occurs only with electrons which are strongly bound to the atom, Fig. 12.16, this interaction is considered to be one between a photon and the atom as a whole. Similarly, pair production is always associated with the presence of a nucleus (only very rarely does it take place in the field of some other charged particle), which is necessary to conserve momentum in the process. It is, therefore, an interaction between a photon and a nucleus. The Compton process, however, is an interaction between a photon and an individual electron so that the probability of a Compton scattering per atom must be multiplied by the number of electrons per atom of scatterer, Z. This explains the presence of the factor Z in the Compton contribution to μ_l in 12.24, whereas the other two contributions depend on the number of atoms per cubic centimeter, N_0, only.

By dividing the linear absorption coefficient μ_l by the density of the absorbing material, we obtain the **mass absorption coefficient** μ_m,

$$\mu_m = \frac{\mu_l}{\rho} \tag{12.25}$$

Division of ρ_m by the number of atoms per gram, N/A, ($N = $ Avogadro's number), gives the **atomic absorption coefficient** μ_a,

Therefore
$$\mu_a = \frac{\mu_m}{N/A}$$

$$= \frac{\mu_l}{N_0} \qquad (12.26)$$

Example 12.5. The radioisotope Na^{24} emits γ-rays of 1.378 and 2.754 Mev energies, respectively, in succession. Calculate the relative intensities of the two components after they have passed through 27.50 grams/cm² of lead (density 11.0 grams/cm³). The linear absorption coefficients are 0.48 cm^{-1} for the harder, and 0.62 cm^{-1} for the softer component.

The thickness of the interposed lead is

$$x = \frac{27.50}{11} \text{ cm} = 2.5 \text{ cm}$$

The attenuation of the two components is given by

$$\frac{I_1}{I_0} = \exp(-\mu_{l1}x) \quad \text{and} \quad \frac{I_2}{I_0} = \exp(-\mu_{l2}x)$$

Therefore
$$\frac{I_1}{I_2} = \exp(\mu_{l2} - \mu_{l1})x = \exp(0.62 - 0.48) \times 2.5$$
$$= \exp(0.35) = 1.42$$

12.5 Compton Scattering

The first of the three effects that account for the attenuation of γ-radiation in matter is the **Compton effect** which can be understood in terms of a collision of a photon with a free electron. The description of the electron as "free" has to be accepted in a relative sense, as we are dealing with atomic electrons which are bound to the atoms of the absorbing medium. Nevertheless, if the γ-ray energy is sufficiently greater than the atomic binding energy of the struck electron, the latter can be considered as a "free" electron. For all practical purposes, this means that for γ-radiation of energy of about 0.1 Mev and above, interacting with an electron, the latter can be considered as being free. For γ-radiation of lower energies the photoelectric effect becomes much more important than the Compton effect as an effective mechanism for γ-ray attenuation.

The Compton effect can be described as an inelastic collision between a photon of energy $E_0 = h\nu_0$ with an electron initially at rest, where the photon emerges with diminished energy $E_1 = h\nu_1$, scattered at an angle ϕ

with the original direction of incidence. The electron moves away from the point of collision at an angle θ and carries away in the form of kinetic energy the energy lost by the photon in the collision (Fig. 12.12). Application of the laws of conservation of energy and momentum lead to the expressions (see Appendix A):

$$E_0 = E_1 + m_0 c^2 \left[\left(1 - \frac{v^2}{c^2} \right)^{-\frac{1}{2}} - 1 \right] \tag{12.27}$$

$$\frac{E_0}{c} = \frac{E_1}{c} \cos \phi + \frac{m_0 v}{\left(1 - \frac{v^2}{c^2} \right)^{\frac{1}{2}}} \cos \theta \tag{12.28}$$

$$\frac{E_1}{c} \sin \phi - \frac{m_0 v}{\left(1 - \frac{v^2}{c^2} \right)^{\frac{1}{2}}} \sin \theta = 0 \tag{12.29}$$

In these equations the relativistic expressions for the energy and momentum of the electron (rest mass m_0) and the particle properties of the photon have been used. Elimination of the electron speed v and its scattering angle θ leads to a relation between the incident γ-ray wavelength λ_0 and the wavelength λ_1 of the scattered radiation, which is

$$\lambda_1 - \lambda_0 = \Delta\lambda = \frac{c}{v_1} - \frac{c}{v_2} = \frac{h}{m_0 c} (1 - \cos \phi) \tag{12.30}$$

where $\Delta\lambda$ is known as the **Compton shift**. The constant $h/m_0 c$ is the **Compton wavelength**, which is a universal constant having the value 0.02417 Å. By inspecting 12.30, it is readily seen that the Compton shift depends only on the scattering angle ϕ and, for a given ϕ, is independent of the wavelength or energy of the incident γ-radiation.

The fractional energy loss, however, is very markedly dependent on the energy of the incident γ-radiation, since it follows from 12.30 that

$$\frac{\Delta E}{E_0} = \frac{1}{1 + (m_0 c^2 / E_0)/(1 - \cos \theta)} \tag{12.31}$$

This shows that the Compton shift in energy becomes increasingly more important with rising γ-ray energy, where a Compton scattering can cause a considerable reduction in the energy of a very energetic γ-ray, Fig. 12.12a.

The Compton cross section σ_C increases with decreasing γ-ray energy, approaching a numerical value of 0.6651 barn for very low γ-ray energies ($E < 0.005$ Mev), and then becomes independent of the energy. This result was obtained by J. J. Thomson on the basis of classical electromagnetic theory and is known as the Thomson cross section,

$$\left[\sigma_{\text{Thomson}} = \frac{8\pi}{3} \left(\frac{e^2}{mc^2} \right)^2 \right].$$

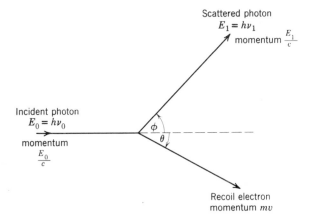

FIG. 12.12. Compton scattering of γ-radiation.

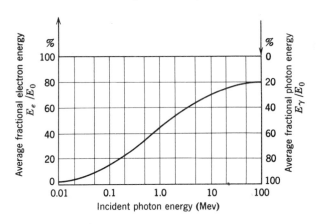

(a) The sharing of energy on the average by Compton electron and scattered photon resulting from a Compton scattering as a function of the incident photon energy.

For higher energies a quantum mechanical expression, known as the **Klein-Nishina** equation, is required to account for the known experimental results. The Klein-Nishina formula can be expressed in the form

$$\sigma_{\text{Compton}} \text{ (barns)} = \frac{1 + (r - 1)^2}{4r^3} \log (1 + 2r)$$

$$+ \frac{r^2(1 + r) + 2(1 + 2r)^2}{2r^2(1 + 2r)^2} \tag{12.32}$$

where

$$r = \frac{E_0}{m_0 c^2}$$

The Compton coefficient of attenuation μ_{Comp} according to 12.24 is therefore obtained by multiplying 12.32 by $N_0 Z$. Equation 12.32 shows that σ_{Comp} is independent of the properties of the absorber and dependent only on the γ-ray energy. Its variation with energy is given in Table 12.3 and is shown in Fig. 12.13.

TABLE 12.3

$E_0/m_0 c^2$	E_0	σ_{Comp} (barn)
0.10	0.0511	0.560
0.20	0.102	0.490
0.30	0.153	0.441
0.40	0.204	0.403
0.50	0.255	0.374
1.00	0.511	0.287
2.00	1.022	0.209
5.00	2.555	0.127
10.00	5.108	0.082
20.00	10.22	0.050

The mass coefficient of scattering μ_m, according to 12.23 and 12.24 is equal to

$$\mu_{m(Comp)} = \frac{\mu_{l(Comp)}}{\rho}$$

$$= \frac{N_0 Z}{\rho} \sigma_{Comp}$$

$$= N_{Avogadro}\left(\frac{Z}{A}\right)\sigma_{Comp} \tag{12.33}$$

so that $\mu_{m(Comp)}$ varies slightly with Z. For light elements $Z/A \simeq \frac{1}{2}$, so that $\mu_{m(Comp)}$ is nearly the same for these elements.

The variation of $\mu_{l(Comp)}$ with energy for lead and aluminum is shown in Fig. 12.15.

As is seen from Fig. 12.13 the Compton absorption coefficient consists of two distinct portions, a true absorption portion and a scattering part. The reduction of the beam intensity is achieved in part by the recoil electron abstracting some of the incident beam energy and in part by the scattered photon moving out of the original beam direction. We can, therefore, separate these contributions by writing

Total absorption coefficient = scattering absorption coefficient
+ true absorption coefficient

Or, in terms of the cross sections,

$$\sigma_C = \sigma_s + \sigma_a \tag{12.33a}$$

This separation is important in connection with the biological effects of radiation where only the truly absorbed portion of the radiation is responsible for the energy transfer to the tissue through ionization and related effects.

In this connection, it is convenient to define an **energy absorption coefficient** μ_e which refers to the energy transfer from the radiation to the absorber as

$$\mu_e = \mu_{ph} + \mu_{pp} + f\mu_C \qquad (12.33b)$$

Here, f is the fraction of the incident γ-radiation energy absorbed by the

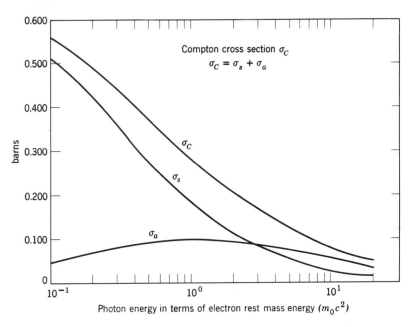

FIG. 12.13. Compton cross sections as function of γ-ray energies.

recoil electrons and integrated over all values of the scattering angles for the Compton collisions. Or, in terms of the cross sections, by 12.24,

$$\mu_e = N_0\sigma_{ph} + N_0\sigma_{pp} + fN_0Z\sigma_C \qquad (12.33c)$$

The photoelectric and pair producing contributions to the attenuating process need not similarly be divided into partial contributions since these processes absorb essentially all the radiation energy in a single interaction. The reduction in the energy absorption coefficient as compared to the total absorption coefficient is entirely ascribed to the scattered portion of the radiation in Compton collisions.

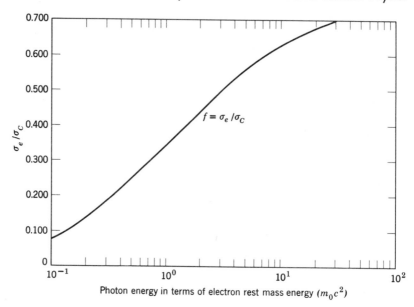

FIG. 12.14. Ratio of energy absorption portion of the Compton cross section σ_e and the Compton cross section σ_C as function of γ-energy.

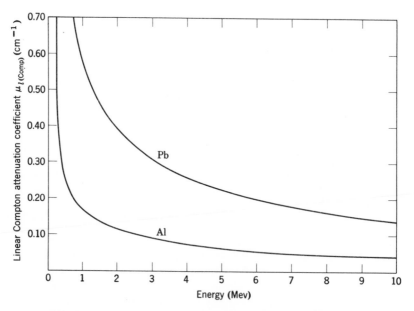

FIG. 12.15. Linear Compton attenuation coefficient for Pb and Al.

The Compton cross section as given in Table 12.3 and its partial contributions according to 12.33a are shown in Fig. 12.13, and the energy absorption portion of the Compton cross section $f\sigma_C$ over σ_C are shown in Fig. 12.14.

12.6   Photoelectric Absorption

The second of the physical processes that lead to the attenuation of γ-radiation passing through matter is the complete absorption of a photon

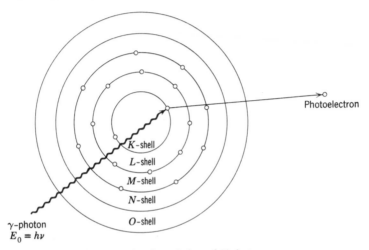

FIG. 12.16. Photoelectric emission of K-electron.

by an atom of the absorbing material, thereby causing an electron to become detached from the atomic configuration which is ejected from the atom with reasonably high kinetic energy. This process is the **photoelectric effect.** Except for the absorbers of low Z, this effect is the predominant type of γ-ray interaction with matter for energies below about 0.1 Mev. The complete absorption of the photon is possible in this mode of interaction without violating the momentum conservation requirement because the γ-ray interacts with the atom as a whole, which carries away momentum as it recoils after the collision. The most likely interaction is one between the photon and the most tightly bound electrons, i.e., the two K-shell electrons, which occurs in about 80% of the photoelectric absorptions, if the incident photon is sufficiently energetic, i.e., greater than the atomic binding energy E_K of the K-electrons. The kinetic energy of the emitted electron will be given by the difference of the radiation energy and E_K.

$$E_{\text{kin}} = h\nu - E_K \tag{12.34}$$

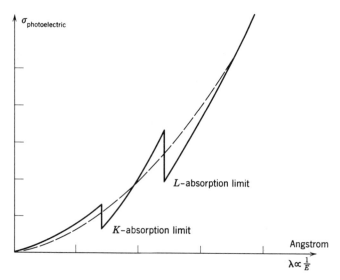

FIG. 12.17. Photoelectric absorption cross section in the region of absorption edges.

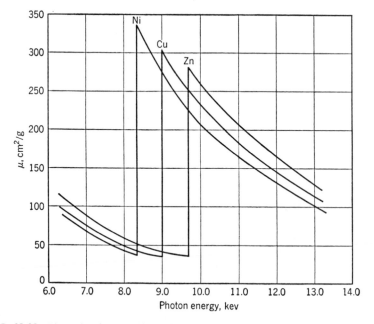

FIG. 12.18. Photoelectric mass absorption coefficients for Ni, Cu, and Zn as obtained experimentally, showing the K-absorption edges. (From D. Halliday, *Introductory Nuclear Physics*, John Wiley and Sons, 1955.)

Although the incident γ-ray is completely destroyed in a photoelectric absorption, it should be realized that the removal of a K-electron gives rise to the subsequent emission of X-rays as the outer electrons fill the gaps left in the lower energy levels of the atom.

The total photoelectric absorption coefficient is obtained by adding the absorption coefficients for all the electrons of the atom and, for practical purposes, it is taken to be ~25% greater than the absorption coefficient for the K-shell electrons alone.

As the photon energy decreases below the binding energy of the K-shell, there will occur a sudden drop in the absorption coefficient, and similar drops will appear as the energy falls below the binding energies of the $L, M, \ldots$ shells. This is shown schematically in Fig. 12.17 and experimental results are reproduced in Fig. 12.18.

The photoelectric absorption cross section σ_{photo} of 12.24 varies in a complicated manner with the γ-ray energy and with Z of the absorber. No simple expression is known which is valid over wide ranges of energy and for all values of Z. It can, however, be expressed in this form

$$\sigma_{ph(\text{barns})} \simeq \frac{AZ^n}{(h\nu)^m} \tag{12.35}$$

where n lies between 4 and 5, m between 1 and 3, and $A = 1.25 \times 10^{-9}$ if $h\nu$ is expressed in Mev. For practical purposes of calculation, the following numerical values are found satisfactory:
For

$$h\nu > 0.5 \text{ Mev} \qquad n \simeq 4.5, m \simeq 1$$
$$h\nu < 0.5 \text{ Mev} \qquad n \simeq 4, \quad m \simeq 3$$

The photoelectric absorption cross sections for some elements are shown in Fig. 12.19.

12.7   Pair Production

The third mechanism that contributes to the attenuation of γ-radiation in matter is that of pair production. This is in effect the conversion of radiation energy into mass energy, which was first observed by Anderson in cloud chamber photographs. In this process a photon is destroyed and an electron pair (an electron and a positron) are created. This can only take place in the vicinity of a nucleus (occasionally, but rarely, in the electric field of some other charged particle) to make conservation of momentum possible, and the created particles must have equal and opposite charges according to the principle of conservation of electric

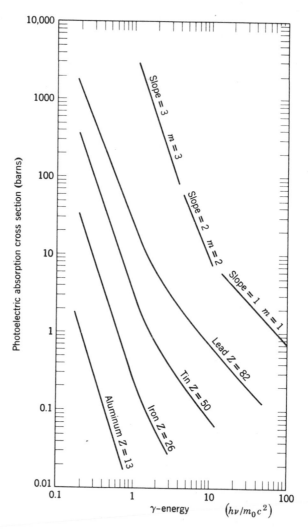

FIG. 12.19. The photoelectric absorption cross section for aluminum, iron, tin, and lead and its variation as $(h\nu)^m$, for a given element (Z).

charge. Applying the principle of conservation of energy to this process, we must have that

$$hv = E_0 = 2m_0c^2 + E^+{}_{kin} + E^-{}_{kin} \qquad (12.36)$$

rest mass energy

kinetic energy of electrons

where we have neglected the small amount of energy carried away by the recoiling nucleus. Equation 12.36 shows that the minimum γ-ray energy

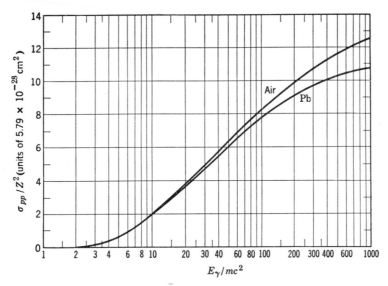

FIG. 12.20. The cross section for pair production as a function of γ-energy in air and in lead. (From E. Segré, *Experimental Nuclear Physics*, vol. I, Part II, John Wiley and Sons, 1953.)

required to create an electron pair is equal to $2m_0c^2$, or 1.022 Mev. The photon energy in excess of this amount can be shared between the two particles in any proportion.

The pair production process becomes increasingly important for γ-rays of energies above the threshold energy of 1.022 Mev. The cross section for pair production, according to Bethe and Heitler, is proportional to $Z(Z + 1)$, i.e., $\sim Z^2$, varying slowly with the energy, approximately as $\log E_0$, so that γ-ray absorption through pair production becomes very important for heavy elements at high energies. The behavior of the pair production cross section is indicated in Fig. 12.20.

The increase in the pair production cross section with γ-ray energy is in

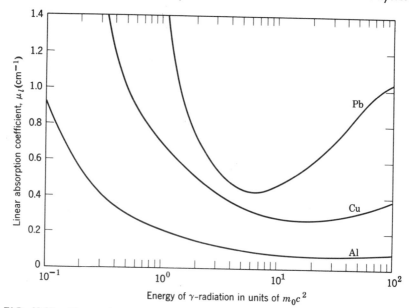

FIG. 12.21. Linear absorption coefficient for γ-radiation in Pb, Cu, and Al as a function of γ-energy.

contrast to the behavior of the cross sections for the Compton and photo-electric effects, both of which fall off with increasing photon energy. We summarize the removal cross sections for γ-radiation per atom of absorber in Table 12.4.

TABLE 12.4

Attenuation Process	Dependence on Z	Dependence on E
Compton	Z	$1/E$
Photoelectric	$Z^{4.5}$	$1/E$ for $E > m_0c^2$
		$1/E^3$ for $E < m_0c^2$
Pair production	Z^2	$\log E$

The total linear absorption coefficient for γ-radiation in Pb, Cu, and Al as a function of radiation energy is shown in Fig. 12.21 and for Pb the individual contributions due to the Compton, photoelectric, and pair production processes are shown in Fig. 12.22.

Table 12.5 gives an approximate classification of the energy regions for which each of the three processes predominates in the case of a light element (Al), a medium heavy element (Cu), and a heavy element (Pb).

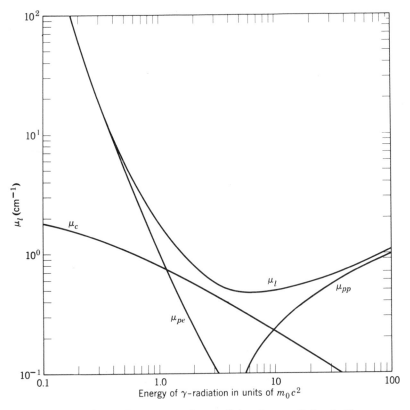

FIG. 12.22. Linear attenuation coefficient for γ-radiation in Pb.

TABLE 12.5

Attenuation Process	Al	Cu	Pb
Photoelectric	$E < 0.05$ Mev	$E < 0.1$ Mev	$E < 0.5$ Mev
Compton	$0.05 < E < 15$ Mev	$0.1 < E < 10$	$0.5 < E < 5$ Mev
Pair production	$E > 15$ Mev	$E > 10$ Mev	$E > 5$ Mev

PROBLEMS

(1) Find the range of a 2 Mev deuteron in air.

(2) Calculate the range in aluminum of a 50 Mev fission fragment, making a reasonable assumption about its mass and charge.

(3) Calculate the range of a 70 Mev fission fragment in zirconium.

(4) Using the data for the α-emitters listed in Table 12.6, draw a suitable linear graph to test the relation $R = cE^n$ and determine the values of c and n from your graph.

TABLE 12.6

α-Emitter	Energy E (Mev)	Mean Range R (cm)
Th^{232}	4.0	2.5
U^{233}	4.8	3.3
U^{235}	4.5	3.0
U^{238}	4.2	2.7
Pu^{239}	5.1	3.6

(5) Calculate S_a, S_e, S_m and the thickness equivalent to 1 cm of air for α-particles of 7.68 Mev in Al, Cu, and Au, given the following relative stopping powers and densities:

Element	Relative Stopping Power	Density (gram/cm³)
Al	1700	2.70
Cu	3800	8.93
Au	4950	19.33

(6) Calculate the energy in Mev of an α-particle having the same speed as a 70 Mev Ba^{138} fission nucleus.

(7) Calculate the range of a 1 Mev β-particle in Al and in Au.

(8) Compare the radiation loss with the ionization loss for 1 Mev β-particles in Al and Pb.

(9) The β-spectrum emitted from the pure β-emitter (i.e., no γ-ray emission accompanies the β-emission) P^{32} has a maximum energy of 1.71 Mev. Calculate the range for this β-spectrum.

(10) Calculate the β-energy for which the radiation and ionization losses are equal in Pb and repeat for Cu.

(11) The radiation loss for electrons occurs at a rate which is given approximately by the expression:

$$-\left(\frac{dE}{dx}\right)_{\text{rad}} = 0.772 \times 10^{-26} Z(Z+1)NE(15.8 - \log Z)$$

By integration, find the **radiation length** for the absorber, which is defined as that thickness of absorber that will reduce the electron energy through radiation loss by $(1/e)$th of its initial energy.

(12) Calculate the maximum energy that can be transferred to the electron in a Compton scattering process, and show that for 1.533 Mev γ-radiation this amounts to 1.314 Mev.

(13) In an absorption experiment with 1.14 Mev γ-radiation from Zn^{65}, it is found that 25 cm of Al reduce the beam intensity to 2%. Calculate the half-value thickness and the mass absorption coefficient of aluminum for this radiation.

BIBLIOGRAPHY

Bleuler, E., and G. J. Goldsmith: *Experimental Nucleonics*, Rinehart, 1952.

Davisson, C. M., and R. D. Evans: "Gamma-Ray Absorption Coefficients," *Rev. Modern Phys.*, **24**, 79 (1952).

Dienes, G. J.: "Radiation Effects in Solids," *Ann. Rev. Nucl. Sci.*, vol. 2, 187, 1953.

Evans, D. H.: *The Atomic Nucleus*, McGraw-Hill, 1955.

Fano, U.: "Gamma Ray Attenuation," *Nucleonics*, vol. 11, No. 8, No. 9 (August, September 1953).

Friedlander, G., and J. W. Kennedy: *Nuclear and Radiochemistry*, Wiley, 1955.

Geneva Conference on the Peaceful Uses of Atomic Energy—1955:
  P/913: Lassen, N. O.: "Energy Loss and Total Charges of Fission Fragments Passing Through Matter," vol. 2, 214.

Second Geneva Conference on the Peaceful Uses of Atomic Energy—1958:
  P/2452: Barendregt, S. M., and A. Imam: "Measurement of Absorption of Beta Rays in Solids and Gases," vol. 14, 481.

Glendenin, L. E.: "Determination of the Energy of Beta Particles and Photons by Absorption," *Nucleonics*, **2**, No. 12 (December 1944).

Goldstein, H.: *Fundamental Aspects of Reactor Shielding*, Addison-Wesley, 1959.

Halliday, D.: *Introductory Nuclear Physics*, Wiley, 1955.

Harrison, J. R.: *Nuclear Reactor Shielding*, Temple Press, 1958.

Hine, G. J., and G. L. Brownell: *Radiation Dosimetry*, Academic Press, 1956.

Knipp, J. R., and R. C. Ling: "On the Ionization Yields of Heavy Particles," *Phys. Rev.*, **82**, 30 (1950).

Price, B. T., Horton, C. C., and Spinney, K. T.: *Radiation Shielding*, Pergamon Press, 1957.

Segré, E. (Ed.): *Experimental Nuclear Physics*, vol. I, part II, Wiley, 1953.

Uehling, E. A.: "Penetration of Heavy Charged Particles in Matter," *Ann. Rev. Nucl. Sci.*, vol. 4 (1954).

Weyl, C., and S. R. Warren: *Radiological Physics*, C C Thomas, 1951.

Yagoda, H.: *Radioactive Measurements with Nuclear Emulsions*, Wiley, 1949.

chapter 13

Radiation Detection and Measurement

13.1 Introduction

The methods used for the detection of nuclear particles and of γ-radiation are almost exclusively based on the ionization produced by particles in their passage through matter. In the case of neutrons and γ-radiation, since they carry no charge, the ionizations produced are caused by secondary charged particles. In the interaction of γ-radiation with matter, charged particles are liberated, as was described in the preceding chapter, which in turn produce ionization effects that can be detected. Similarly, with neutrons we utilize certain neutron reactions which result in the production of charged nuclear particles that reveal their presence by the ionization they produce.

Of the many kinds of detectors that are currently being used for detecting, monitoring, and measuring nuclear radiations we shall select and describe only a few basic methods and instruments.

13.2 Lauritsen Electroscope

Much of the pioneer work in radioactivity research was done with the ordinary gold leaf electroscope, whose principle of operation is used in the modern and compact form of the Lauritsen electroscope (Fig. 13.1).

The central part of this instrument consists of a small metal frame to which is attached a T-shaped tiny (3 to 5 microns) gold-coated quartz fiber about 6 mm long. The gold coating is applied to make the quartz fiber conducting. When the frame and the attached quartz fiber are charged, the fiber is repelled from the frame and it assumes an equilibrium position under the joint effects of an electrostatic force of repulsion and an elastic restoring force in the quartz. If an ionizing particle causes ions to appear in the surrounding space, the charge on the metal frame and fiber will become partially neutralized and the deflection of the quartz fiber will diminish. The fiber deflection can be observed by means of a microscope having a graduated scale in its eyepiece. Since the deflection is not quite linear with charge, it is necessary to take readings always over the same portion of the scale.

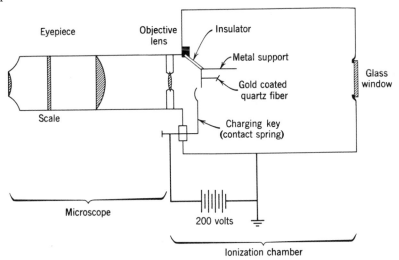

FIG. 13.1. Diagram of Lauritsen electroscope.

A modified and sturdier variant of this electroscope is the pencil-type pocket dosimeter which has become standard equipment for nuclear reactor personnel.

13.3 Ionization Chambers

An ionization chamber consists essentially of two conductors which are insulated from each other and are maintained at different potentials, the whole being contained in a gas-filled chamber (Fig. 13.2). When ion pairs are produced by an ionizing particle traversing the space between the two conductors, which can be either parallel plates or, more frequently, a central wire surrounded by a cylindrical conductor, each ion type will move towards the electrode of opposite polarity. If the entry of ionizing radiation is at a steady and sufficient rate, the ions flowing to the electrodes will appear as a steady current flow that can be measured directly. When the ionization chamber is being used in this manner where it measures the total quantity of charge due to the entry of ionizing particles over a certain time interval, it is operating as an **integrating** instrument. The Lauritsen electroscope can similarly be classified as an integrating instrument because it, too, measures the integrated effect of ionizing particles entering it over a certain period of time.

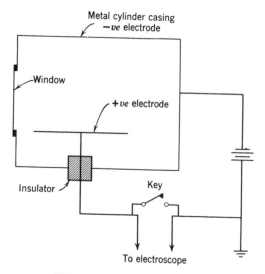

FIG. 13.2. Ionization chamber.

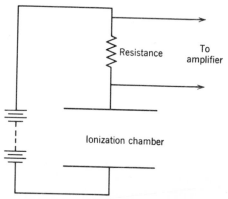

FIG. 13.3. The ionization current flows through a high resistance, causing a voltage drop across the resistance which can be amplified electronically.

Ionizing chambers can also be operated so as to indicate separately the entry or passage of individual ionizing particles. When functioning in this manner they are operating as nonintegrating or **counting** instruments, often called **ion pulse chambers**.

The integrating type of operation is suitable for measuring very high intensities of radiation when the rate of individual ion pulses formed in the chamber is large, each contributing to a mean ionization current which is allowed to flow through a high resistance as in Fig. 13.3. The currents are usually too small to be measured directly and voltage amplification is necessary.

Example 13.1 Calculate the ionization current produced by a beam of α-particles of 5 Mev energy, entering an ionization chamber at a rate of 1 per sec. Each α-particle produces

$$\frac{5 \times 10^6 \text{ ev}}{35 \text{ ev/ion pair}} = 1.43 \times 10^5 \text{ ion pairs}$$

Therefore   total current flow $= 1.43 \times 10^5 \times 1.6 \times 10^{-19}$ coulomb/sec

$$= 2.3 \times 10^{-14} \text{ amp}$$

13.4   Ionization in Gases

The different methods of operating ionization detector instruments are based on the varying behavior, with the potential gradient that exists between the electrodes, of the ion pairs produced by a charged primary particle in its passage through a gas, and on their interaction with the gas molecules. As the voltage difference between the electrodes is increased the ionization current flowing to the collector plate increases at first almost linearly, and then more slowly, until it finally approaches asymptotically a current value, called the **saturation value** (Fig. 13.4). A further raising of applied voltage will not result in an increased current flow. It is, however, possible to reach a higher saturation current by increasing the primary ionizing radiation (Fig. 13.5).

The response of the ionization current to the variation of applied voltage difference between the electrodes as shown in Fig. 13.4 and Fig. 13.5 can be explained in terms of the recombination of ions that takes place in the gas. When ions first appear in the gas following the passage of ionizing radiation, the negative ions (electrons) and the positive ions will be attracted to opposite electrodes and will each move with a certain drift velocity which, among other factors, will depend on the potential difference between the electrodes. Because of frequent collisions with gas molecules their motion will not be accelerated but will, rather, correspond to a steady drift velocity which is superimposed on their kinetic motion. The drift velocity of the more massive positive ions is, in general, only 1/100 of that of the electrons. For low collecting voltages the separation and collection of the two ion types will be relatively slow, so that there is always taking place in the gas a certain amount of recombination of positive and negative ions before they can reach the collecting electrodes because of the mutual force of attraction that exists between the oppositely charged ions. But, any neutralization of charges through recombination will cause a reduction in the measured ionization current.

As the electric field between the electrodes is increased, the velocity with which the ions move towards the opposing electrodes increases, thereby decreasing the likelihood and the amount of recombination until eventually

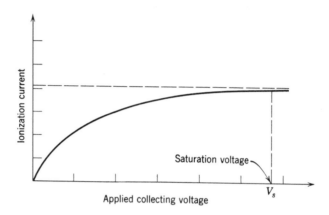

FIG. 13.4. Saturation curve. Increasing the voltage above V_s will not measurably increase the ionization current.

when the field becomes sufficiently high, recombination of ions is reduced to a minimum, and the maximum possible amount of ions (nearly all) is collected by the electrodes. This condition of operation, where the applied voltage is high enough to prevent recombination, corresponds to the saturation current of Fig. 13.4. The value of the saturation current is proportional to the initial number of ion pairs formed in the gas (Fig. 13.5). The ionization chamber is usually operated in this saturation region where it is independent of the applied voltage and where the electrical charge collected by the electrodes is equal to the charge carried by the primary ions produced in the gas.

A well-known design of ionization chamber, commonly known as Cutie Pie, is often used as monitor and for radiation surveys. Ionization chambers can be used to detect most kinds of radiation by special design adaptations. When thick walls are employed in their design, only the penetrating γ-radiation will be detected while α- and β-radiation is screened out. With thinner walled chambers β- and γ-radiation will be detected whereas α-radiation is kept out. In other types of ionization chambers the response to different types of radiation can be adjusted by the use of different window coverings.

A common method employed for the detection of slow neutrons is based on the reaction

$$B^{10} + n^1 \rightarrow Li^7 + He^4$$

which has a thermal cross section of 3813 barns for the pure B^{10} isotope reaction. In the natural composition of $\sim 19\%$ B^{10} and 81% B^{11}, the

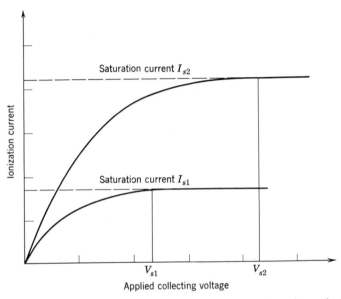

FIG. 13.5. The saturation value of the current depends on the primary ionization radiation.

cross section is reduced to ~ 755 barns which is still a large value. The boron is sometimes employed as a solid for lining the inner walls, and sometimes in the form of borontrifluoride gas or some other suitable boron compound which is introduced into the detection chamber.

In the (n, α) reaction with B^{10}, an energy of 2.314 Mev is shared by the α-particle and the recoiling Li^7 nucleus, of which the α-particle carries away 1.473 Mev and the Li^7 nucleus retains 0.841 Mev as kinetic energy and the rest as excitation energy.

Another reaction which has been used for the detection of slow neutrons is

$$Li^6 + n^1 \rightarrow He^3 + He^4 + 4.6 \text{ Mev}$$

with a cross section of ~ 945 barns for the pure Li^6 isotope (natural abundance $\sim 8\%$).

Another possible, although less frequently employed reaction for the detection of slow neutrons, is the following:

$$He^3 + n^1 \rightarrow H^3 + H^1$$

in which the proton and triton share an energy of 0.76 Mev.

Other, more indirect methods of detection of slow neutrons are available in the utilization of the (n, γ) reaction with many nuclei to produce radioisotopes which usually emit γ-radiation and β-particles which can be

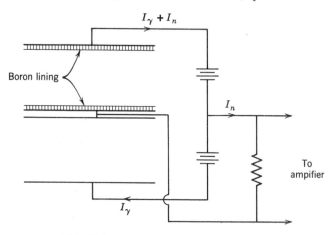

FIG. 13.6. γ-compensated ionization chamber.

detected. The fission reaction of uranium with neutrons has also been used for neutron detection, in view of the fact that the high-energy fission fragments produce easily detectable ionization. By using the pure isotopes of uranium one can discriminate between slow neutrons and fast neutrons, since only fast neutrons can fission the U^{238} isotope. Another method of fast neutron detection makes use of their elastic collision with hydrogen atoms in which the resultant fast recoil protons produce the detectable ionization. The detection chamber is either filled with hydrogen gas or has its walls lined with hydrogeneous materials, such as thin sheets of polyethylene.

If we want to discriminate between neutron and γ-radiation when both are present, a **compensated chamber** arrangement can be used, where a chamber consisting of two identical halves is employed. One-half of the chamber is sensitive to both γ-radiation and neutrons by including a boron compound, whereas the other half is sensitive only to γ-radiation. By a suitable electronic circuit arrangement the γ-ray induced responses can be canceled out while allowing only the neutron induced output to be recorded (Fig. 13.6).

13.5 Gas Amplification

The region of saturation (Fig. 13.4) usually extends over a range of several hundred volts. If the potential difference between the central wire and the outer electrode is increased beyond the region of saturation, the current flow across the ionization chamber will again begin to rise (Fig. 13.7). The mechanism responsible for the increased current flow is the

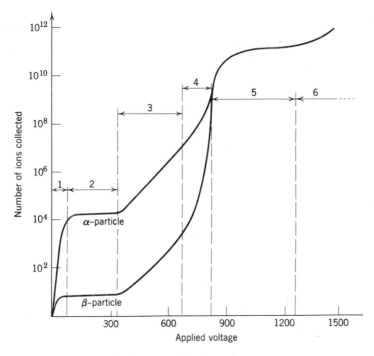

1. Ion recombination region
2. Ionization chamber region
3. Proportional counter region
4. Limited proportionality region
5. Geiger-Müller counter region
6. Continuous discharge region

FIG. 13.7. Operating regions of an ionization chamber.

creation of additional ions by the first generation primary ions. As the potential difference between the electrodes is raised past the region of saturation, some of the primary ions formed in the chamber will gain sufficient energy in the electric field to produce fresh ions in collisions with the molecules of the gas, which in turn may acquire sufficient energy to produce still more ions. This successive build-up of ions, often called avalanching, will cause a considerable multiplication of the initial ionization current, with ten or more ions produced per single primary ion. This effect is called **gas amplification**.

The amplification factor will be essentially the same, whatever the initial ionization, so that the total ionization produced will be proportional to the primary ionization. The difference in the ionization produced by an α-particle and by a β-particle will, therefore, be even more apparent because of this proportional magnification. An ionization chamber operating in this voltage region (Fig. 13.7) is called a **proportional counter**. Gas amplification factors of the order of 10^4 are quite common for these counters. With the cylindrical type of ionization chamber, Fig. 13.8, it is possible to achieve a high electrical field near the central wire electrode, which is necessary for an avalanche to set in without having to employ extremely high potentials. Ordinarily, the range of operation lies somewhere between 600 to 900 volts, depending on various design factors, although somewhat higher potentials may sometimes be desirable. The electric field in a commonly used counter construction can be as high as 10^5 volts per cm.

For a cylindrical counter, the electric field E at a distance r from the central axis is

$$E = \frac{V}{r} \bigg/ \log \frac{R}{r_0} \tag{13.1}$$

where R is the radius of the outer cylinder, r_0 the radius of the central wire, and V, the applied voltage between the electrodes. The avalanche ionization takes place very close to the central electrode, most likely within the last few mean free paths of the electrons from the central anode and probably at one point only.

Proportional counters are commonly used for detecting and measuring strongly ionizing radiation (α-particles and protons) in the presence of strong background radiation of small specific ionization (β- and γ-radiation). By comparing the counts at lower operating voltages with those at higher voltages within the proportional counting region, the separate contributions of the highly ionizing particles and those of low specific ionization can be determined. At low operating voltages the observed counts are due primarily to the former particles, whereas for the high voltage counting, contributions are made by both kinds of ionizing particles. Special electronic circuits have been designed to allow only pulses larger than a certain desired pulse height to be recorded while discriminating against smaller ones. These circuits are known as **pulse analyzers** or **pulse height discriminators**.

By using two such analyzers, each set for a different minimum pulse height, we can select pulses with heights lying between these two values and exclude all other pulse heights. This is done by subtracting from each other electronically the output voltages of the two analyzers. If V_1 is the minimum pulse height passed by the first analyzer and V_2 that of the second, only pulses with heights lying between V_1 and V_2 can be selected to pass through and to be recorded. This arrangement is known as a **single channel pulse height analyzer.**

The pulse height ΔV for a counter capacitance C, gas amplification M, and number of electrons produced by the primary ionizing particle N, is given by

$$\Delta V = \frac{MNe}{C} \tag{13.2}$$

13.6 Proportional Counters

For proportional counters the size of the discharge pulse for a given applied voltage is proportional to the number of ions formed by the primary ionization process. The general construction features of a typical counter are shown in Fig. 13.8. It consists of a metal chamber with a very thin wire in the center which is insulated from the chamber casing. This central wire is always made positive with respect to the metal chamber wall and serves as a collecting electrode which is connected to a pulse amplifier. Ionizing particles can enter the chamber either through a thin aluminum or mica window at one end or in the wall of the counter. The chamber is filled with a gas at a pressure that can differ for various types of counters, from below atmospheric to a little above and, in yet another type, the gas is made to flow continuously through the chamber. Although most gases are suitable as a filler, methane is often preferred (with an admixture of some argon) because of the high gas amplification that can be reached with this gas. For a satisfactory operation of such a counter at atmospheric pressure, voltages above 1200 volts are usually required. Operation at atmospheric pressure permits the introduction of the radioactive sample into the chamber directly, thus eliminating errors due to window absorption and geometry corrections. The pulse heights in proportional counters are usually of the order of millivolts and, therefore, require amplification by electronic means.

The proportional counter is a very fast counter and very high counting rates are possible with it. Separate pulses entering the counter at a rate of as high as 10^6 per sec can be resolved with a properly designed counter. By **resolving time** we understand the shortest time interval between two successive particles that can be detected or resolved by the counter. This depends on the *speed* of the counter. By using counters of small diameters, 5 mm or less, a resolving time of 10^{-7} sec can be achieved.

If the primary ionizing particles arrive in too rapid a succession, a mechanical counter, which is generally used to record the arrival of particles in the chamber, cannot respond to all arrivals. The output from

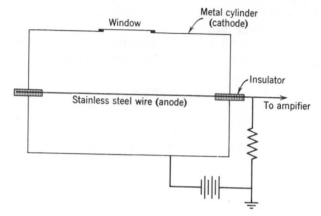

FIG. 13.8. Proportional counter.

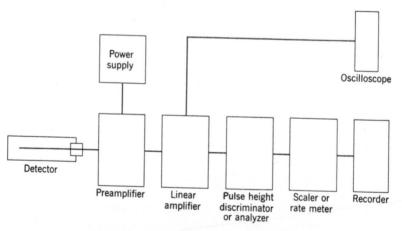

FIG. 13.9. Block diagram of counting circuit.

the amplifier is therefore first passed through a **scaling circuit** before being fed into the mechanical counter. A **scaler** is an electronic circuit arrangement that feeds a predetermined fraction of the actual particle counts to the mechanical counter. A block diagram of a typical counting circuit is shown in Fig. 13.9.

Another characteristic quality of a counter is its **counting efficiency**. This is the fraction of all the particles passing through the sensitive volume of the counter which are actually detected by the counter.

A disadvantage of the proportional counter is the need for a highly stable operating voltage, especially for high gas pressure counters, since in the region of proportionality, a slight change in the applied counter voltage will alter the gas amplification and, hence, the output of the proportional counter.

The proportional counter can be adapted to the use as neutron counter by methods described in section 13.4, and in this form it is being employed to an increasing extent in nuclear reactor operation.

13.7 Geiger-Müller Counters

As the applied voltage is further increased beyond the region of proportionality, avalanche ionization will begin to set in at distances farther away from the central conductor until, eventually, at a sufficiently high voltage, the ionization avalanche will spread along the entire length of the wire. This behavior distinguishes this region, which is called the **Geiger-Müller region**, from the region of proportionality where the electron from an ion pair produces an avalanche at one point only; thus the avalanche remains localized instead of spreading rapidly along the central wire.

The Geiger-Müller region in Fig. 13.7 is reproduced on a larger scale in Fig. 13.10. Although covering the same region of operation the two graphs represent different quantities measured. In Fig. 13.7 the total number of ions collected is shown along the ordinate. In Fig. 13.10 the **counting rate** is shown along the ordinate. The applied voltage at which the tube begins to register counts is called the **starting voltage** of the counter. It should, however, be noted that pulses are produced at voltages below this value in accordance with the curve of Fig. 13.7, although they are not being recorded by the associated electronic circuits, because these are designed to operate only with pulse heights above a certain minimum value suitable for the Geiger-Müller region of tube operation. This minimum output voltage is usually 0.25 volt, which is 50 to 100 times greater than the typical pulse height in the proportional counter region.

As the applied voltage is increased above the starting voltage, the counting rate increases rapidly until it reaches the **threshold voltage** of the Geiger-Müller region when the count rate begins to level off very markedly. The threshold voltage of a typical Geiger-Müller tube is in the vicinity of 900 volts, and for the next 200 to 300 volts the counting rate remains almost (but not quite) independent of the applied voltage. This extended region of operation is called the **Geiger plateau**. It usually has a slight positive slope which will influence the counting rate somewhat with change of operating potential.

The construction of the Geiger-Müller counter is very similar to that of the proportional counter. The central electrode is usually a finely drawn tungsten wire of about 0.01 cm diameter. The outer electrode can be contained inside a glass envelope or can be on the outside acting in the

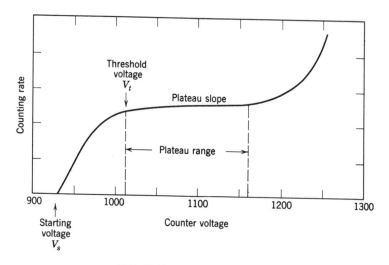

FIG. 13.10. Geiger-Müller region.

dual role of electrode and container (Fig. 13.11). For low counting rates (cosmic ray research), the outer electrode can be in the form of a fine spray of graphite in lacquer which is deposited on the glass envelope. The counting chamber is filled with a gas mixture of some 90% argon and 10% alcohol at a pressure of 10 cm Hg. The applied voltage is usually in the neighborhood of 1000 volts, which is high enough to bring the counter into the Geiger-Müller operating region. The value of the operating potential is not critical if it is chosen somewhere near and a little below the center of the plateau. With proper choice of counter gas and careful attention to the working of both the central wire electrode and the inner surface of the cylindrical electrode, the slight variation in the counting rate with applied operating potential can be reduced to a minimum.

In the Geiger-Müller region the ionization pulse depends on the general characteristics and construction of the tube, such as its physical dimensions, voltage, type of gas employed, and no longer on the initial ionization produced by the primary particle. The latter serves merely to initiate the avalanche and a single ion pair is sufficient to trigger it. As is apparent from Fig. 13.7 the ionization current across the chamber is independent of the primary ionization and does not discriminate among the various types of radiation as is the case for a counter operating in the region of proportionality. The primary ionization that triggers the avalanche can produce a gas amplification of $\sim 10^8$ or more, which results in a pulse height of several volts, even as high as 50 volts in some cases. This output would be strong enough to operate a mechanical counter directly without the need

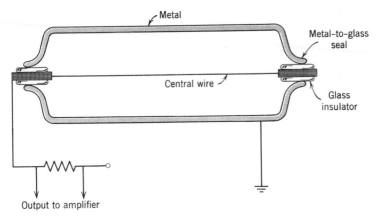

FIG. 13.11. Simple Geiger tube and circuit.

of prior amplification, although normally counters are always fed through an electronic amplifying circuit. Since the voltage pulse is independent of the specific ionization of the original particle entering the tube, the Geiger-Müller counter does not distinguish between the different types of particles or radiation.

The much more rapid spread of the discharge in the Geiger-Müller region as compared to that in the region of proportionality is ascribed to the release of photoelectrons from the surface of the counter electrodes by radiation, that is emitted from gas atoms in the region of the first avalanche which are excited by collisions with very fast electrons. The applied voltage in the Geiger-Müller region is high enough for the electrons to raise some atoms to excited states, followed by the subsequent emission of ultraviolet radiation which causes the avalanche of electrons that extends over the whole length of the tube.

The electrons produced in the avalanche or series of avalanches move with high speed and are collected by the anode wire within the short period of 1 μsec or less, but the positive ions which originate near the central wire move much slower and require about 200 μsec to reach the outer cathode. Their continued presence in the neighborhood of the central anode after the disappearance of the electrons constitutes a positive space charge that effectively reduces the electric field intensity near the wire, so that no further ionization pulses can be detected for as long as the space charge depresses the electric field in the space surrounding the anode to below the threshold value necessary to produce a pulse. As the positive ions move close enough to the surface of the cathode they will detach electrons from the metal surface and so neutralize their charge. This electron capture will, in general, leave the atoms in an excited energy state from which they make a transition to the ground state by emitting the excess energy in the form of radiation, which as a rule contains some photons of high enough energy to liberate photoelectrons from the cathode. These photoelectrons will set up a new avalanche, and the process just described will be repeated so that a single avalanche will give rise to a whole series of ensuing avalanches. The counter would therefore be kept in a continuous state of avalanching, unless provisions were made to suppress this continuous discharge.

The methods used to prevent a continuous series of pulses from taking place in the Geiger-Müller counter are called **quenching**. The inclusion of a **quenching agent** in the counter gas is an almost universally used method; counters that employ an admixture of gas to quench continued discharges are called **self-quenching counters**.

Another method of quenching is the use of an external quenching circuit of resistance-capacitance coupling to the tube with the purpose of reducing the effective counter voltage to below its threshold value until all the ions have been collected.

Polyatomic gases such as alcohol, amyl acetate, or xylene can be used as quenching agents together with a simple gas like argon in various proportions. The function of the organic gas is the suppression of the release of electrons from the counter wall when the positive ion sheath reaches the cathode. In order to be suitable as a quenching agent a gas must have an ionization potential which is smaller than that of the main tube filler; it must have strong and broad absorption bands in the ultraviolet region, and, finally, when it absorbs excitation energy it must dissociate rather than re-emit it in the form of radiation or transfer it to a metallic electron. For an argon-alcohol gas mixture the ionization potential of argon exceeds that of alcohol by 4.4 ev. It is therefore energetically possible for an electron to be transferred from an alcohol molecule to an argon ion in a collision between the two, but no transfer of an electron from an argon molecule to an alcohol ion is possible. This will favor the neutralization of the argon ions and the creation of alcohol ions instead; thus, by the time the ion sheath reaches the cathode after the initial pulse, this will consist almost entirely of alcohol ions as a result of numerous collisions between the two gases. The alcohol ions are neutralized on reaching the cathode and dissociate rather than emit excitation energy which would cause secondary emission of photoelectrons from the cathode. Since each discharge causes the dissociation of a large number of organic molecules, counters employing them have necessarily a limited useful life. Some counters employ halogen gases as quench gases which do not dissociate but re-emit the

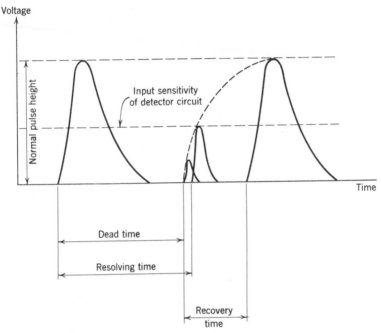

FIG. 13.12. The figure shows pulse amplitude, dead time, resolving time, and recovery time. For an amplifier of high sensitivity, the recovery time and dead time are very nearly equal.

excitation energy in the form of radiation of frequency below the photoelectric threshold frequency. The life of halogen counters is, therefore, not limited to a definite number of counts.

The presence of the positive ion sheath around the central wire makes the counter inoperative for a period of time known as the **dead time**, which is about the time taken by the positive ions to reach the cathode. The counter will require a further short time before it fully recovers; this is called the **recovery time**. They each last about 10^{-4} sec. The Geiger-Müller counter will be able to resolve a new pulse within a period less than the full recovery time, depending on the input sensitivity of the detector circuit, although the pulse will not reach its normal height until the full recovery time has elapsed. This is shown in Fig. 13.12.

Any pulses that arrive in the tube before the elapse of a time interval equal to the resolving time after the previous count will not be recorded by the Geiger-Müller counter. To eliminate counting errors due to this period of uncertainty electronic circuits are employed that introduce an accurately known dead time τ after each count, during which the voltage across the tube is held below the critical voltage necessary to operate the tube. The true count rate N can then be obtained from the observed count rate n by means of the relation

$$N = \frac{n}{1 - n\tau} \tag{13.3}$$

13.8 Scintillation Counters

The scintillation flashes of α-particles incident on copper activated zinc sulfide crystals had been used as the earliest method of detecting individual

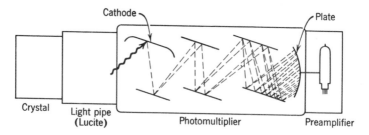

FIG. 13.13. Scintillation counter with photomultiplier.

particles emitted by radioactive materials by Rutherford and his collaborators. The advent of the photomultiplier tube has obviated the need for visual observation of the light flashes and has overcome the limitations inherent in this method of observation, and so has helped to establish the scintillation counter as the foremost method of detection of nuclear radiations in present-day nuclear research.

The schematic diagram of a scintillation counter in Fig. 13.13 shows its two main components: the phosphor crystal in which radiation energy imparted to it is converted into light energy, and the photomultiplier tube in which the light energy is further converted into electrical energy. The photons which are generated in the crystal by the incident nuclear radiation strike the photosensitive cathode and emit secondary electrons. These are collected by a second electrode where they liberate more secondaries, which in turn are focused on to a third electrode. This process is allowed to be repeated in several successive stages by focusing the electrons from one surface to the next.

The collecting electrodes, called **dynodes**, are each at a higher potential than the preceding one and their surfaces are specially treated, so that for each incident electron several secondaries are emitted. For a secondary emission coefficient of five electrons emitted for each incident electron and a total of 10 dynodes, an amplification of 5^{10} or 10^7 is obtained. By a proper cascade arrangement of the dynodes a multiplication factor of 10^{11} can be attained without great difficulty.

There are many organic as well as inorganic materials, generally called phosphors, such as naphthaline and anthracene crystals or sodium and potassium iodide, that can be used as the light sensitive agents. Sodium iodide activated with thallium is usually chosen for γ-ray counting because of its large absorption coefficient, whereas zinc sulfide is suitable for α counting and anthracene for β counting. For slow neutron detection, lithium iodide activated with europium has been found suitable.

The scintillation counter has certain decided advantages over the Geiger-Müller counter, which account for its increased application as a nuclear radiation detector. Its pulse heights are proportional to the energy of the incident radiation so that it can be applied to the investigation of the energy distribution of nuclear radiations. It is the most efficient detection device for γ-radiation, reaching counting efficiencies of 50% without difficulty, compared to the 1% efficiency of a Geiger-Müller counter. With large size and highly transparent phosphors even higher efficiencies can be achieved. Scintillation counters have very short dead times and resolving times (of the order of 10^{-9} sec), permitting very high counting rates to be attained, especially with certain organic phosphors.

In general, inorganic phosphors are more efficient than organic ones, but the pulses from organic crystals, although smaller than from inorganic materials, are much shorter, with higher counting rates thus being possible. Since inorganic crystals have higher densities than the organic kind, it is easier to absorb high-energy radiation completely in these crystals. This is necessary if the full pulse height corresponding to the energy of the particle is to be recorded and compared. Scheelite ($CaWO_4$) with its high density of 6.06 grams/cm^3 is especially suited for the detection of γ-radiation.

In addition to the solid phosphors, liquid phosphors have been developed which are favored when large collecting volumes are required. In order to assure the efficient collection of the light from the phosphors the crystal can be surrounded with aluminum foil to reflect the light back, leaving uncovered only the side in contact with the photocell.

13.9 Cerenkov Radiation and Cerenkov Counters

When charged particles of high speed pass through a transparent dielectric medium, they can give rise to the emission of visible light which generally falls into the blue end of the optical spectrum. The properties of this radiation were first investigated by Mallet and later, more exhaustively, by Cerenkov with whose name they have become associated, being known as **Cerenkov radiation**. The Cerenkov radiation does not manifest the line or band structure which is a common characteristic of ordinary fluorescent radiation but is, instead, continuous over a certain range of the optical spectrum.

The condition that must be fulfilled for a production of Cerenkov radiation to be possible is that the phase velocity of light in the transparent medium must be smaller than the velocity of the charged particle in the medium. If v is the particle velocity, c the velocity of light in vacuum, and n the refractive index of the medium, this condition can be stated as

$$v > \frac{c}{n} \tag{13.4}$$

This relation determines a threshold velocity v_t (or a threshold energy E_t corresponding to v_t) which the charged particle must exceed before Cerenkov radiation can be produced. It is given by

$$v_t = \frac{c}{n} \tag{13.5}$$

For electrons in water the threshold energy is 0.26 Mev, as can readily be verified by using the relativistic relation between particle velocity v, total energy E, and the rest energy E_0 (see Appendix A).

$$\frac{E_0^2}{E^2} = 1 - \frac{v^2}{c^2} \tag{13.6}$$

with $v = c/n = (\frac{3}{4})c$ for water, and $E_0 = 0.51$ Mev for electrons.

The Cerenkov radiation is emitted in a direction making an angle θ with the path of the charged particle such that (Fig. 13.14)

$$\cos \theta = \frac{c}{nv} \tag{13.7}$$

This means that the radiation travels outward from points along the charged particle track such that the wave front lies on the mantle of a right circular cone of half-angle $\pi/2 - \theta$ (Fig. 13.15).

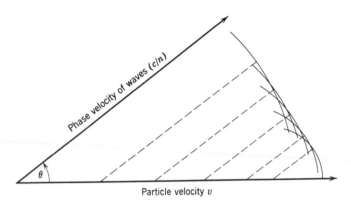

FIG. 13.14. The wave front of the radiation propagates with a speed c/n, the normal to the wave front making an angle θ with the particle track where

$$\theta = \cos^{-1} \frac{c/n}{v}$$

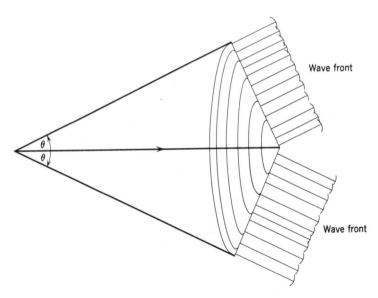

FIG. 13.15. The radiation spreads out in a direction perpendicular to a conical surface as shown in the figure.

Since v cannot exceed c, the largest possible angle $\theta = \theta_{max}$ in a given medium is

$$\theta_{max} = \cos^{-1}\left(\frac{1}{n}\right) \tag{13.8}$$

which for water is about 41°

The characteristic blue glow that surrounds the fuel core in pool type reactors (Fig. 7.9d) or that emanates from "hot" fuel elements that are being stored under water for "cooling" is Cerenkov radiation produced by high speed electrons, mostly Compton electrons passing through the water. As a rule nuclear particles heavier than electrons do not have a high enough energy to give rise to Cerenkov radiation. This follows readily from a simple numerical estimate by means of Eq. 13.6. Since the core or fuel elements are an extended source and the emitted electrons show a distribution over a wide range of energies and angles, the directional properties of the Cerenkov radiation will not be apparent and, as a result, the radiation appears diffuse.

The emission of Cerenkov radiation by high-speed charged particles has been used for their detection by combining the transparent dielectric in which the radiation originates with a photomultiplier tube to form a **Cerenkov counter**. This method has become quite common and a more detailed description can be found in the references cited at the end of this chapter.

Soon after Cerenkov's work was published, a satisfactory explanation of the Cerenkov radiation was first given by Frank and Tamm, who applied the laws of classical electrodynamics to this phenomenon. According to this description a charged particle traversing a dielectric medium causes polarization of the molecules adjacent to its path. The electric charge distribution within these molecules will be distorted as the charged particle attracts the oppositely charged components of a molecule and repels the components of the molecule with charges of the same kind as its own (Fig. 13.16). As the particle moves on, the molecules resume their original position and charge distribution and emit a pulse of electromagnetic radiation in this process of readjustment. In general, the radiation pulses emitted in succession by the molecules along the path of the charged particle destroy each other by interference. However, if the speed of the charged particle in the dielectric medium exceeds the speed of the radiation in the medium the optical interference between the successive wavelets is constructive and can then be observed as a light pulse (Fig. 13.14). The phenomenon is very similar to that of an acoustical shock wave that appears when an object travels through air at supersonic speed or to the bow wave that spreads out from a ship which is traveling at a speed greater than that of the surface waves on the water.

According to the calculations of Frank and Tamm, the light intensity produced by radiation of a given frequency ν (more accurately, within a small spread of frequencies $\Delta \nu$ about ν) is proportional to $1 - c^2/(\nu n)^2$, so that a good medium yielding relatively high light intensity should have a large value of n. If the medium is to be used as a detector of Cerenkov radiation, it should also have a low dispersive power and good transparency. A suitable material for Cerenkov radiation detection is lucite which is commonly used in Cerenkov detectors.

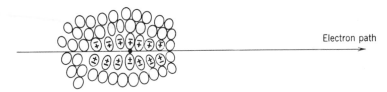

Electron path

FIG. 13.16. The molecules in close proximity to the passing charge (electron) suffer a momentary charge displacement in their internal structure with the positive charges being displaced toward the electron and the negative charges being repelled. As the electron passes out of their vicinity the cluster of disturbed molecules returns to its original distribution, the net result being a pulsation of charge of short duration causing the emission of a pulse of electromagnetic radiation (light).

The energy loss of a charged particle through Cerenkov radiation is negligible as compared to energy loss through ionization and it was, therefore, not considered in connection with energy losses of electrons passing through matter in section 12.3.

PROBLEMS

(1)   What ionization current would result from a beam of 3 Mev deuterons entering an ionization chamber at a rate of 1000 per sec?

(2)   The efficiency of a Geiger counter is the probability of the counter registering the passage of a charged particle. It can be shown that this is given by

$$1 - \exp\left(-\frac{dE}{dx}\frac{l}{I_m}\right)$$

where l is the path length of the particle in the counter and dE/dx and I_m are the same as in Chapter 12.

Calculate the efficiency of a counter filled with argon for high-speed electrons, assuming a value of 350 ev per cm for dE/dx and a path length of 0.2 cm.

(3)   The output capacitance of a counter is 20 $\mu\mu$f. Calculate the voltage pulse height for a current pulse of 10^8 electrons.

(4)   A slow neutron entering a U^{235} fission chamber releases fission fragments of a total energy of 200 Mev. If the capacitance of the collector system is 25 $\mu\mu$f,

calculate the resultant pulse height, assuming an ionization energy of 35 ev/ion pair.

(5) The absorption of a quantum of Cu K_α-radiation (wavelength 1.542 Å) produces a voltage pulse of 2.5 mv. Calculate the pulse produced by the absorption of a quantum of Mo K_α-radiation (wavelength 0.711 Å).

(6) Calculate and compare the total ionization produced by a 2.5 Mev α-particle and a 2.5 Mev β-particle in xenon.

(7) Calculate the counter voltage required to produce a field of 10^5 volts/cm near the central wire of a counter if the radii of the cylindrical electrodes are 0.004 cm and 1.2 cm respectively.

(8) Prove Eq. 13.3 and apply it to calculate the counting error for a dead time of 3×10^{-4} sec at an output rate of 60 counts/sec.

(9) A proportional counter has a gas multiplication factor of 1000. Estimate the number of mean free paths in which this multiplication takes place and calculate the distance from the central wire within which the multiplication occurs, assuming a mean free path of 2×10^{-4} cm for the electrons in the gas.

(10) A Geiger-Müller counter with a cathode radius of 1 cm and an anode wire radius of 0.005 cm contains argon at atmospheric pressure. Assuming a mean free path of 10^{-4} cm for the electrons in the tube, calculate the maximum distance from the wire at which it would be possible for an electron to ionize an argon atom (ionization potential 15.7 volts) for an applied counter voltage of 900 volts.

(11) A Geiger-Müller counter has a plateau slope of 3% per 100 volts. If the operating point is at 1100 volts, what is the maximum permissible voltage fluctuation if the counting is not to be affected by more than $\frac{1}{10}$%?

BIBLIOGRAPHY

Birks, J. B.: *Scintillation Counters*, McGraw-Hill, 1953.

Bleuler, E., and G. J. Goldsmith: *Experimental Nucleonics*, Rinehart, 1952.

Brown, C.: "Theory and Operation of Geiger Counters," *Nucleonics*, **3**, Nos. 1, 2, 3 (January, February, March 1945).

Curran, S. C.: *Luminescence and the Scintillation Counter*, Academic Press, 1953.

Engstrom, R. W., and J. L. Weaver: "Are Plateaus Significant in Scintillation Counting?," *Nucleonics*, **17**, No. 2 (February 1959).

Fretter, W. B.: *Introduction to Experimental Physics*, Prentice-Hall, 1954.

Friedlander, G. and J. W. Kennedy: *Nuclear and Radiochemistry*, Wiley, 1955.

Hine, G. J., and G. L. Brownell: *Radiation Dosimetry*, Academic Press, 1956.

Hoag, J. B., and S. A. Korff: *Electron and Nuclear Physics*, van Nostrand, 1948.

Jelly, J. V.: "Cerenkov Radiation," *Progress of Nucl. Phys.*, 3 (1953).

Jelly, J. V.: *Cerenkov Radiation and its Applications*, Pergamon, 1958.

Jordan, W. H., and B. R. Bell: "Scintillation Counters," *Nucleonics*, **5**, No. 4 (April 1947).

Korff, S. A.: *Electron and Nuclear Counters*, van Nostrand, 1955.

Lapp, R. E., and H. L. Andrews: *Nuclear Radiation Physics*, Prentice-Hall, 1954.

Lapsley, A. C.: "Neutron and Gamma Measurements for in-Pile Monitoring," *Nucleonics*, **16**, No. 2 (February 1958).

Marshall, J: "Cerenkov Counters," *Ann. Rev. Nucl. Sci.*, vol. 4 (1954).

McKenzie, J. M.: "Making Fission Counters for Neutron Monitoring," *Nucleonics*, **17,** No. 1 (January 1959).

Overman, R. T., and H. M. Clarke: *Radioisotope Techniques*, McGraw-Hill, 1960.

Pollard, E. C., and W. L. Davidson: *Applied Nuclear Physics*, Wiley, 1951.

Price, W. J.: *Nuclear Radiation Detection*, McGraw-Hill, 1958.

Second Geneva Conference on the Peaceful Uses of Atomic Energy—1958:

P/1465: Sharpe, J., and E. E. Thomson: "Photomultiplier Tubes and Scintillation Counters," vol. 14, 311.

Segré, E. (Ed.): *Experimental Nuclear Physics*, vol. I, Wiley, 1953.

Sharpe, J.: *Nuclear Radiation Detectors*, Wiley, 1955.

Swank, R. K.: "Characteristics of Scintillators," *Ann. Rev. Nucl. Sci.*, **4** (1954).

Trice, J. B.: "Miniature Fission Chamber," *Nucleonics*, **16,** No. 7 (July 1958).

Washtell, C. C.: *Introduction to Radiation Counters and Detectors*, Newnes, 1958.

Wilkinson, D. H.: *Ionization Chambers and Counters*, Cambridge Univ. Press, 1950.

Wolfgang, R., and C. F. Mackay: "New Proportional Counters for Gases," *Nucleonics*, **16,** No. 10 (October 1958).

"Radiation," *Scientific American*, September 1959.

"Scintillation Counting Today," *Nucleonics*, **12,** No. 3 (March 1954).

"Special Report on Scintillation Counting," *Nucleonics*, **16,** No. 6 (June 1958).

Radiation Protection and Health Physics

14.1 Introduction

Nuclear reactors are sources of very intense radiations of various types which can cause serious injuries to personnel in the vicinity of the reactor unless proper methods of shielding are adopted for their protection. The function of the reactor shield is to absorb most of the radiation emanating from the reactor and thus to reduce its intensity to a level where it no longer presents a health hazard and where it does not seriously interfere with the proper functioning of electrical control and experimentation facilities which are installed in close proximity to the reactor.

14.2 Radiation Damage

Most materials undergo physical or structural changes when they are subjected to high intensity nuclear radiation. The most pronounced effects of this nature occur with organic materials such as biological tissue where heavy irradiation can bring about permanent chemical and structural changes. The tissue cells can either be completely destroyed or can become so severely damaged that their normal functioning is brought to an end.

We saw in the two preceding chapters that nuclear radiations can cause ionization and electronic excitation of the constituent atoms or molecules with which they interact. Although the exact nature of the radiation effects on biological tissue is still not known, it is clear, however, that the cell damage is caused by the disruption of chemical bonds of the complex molecules that make up the cell tissue. Damage can also be caused in inorganic as well as in organic matter by the actual displacement of struck atoms from their normal positions in the lattice structure of the material to so-called **interstitial** positions. Furthermore, nuclear radiation can cause the transmutation of indigenous atomic nuclei, leading to the formation of nuclei which are foreign to the organic tissue and which may themselves be radioactive.

Healthy human tissue has a high recuperative power, so that if the extent of damage to individual cells and the total number of destructions of entire cells are not excessive, permanent damage to the body can be avoided. The direct interaction between nuclear radiation and a **cell nucleus**, however, leads almost always to the total destruction of the cell. Since the cell nucleus occupies only a very small fraction of the cell volume, this type of cell damage will be much less frequent than damage to the outer portions of the tissue cells.

The permissible amount of radiation damage to human tissue that will not eventually lead to permanent injury is still a matter of uncertainty. It no doubt varies from one individual to another just as the differences among individuals vary in their resistance to other forms of health hazards. The general trend during the years since radiation damage has been recognized as a serious health hazard has been to reduce successively the permissible limits of radiation exposure.

14.3 Internal Irradiation Damage

Exposure to radiation can come about through external irradiation or through internal irradiation after radioactive materials have entered the body by inhalation or by ingestion. Internal irradiation can be especially harmful because of the proximity of the radioactive emitter to vital organs of the human body which are protected to some extent against external irradiation by layers of skin and tissues, and because of the possible protracted and concentrated irradiation of select regions of the body by the ingested material. The duration of the irradiation from internal sources of radiation depends entirely on the natural life of the radioactive material and on the biological process of natural elimination; thus it is difficult to arrest and control radiation damage in any other way once the radioactive material has entered the body. The danger of radiation damage is enhanced because certain organs seem to be particularly favored as host tissue by certain radioactive isotopes which concentrate selectively in them. It is well known, for example, that Ra^{226}, Pu^{239}, and Sr^{90} favor bone tissue, or I^{131}, the thyroid gland from which they are only very slowly eliminated. Bone marrow and the gastro-intestinal and reproductive organs are especially radio-sensitive tissues, with kidneys, liver, lungs, and the skin somewhat less sensitive. The muscles, fully grown bone, and the nerve cells are much more resistant to radiation exposure than the former two groups.

14.4   Acute and Chronic Exposure

Radiation damage is much more severe in cases of **acute exposure**, which is the exposure to a large dose of radiation within a relatively short time interval, than in cases of **chronic exposure**, where the exposure is stretched over longer periods of time, although the total amount of radiation received may be the same in both cases. This seems to indicate that the human body is able to recuperate and repair radiation damage that is kept within certain limits and below a certain **threshold**. This fact is the basis of health protection provisions that are currently being employed for personnel who have to work with radioactive materials and with installations that give rise to nuclear radiations. As it is not possible to exclude radiation exposures completely and absolutely, all protection methods aim at reducing radiation doses received to below the threshold amount that would induce permanent injury. There is, however, as yet no certainty that even with these limited exposures there may not build up in the exposed organism cumulatively harmful effects which may not appear until a number of years have elapsed. Such cumulative and deleterious effects are believed to be very likely with the genetic cells where harmful effects due to radiation exposure may reveal themselves in future generations.

14.5   Radiation Intensity

Before meaningful safety levels for permissible amounts of irradiation can be fixed, it is necessary to adopt suitable units of radiation. Of the many units that have been proposed a few have found sufficiently widespread acceptance to warrant their adoption as standards of common usage. We must distinguish between units of radiation and units of energy dissipation or energy absorption.

Units of radiation are the **intensity** of radiation and the **quantity** of radiation The intensity of radiation is the amount of radiation energy that passes through unit area perpendicular to the radiation in unit time, and the quantity of radiation is the time integral of the intensity.

If ϕ particles or photons, each carrying an amount of energy E, cross unit area per unit time, then

$$\text{Intensity } I = \phi E \text{ (ergs/cm}^2 \text{ sec)} \qquad (14.1)$$

$$\text{Quantity } Q = \int \phi E \, dt \text{ (ergs/cm}^2) \qquad (14.2)$$

The intensity I is the product of the flux and the energy, also called the energy flux.

14.6   Radiation Units and Radiation Dosage

If μ_e is the **linear energy absorption coefficient**, the rate R at which energy is absorbed per cubic centimeter of material from the incident radiation is by 4.28

$$R = \mu_e \phi E \qquad\qquad (14.3)$$

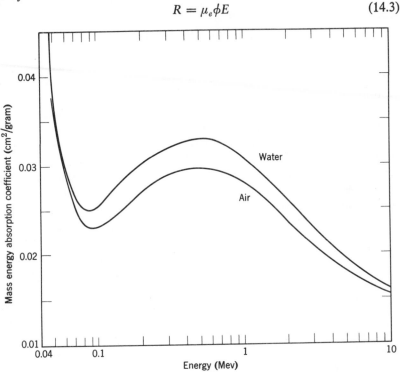

FIG. 14.1. Mass energy absorption coefficients of air and water for γ-radiation.

since, by 12.22, μ_e is the macroscopic cross section for this process. The energy absorption coefficient depends on the absorber and varies with the energy of the radiation. For the absorption of γ-radiation in air and for γ-energies lying between 0.1 Mev and 3 Mev the value of μ_e is about 3.5×10^{-5} cm^{-1}. Values of the **energy mass absorption coefficient** μ_e/ρ for air and water are shown in Fig. 14.1.

The energy absorption coefficients are smaller than the total absorption coefficients of Chapter 12 because the latter include also the attenuation contributed by scattering losses from the incident radiation.

It follows from Eq. 14.3 that, since μ_e is not the same for all energies, the rate of energy absorption in a given material depends jointly on the radiation intensity I and on the absorption coefficient μ_e. Thus, the same intensity of radiations of different energies will, in general, be absorbed at different rates.

The amount of radiation dissipated in or absorbed by a specified mass or volume of material is commonly described as a **dose** of radiation. Since the absorption of radiation in matter depends not only on the quantity of incident radiation but through μ_e also on the energy of the incident radiation, the term dose should be reserved strictly to describe the radiation absorption only.

The prevalent unit of dose (or dosage) which is derived from one that was originally set up for X-rays is the **roentgen** (r). It is defined as that quantity of X- or γ-radiation which, on passing through dry air at STP, will liberate a number of secondary particles in 1 cm³ of air which will produce in air ions carrying 1 esu of electricity of either sign.

The unit **dosage rate** which is derived from this is the roentgen per second (r/sec) with an absorption equivalent to that of 1 r/sec.

It should be noted that the r is a unit for X- and γ-radiation only, and units corresponding to it have been established for other radiations. For γ-radiation of energy in excess of $\sim$3 Mev the pair-creation process becomes significant, so that a large portion of the radiation energy is used up in the creation of electron restmass energy and, consequently, is not available for ion production. It is therefore impractical to use the r unit for γ-radiation above this energy. Furthermore, it should be understood that the restriction in the definition to a volume of 1 cm³ applies only to the secondary particles produced by the radiation. The ionization caused by the secondary particles, however, is not so restricted, but can take place anywhere in the surrounding space. The ionization produced by the radiation is a reliable indication of its biological effectiveness since the biological damage caused by radiation has been found to depend on the energy liberated in the tissue.

Example 14.1. Calculate the energy transfer in air that corresponds to 1 r.

Since a singly charged ion carries a charge of 4.80×10^{-10} esu, the number of ion pairs carrying a total combined charge of 1 esu is

$$\frac{1}{4.80 \times 10^{-10}} = 2.083 \times 10^9 \text{ ion pairs}$$

Taking the energy required to create 1 ion pair in air as 35 ev, we have for the energy transfer per roentgen in air

$2.083 \times 10^9 \times 35 \text{ ev/cm}^3 = 7.29 \times 10^{10} \text{ ev/cm}^3$

$$= (7.29 \times 10^{10})(1.6 \times 10^{-12}) \text{ erg/cm}^3 = 0.1166 \text{ erg/cm}^3$$

$$= \frac{0.1166 \text{ (erg/cm}^3)}{0.001293 \text{ (gram/cm}^3)} = 90 \text{ erg/gram}$$

The energy transfer per roentgen in materials other than air will depend on the absorption properties of the material and, in general, will be different for different materials. Nevertheless, the roentgen unit is uniquely determined in terms of the ionizing properties of dry air and 1 r is the same for all materials, although the energy abstraction from the radiation may vary for different materials. Since the mass absorption coefficients for X-radiation in air and in biological tissue, which consists mainly of water, are about the same (within the energy range of interest), Fig. 14.1, the amount of energy transferred from 1 r of X-radiation to air will be nearly the same as that transferred to the same mass of tissue. In fact, the energy deposited in tissue by 1 r is 100 ergs/gram, as compared to 90 ergs per gram for air. The amount of energy absorbed in tissue was the basis for a now obsolete unit of dose, which had been extended to apply to all types of radiation. That unit was the **roentgen equivalent physical** (rep), which was defined as that quantity of ionizing radiation (including neutrons) which led to the transfer in tissue of an amount of energy of 100 ergs/gram.†

This unit has now been superseded by the international unit of absorbed dose, called the **rad**, which is the amount of radiation that deposits 100 ergs/gram in any material. For practical purposes of radiation protection, we can use 1 rad as equal to 1 rep in soft tissue.

14.7 Relative Biological Effectiveness (rbe)

Besides depending on the total amount of ionization, it is found that the radiation damage is determined also to a marked degree by the specific ionization of the incident radiation. For equal doses, the more heavily ionizing radiations like α-particles, slow protons, and fission fragments are more damaging than β-particles and γ-radiation which cause a more diffuse ionization. To take account of the differing biological effectiveness of various radiations, we use the **relative biological effectiveness** (rbe) which is defined by

$$\text{rbe} = \frac{\text{absorbed dose (erg/gram) of X-radiation}}{\text{absorbed dose (erg/gram) of radiation considered}} \quad (14.4)$$

with reference to a particular type of damage. The energy of the X-radiation used here as the standard of comparison is usually taken as 250 kev.

Another unit of radiation dose which takes into consideration the different degress of biological effectiveness of various radiations is the **roentgen equivalent man** (rem). The rem is defined as that dose of any

† Based on the more recent value of 35 ev/ion pair the figure given in the text results, compared to a lower value used in the original definition.

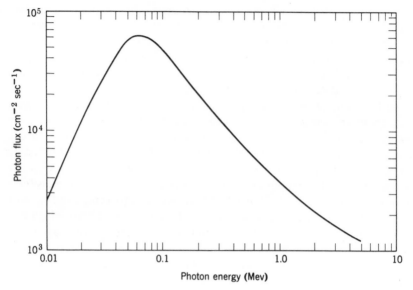

FIG. 14.2a. Photon flux for different photon energies to give the equivalent exposure of 0.3 rem per 40 hr week.

ionizing radiation which is biologically equivalent to the dose of 1 r of X- or γ-radiation. Evidently, we have the relation

$$\text{Dose in rem} = \text{rbe} \times \text{dose in rads} \qquad (14.5)$$

The rbe of various types of radiation is given in Table 14.1.

TABLE 14.1

Radiation	rbe
γ-radiation	1
β-particles	1
Slow neutrons	3 to 5
Fast neutrons	10
Protons	10
α-particles	10 to 20

The **maximum permissible exposure (mpe)** or **maximum permissible level (mpl)** is that dose of whole body exposure to external radiation extending over many years which will not cause any permanently injurious effects.

A corresponding limit on the permissible ingestion is called the **maximum permissible concentration**.

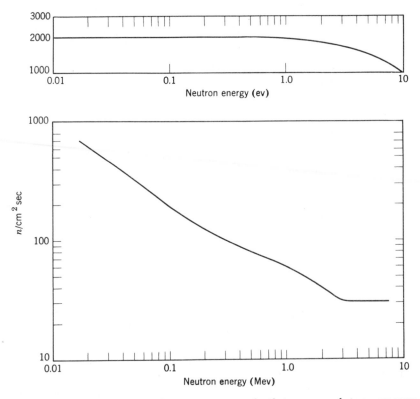

FIG. I4.2b. Neutron flux at different neutron energies that corresponds to an exposure of 0.3 rem per 40 hr week.

The total dose received during a person's lifetime should not exceed 200 rem and the weekly dose should be kept below 0.3 rem.

The radiation flux corresponding to an exposure limit of 0.3 rem per week (40 hr) is shown in Table 14.2 and Fig. 14.2a and 14.2b for γ-radiation and for neutrons.

Example 14.2. Calculate the photon flux rate corresponding to a dosage rate of 1 r/sec.

$$1 \text{ r/sec} = 7.29 \times 10^{10} \text{ ev/cm}^3 \text{ sec}$$

and

$$R = \mu_e \phi E$$

Therefore

$$\mu_e \phi E = 7.29 \times 10^{10} \text{ ev/cm}^3 \text{ sec}$$

Therefore

$$\phi = \frac{7.29 \times 10^{10}}{\mu_e E} \text{ photons/cm}^2 \text{ sec}$$

For a 1 Mev γ-radiation, $\mu_e = 3.5 \times 10^{-5}$ cm^{-1}, so that in this case

$$\phi = \frac{7.29 \times 10^{10}}{3.5 \times 10^{-5}} \times 10^6 = 2.1 \times 10^9 \text{ photons/cm}^3 \text{ sec}$$

TABLE 14.2

Energy	Neutrons (n/cm^2 sec)	γ-radiation (photons/cm^2 sec)
0.025 ev	2000	
1.0 ev	2000	
10 ev	1000	
0.05 Mev	350	6×10^4
0.1 Mev	200	4.6×10^4
0.5 Mev	80	7×10^3
1.0 Mev	60	3.8×10^3
2.0 Mev	40	2.2×10^3
3.0 Mev	30	1.7×10^3
4.0 Mev	30	1.4×10^3
5.0 Mev	30	1.2×10^3

14.8   Radiation from a Point Source

If the radiation emanates from a point source which emits the radiation isotropically, the dosage received at a point in space will also depend on its distance from the point source. If we ignore for the moment the small attenuation of radiation in air, we can say that the intensity of radiation varies as the inverse square of the distance from the source. If the source strength is S particles or photons per second per square centimeter, the number of particles ϕ (or photons) passing through unit area at a distance R from the source will be obtained by dividing the source strength S by the area of a sphere of radius R:

$$\phi = \frac{S}{4\pi R^2} \tag{14.6}$$

The energy flux or radiation intensity as defined by 14.1 will then be

$$I = \phi E = \frac{SE}{4\pi R^2} \tag{14.7}$$

This rapid decrease of the radiation intensity with distance from the source affords a simple and convenient first-line protection against unnecessary radiation exposure which is employed by trained scientific workers who have to handle radioactive materials. Such materials should always be handled with long tongs held at arms length in order to derive the full benefit of protection from the inverse square attenuation of the radiation intensity. This additional geometrical factor of radiation protection is absent in cases of exposure to collimated or narrow beams of radiation.

A unit which is often used to express the strength of a radiation source is the **roentgen per hour at 1 meter** (rhm).

Example 14.3. Calculate the strength in rhm of a 1 curie source of Co^{60} which emits two photons of 1.17 Mev and 1.33 Mev, respectively, per β-disintegration, assuming a value of 3.5×10^{-5} cm^{-1} for the linear absorption coefficient in air.

By 14.7,

$$I = \frac{3.7 \times 10^{10} \text{ sec}^{-1} (1.17 + 1.33) \text{ Mev}}{4 \times 3.14 \times 10^4 \text{ cm}^2}$$

$$= 0.736 \times 10^6 \text{ Mev/cm}^2 \text{ sec}$$

The absorption rate R is given by 14.3

$$R = \mu_e I$$

$$= (3.5 \times 10^{-5} \text{ cm}^{-1}) \times (0.736 \times 10^6 \text{ Mev/cm}^2 \text{ sec})$$

$$= 25.8 \text{ Mev/cm}^3 \text{ sec}$$

Therefore,   dosage rate $= \dfrac{R}{7.29 \times 10^4 \text{ Mev/cm}^3 \text{ sec/r}}$

$$= \frac{25.8}{7.29 \times 10^4} \text{ r/sec} = 3.54 \times 10^{-4} \text{ r/sec}$$

$$= 3.54 \times 10^{-4} \times 3600 \text{ r/hr} = 1.27 \text{ r/hr}$$

The dosage rate at 1 meter is, therefore, 1.27 rhm.

14.9   Neutron Irradiation Damage

The biological damage caused by neutron irradiation is in the main a result of elastic neutron-proton collisions which lead to the production of high-energy protons. The rate at which energy is absorbed from the neutron radiation is again given by 14.3 with Σ_{el} replacing the absorption coefficient.

$$R = \Sigma_{el} \phi \, \Delta E \qquad\qquad (14.8)$$

The energy ΔE here is not the neutron energy but the average energy loss by a neutron per collision with a proton. We saw in Chapter 6 that this average energy transfer from the neutron to the proton is $\frac{1}{2}E$. We can, therefore, write the rate of energy transfer from the neutrons to the tissue, replacing also the macroscopic cross section by $N_0\sigma_{el}$ as

$$R = N_0\sigma_{el}\phi\left(\frac{E}{2}\right) \tag{14.9}$$

For high-energy neutrons the elastic scattering n-p cross section is roughly inversely proportional to the neutron energy (a good approximation is $\sigma_{el} = \dfrac{10.97}{E + 1.66}$, where E is in Mev and σ_{el} in barns), so that $\sigma_{el}E$ remains fairly constant and the rate of energy transfer can be assumed to be approximately constant and independent of the neutron energy. An estimate for the permissible neutron flux based on a maximum permissible level of 7.5 millir/hr leads to a maximum permissible fast neutron flux of ~60 neutrons/cm² sec (Table 14.2).

For slow neutrons the maximum permissible flux at present is taken to be 2000 neutrons/cm² sec (Table 14.2). The predominant cause of biological damage here is the (n, p) reaction with N^{14} leading to the production of heavily ionizing protons.

14.10   Radiation Shielding and Build-Up Factor

When we considered the attenuation of a collimated beam of γ-radiation passing through matter, we used the total linear absorption coefficient as given by 12.22 and 12.23, since a scattering collision (Compton scattering) between a photon and an electron reduced the beam intensity just as effectively as an absorption collision. On this basis the exponential law of attenuation 12.21 was derived. This law is valid only within the limits of the assumption made in its derivation, namely, that multiple scattering does not contribute to the beam intensity and that the radiation intensity after penetrating a thickness x in the material as given by 12.21 is that of the virgin flux, with no contribution from multiply scattered portions of the original beam which may have rejoined the original beam direction.

This assumption leads to good agreement with experiment also in cases of "poor geometry" (i.e., broad and not well-collimated beams) if the absorber is sufficiently thin. For thick absorbers as represented by the shielding around nuclear reactors the effect of multiple scattering can no longer be ignored. The probability that some of the scattered radiation may, after having undergone several successive scattering collisions, again rejoin the original beam direction is no longer negligible. Experimental results show that intensities calculated on the basis of 12.21 fall significantly below the measured intensities. This difference between the beam intensity as calculated on the basis of the exponential attenuation and the measured intensity is described by the **build-up factor**, B. It is defined as the ratio of the radiation intensity as obtained from a measurement of the total intensity to the intensity as calculated on the basis of the "uncollided virgin flux," which is the flux without the contribution from scattered radiation

$$B \equiv \frac{\phi}{\phi_0 \exp(-\mu x)} \qquad (14.10)$$

As was seen in Chapter 12 the Compton scattering leads only to a partial transfer of energy from the radiation to the absorber, with part of the radiation energy reappearing as a scattered photon of reduced energy. The γ-radiation emitted by a nuclear reactor consists largely of radiation that lies in the 3 Mev region where the Compton scattering is the predominating attenuation process for the heavy elements that are usually employed as reactor shielding material. Since all materials, with the exception of hydrogen, contain roughly the same number of electrons per unit mass ($\sim 3 \times 10^{23}$ electrons/gram) the attenuation of γ-radiation in the energy region where Compton scattering is predominant (1.5 to 3 Mev) is achieved with equal effectiveness with equal masses of all materials. This is seen from an inspection of Fig. 14.3 where the mass absorption coefficient of various materials is plotted against the energy of the γ-radiation.

If we consider now the radiation flux (or intensity) at a distance R from a point source of strength S and take account also of the absorption in the intervening medium (which may be air, water, or any other shielding material), we must modify expressions 14.6 and 14.7 to include also the exponential attenuation factor from 12.21. We then get for the uncollided energy flux, I_0

$$I_0 = \frac{SE}{4\pi R^2} \exp(-\mu_l R) \qquad (14.11)$$

Because of contributions from multiple scattering the experimentally measured flux will be greater by a factor B, where B is the build-up factor, so that we have for the experimental flux I

$$I = BI_0 = B \exp(-\mu_l R)\frac{SE}{4\pi R^2} \qquad (14.11a)$$

The dosage rate is, therefore, correspondingly greater.

The value of B will depend on the radiation energy, on the absorption coefficient and thickness of absorber, as well as on the detector used in the experiment.

We can approach the problem of correcting for the contribution from multiple scattering to the beam intensity of γ-radiation by using, instead of 12.23,

$$\mu_l = \mu_{\text{photo}} + \mu_{pp} + \mu_{\text{Compton}} \qquad (12.23)$$

an effective linear absorption coefficient μ_a, given by†

$$\mu_a = \mu_l - C\mu_c \qquad (14.12)$$

where C is less than unity and represents the fraction of γ-radiation energy

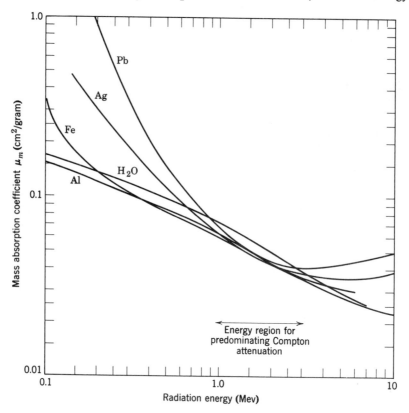

FIG. 14.3. The mass absorption coefficients as a function of different γ-radiation energies for several materials.

that is scattered back into the beam. The fraction of transmitted energy for $C = 1$ and $C = 0$ as well as for $0 < C < 1$ is shown in Fig 14.4.

Using μ_a, instead of μ_l, in 14.11, we get for the energy flux

$$I = \frac{SE}{4\pi R^2} \exp\left(-\mu_a R\right) \qquad (14.13)$$

† Writing μ_{Compton} in the abbreviated form μ_c

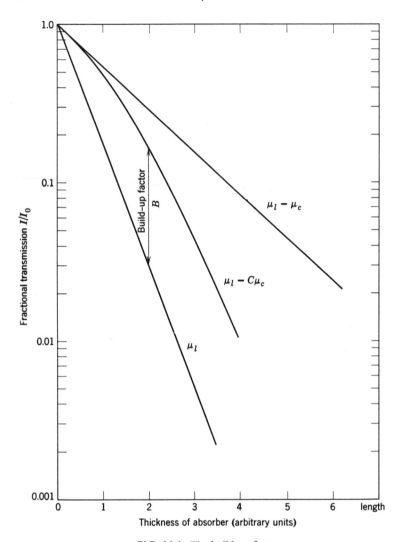

FIG. 14.4. The build-up factor.

Dividing this by the virgin flux, we have by 14.10 and 14.11a

$$\frac{I}{I_0} = B = \exp - (\mu_a - \mu_l)R = \exp(CR\mu_l) \qquad (14.14)$$

This shows that the build-up factor increases rapidly with the thickness R of absorber. The energy build-up factor for a point source in water as a function of $\mu_l R$ is shown in Fig. 14.5.

By writing the energy absorption coefficient as defined by 12.33*b* in the form

$$\mu_e = \mu_{ph} + \mu_{pp} + \mu_C - (1-f)\mu_C = \mu_l - (1-f)\mu_C \quad (14.14a)$$

we see that by identifying the true absorption coefficient μ_a with the energy absorption coefficient μ_e, we obtain by comparing 14.14*a* with 14.12, the relation

$$(1-f)\mu_C = C\mu_l \quad (14.14b)$$

In the energy region where Compton scattering predominates we can set $\mu_l \simeq \mu_C$, and then write 14.14*b* in the simplified form

$$C = 1 - f \quad (14.14c)$$

The value of f as a function of radiation energy E is shown in Fig. 12.14. For distances close to the source we can write 14.14 by expanding $B(R)$ and neglecting higher powers,

$$B(R) \doteq 1 + CR\mu_l \quad (14.15)$$

If C is taken to be of the order of one, the last result can be further simplified to

$$B(R) \doteq 1 + R\mu_l \quad (14.16)$$

where $B(R)$ is referred to as the **linear build-up factor**.

This simplified result for the build-up factor is often used in preliminary calculations. It is of limited validity and gives reliable results for restricted values of Z of the absorber for certain energy ranges only.

The calculations outlined here are satisfactory only for γ-radiation, since sufficient information is still lacking for neutrons to permit a reliable calculation of the build-up factor for neutrons.

Furthermore, the idea of a single radiation source is a great over-simplification, since in nuclear reactors we have to deal with extended radiation sources, which means, in effect, that the point sources must be integrated over the entire reactor volume.

To sum up the discussion, we can say that the dangers from external irradiation in the neighborhood of nuclear reactors come primarily from the fast neutrons and energetic γ-radiation. The methods of protection against radiation damage through overexposure are to reduce and limit the exposure times of personnel to a minimum, to make use of the inverse square law of attenuation by using remote control handling devices whenever possible and necessary, and to employ sufficient shielding. Any shield that reduces the neutron and γ-radiation intensities below the danger level does so automatically and even more effectively for any other particles or radiations that might escape from the reactor assembly.

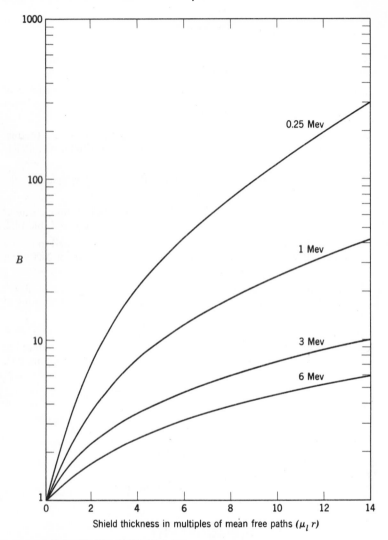

FIG. 14.5. Energy build-up factor for water (isotropic point source).

A good reactor shield should consist of a mixture of hydrogen and other light nuclei and of nuclei of fairly high atomic number which together will slow down fast neutrons by elastic and inelastic collisions and act as an efficient absorber for γ-radiation. These conditions are fulfilled with concrete cement, which has been used extensively in the shielding of stationary reactors.

PROBLEMS

(1)   Calculate the radiation flux intensity at a distance of 60 cm from a point source of a 2 Mev γ-radiation that emits 10^{10} photons per sec.

(2)   Calculate the dosage rate in roentgen per hour due to the source of Problem 1 at the given distance, assuming a value of 3×10^{-5} for the linear energy absorption coefficient.

(3)   How long could an experimenter be exposed continuously to a thermal neutron flux of 10^8 neutrons/cm^2 sec before reaching the maximum permissible exposure of 0.3 rem per week?

(4)   Assuming human soft tissue to be equivalent to water, calculate the energy absorption in tissue which corresponds to 1 r.

(5)   Estimate the maximum permissible fast neutron flux if a dosage rate of 7.5 mr/hr is not to be exceeded, and compare with the value given in Table 14.2.

(6)   What thickness of boron of density 2.34 grams/cm^3 is required to reduce a thermal neutron flux of 10^{13} n/cm^2 sec to the maximum safe level of 2000 n per cm^2 per sec?

(7)   Calculate the safe working distance from a 1 gram source of Ra^{226}, assuming each disintegration to give rise, on the average, to 2.29 photons of energy 0.782 Mev.

(8)   A 2 millicurie source of Co^{60} is contained in a spherical lead container of internal radius 5 cm. If the γ-radiation dose outside the container is reduced to one-fifth the maximum permissible level, calculate the thickness of the container, assuming an emission of 2 photons per γ-disintegration of combined energy 2.5 Mev.

(9)   Show that for a spherical container of internal and external radii r and R, respectively, the fractional transmission $I(R)/I(r)$ can be approximated by

$$\frac{I(R)}{I(r)} = (1 + \mu_l t)\left(\frac{r^2}{R^2}\right) \exp(-\mu_l t)$$

where $t = R - r$.

Repeat the calculation in Problem 8, using this expression.

BIBLIOGRAPHY

Barnes, D. E., and D. Taylor: *Radiation Hazards and Protection*, Newnes, 1958.
Etherington, H. (Ed.): *Nuclear Reactor Handbook*, McGraw-Hill, 1958.
Evans, D. H.: *The Atomic Nucleus*, McGraw-Hill, 1955.
Glasstone, S.: *Principles of Nuclear Reactor Engineering*, van Nostrand, 1955.
Goldstein, H.: *Fundamental Aspects of Reactor Shielding*, Addison-Wesley, 1959.
Harwood, J. J. (Ed.): *The Effects of Radiation on Materials*, Reinhold, 1958.
Moyer, B. J.: *Ann. Rev. Nucl. Sci.*, **8** (1958).
Ohlinger, L. A.: "Shielding from Nuclear Radiations," *Nucleonics*, **5**, No. 4 (April 1947).

Price, B. T., C. C. Horton, and K. T. Spinney: *Radiation Shielding*, Pergamon, 1957.

Ter-Pogossian, M., et al.: "Comparison of Air and Tissue Doses for Radium Gamma Rays," *Nucleonics*, **5**, No. 4 (April 1947).

The Biological Effects of Atomic Radiations, Summary Reports by the National Academy of Sciences, 1957.

U. S. Department of Commerce, National Bureau of Standards Handbooks:

No. 51: *Radiological Monitoring Methods and Instruments.*

No. 52: *Maximum Permissible Concentrations in Air and Water.*

No. 59: *Permissible Dose from External Sources of Ionizing Radiation.*

No. 63: *Protection Against Neutron Radiation up to 30 Mev.*

Van Dilla, M. A., and G. J. Hine: "Gamma Ray Diffusion Experiments in Water," *Nucleonics*, **10**, No. 7 (July 1952).

White, G. N.: *Principles of Radiation Dosimetry*, Wiley, 1959.

Appendix A

A.I Relativistic Expressions for Mass, Momentum, and Energy

If m_0 is the rest mass of a particle and E_0 its rest energy, the Einstein mass energy relation establishes that

$$E_0 = m_0 c^2 \qquad (A.1)$$

If the particle is moving with velocity v, its mass and energy are increased by the factor $(1 - \beta^2)^{-\frac{1}{2}}$, where $\beta = v/c$, so that

$$m = m_0(1 - \beta^2)^{-\frac{1}{2}} \qquad (A.2)$$

and

$$E = mc^2 = m_0 c^2 (1 - \beta^2)^{-\frac{1}{2}} \qquad (A.3)$$

The kinetic energy E_K of the particle is given by the difference between its energy E and its rest mass energy E_0. Hence

$$
\begin{aligned}
E_K &= E - E_0 \\
&= mc^2 - m_0 c^2 \\
&= (m - m_0)c^2 \\
&= m_0 c^2 [(1 - \beta^2)^{-\frac{1}{2}} - 1]
\end{aligned}
\qquad (A.4)
$$

The momentum p of the mass m is

$$
\begin{aligned}
p &= mv \\
&= m_0 v (1 - \beta^2)^{-\frac{1}{2}} \\
&= m_0 c \beta (1 - \beta^2)^{-\frac{1}{2}}
\end{aligned}
\qquad (A.5)
$$

The relativistic relation between p and E can be derived from this expression by evaluating $p^2 c^2$

$$p^2 c^2 = m_0^2 \beta^2 c^4$$

$$E_0^2 = m_0^2 c^2$$

adding

$$
\begin{aligned}
p^2 c^2 + E_0^2 &= m_0^2 c^4 \left(1 + \frac{\beta^2}{1 - \beta^2} \right) \\
&= m_0^2 c^4 (1 - \beta^2)^{-1} \\
&= E^2
\end{aligned}
\qquad (A.6)
$$

For $v \ll c$, $m \doteq m_0$ and $E \doteq E_0$, and Eq. A.6 reduces to the classical relation as follows:

$$p^2c^2 = E^2 - E_0{}^2 = (E + E_0)(E - E_0)$$
$$\doteq 2EE_K$$

Therefore
$$E_K = \frac{p^2c^2}{2E}$$

$$= \frac{p^2c^2}{2mc^2}$$

$$= \frac{p^2}{2m} \tag{A.7}$$

A.2   The de Broglie Relations

For photons,
$$E = h\nu = mc^2$$
$$p = mc$$

and therefore
$$\frac{E}{p} = c$$

or
$$p = \frac{E}{c} = \frac{h\nu}{c}$$

$$= \frac{h}{\lambda} \tag{A.8}$$

This is the de Broglie relation between the momentum p and the wavelength λ for photons.

A similar relation holds for the momentum of a particle of mass m and the associated de Broglie wavelength of the particle

$$\lambda = \frac{h}{p}$$

$$= \frac{h}{mv} \tag{A.9†}$$

The de Broglie relations establish a fundamental connection between the corpuscular properties of a material particle as expressed by its momentum p and its wave properties as expressed by its de Broglie wavelength.

† See A. P. French: *Principles of Modern Physics*, Chapter 7, Wiley, 1958, for a clear presentation of this topic.

A.3 The Heisenberg Uncertainty Principle

This principle is a consequence of the particle wave dualism of matter. According to this principle, the simultaneous determination of the momentum p and the position-coordinate x of a particle is limited by the condition that the products of the uncertainties in the measurement of these quantities cannot be less than h.

If we denote the uncertainties by Δ, then

$$\Delta x \, \Delta p \geqslant h/2\pi \tag{A.10}$$

A similar limitation applies to the possibility of a simultaneous determination of the energy E and the time coordinate t:

$$\Delta E \, \Delta t \geqslant h/2\pi \tag{A.11}$$

Appendix B

B.1 The Neutron Current Density and Fick's Law of Diffusion

If the neutron density is not constant throughout a given volume, there will then take place a net flow of neutrons from regions of higher density to regions of lower density. If we consider a unit area in a volume occupied by a neutron gas, we find that neutrons will cross the unit area in all directions. Unless the neutron density is uniform in the neighborhood of our unit area there will, in general, be an excess of neutrons passing through the unit area in one direction as compared to the number of neutrons crossing it in the opposite direction. This net flow across the unit area will be greatest if we place it normal to the direction of the neutron flow.

The number of neutrons passing in unit time through a unit area which is normal to the direction of flow is the **neutron current density J**. It is a vector quantity, and in Cartesian coordinates it can be stated in terms of its components along the (x, y, z)-axes in this manner:

$$\mathbf{J} = \mathbf{i}J_x + \mathbf{j}J_y + \mathbf{k}J_z \tag{B.1}$$

where **i, j, k** are unit vectors along the three axes.

The value of **J** depends on the space rate of change of the neutron density, $dn/\mathbf{ds}$, in the neighborhood of the point of interest.

The connection between the neutron current density **J** and the space rate of change of the neutron density is given by **Fick's Law of Diffusion**, which states that the two quantities are proportional to each other:

$$\mathbf{J} = -D\left(\frac{dn}{\mathbf{ds}}\right) \tag{B.2}$$

Here, D is the **diffusion coefficient** as given by Eq. 8.1 and $dn/\mathbf{ds}$ is the maximum rate of change of neutron density, also called the **density gradient**, or grad n.

In standard vector notation,

$$\frac{dn}{\mathbf{ds}} = \text{grad } n = \nabla n \tag{B.3}$$

The minus sign in B.2 indicates that the neutron current is in the direction of decreasing neutron density.

For monoenergetic neutrons, since $\phi = nv$, we can also write,

$$\mathbf{J} = -\frac{D}{v}\frac{d\phi}{ds}$$

$$= -D_0(\text{grad }\phi)$$

$$= -D_0\nabla\phi \tag{B.4}$$

$D_0 = D/v$ is the **diffusion constant**, also called the **diffusion coefficient for flux** by some authors. It has the dimensions of a length.

In rectangular coordinates, grad ϕ can be written in a form corresponding to B.1, which is

$$\text{grad }\phi = \mathbf{i}\left(\frac{d\phi}{dx}\right) + \mathbf{j}\left(\frac{d\phi}{dy}\right) + \mathbf{k}\left(\frac{d\phi}{dz}\right) \tag{B.5}$$

Substitution of Eqs. B.1 and B.5 in B.2 leads to the three equations for the components of the current density.

$$J_x = -D_0\frac{\partial\phi}{\partial x} \qquad J_y = -D_0\frac{\partial\phi}{\partial y} \qquad J_z = -D_0\frac{\partial\phi}{\partial z} \tag{B.6}$$

Each of these components represents the net current density along the respective axis and is the difference between a current density component in the positive direction and a current density component in the opposite direction.

Thus

$$J_x = J_{x+} - J_{x-}$$

$$J_y = J_{y+} - J_{y-} \tag{B.7}$$

$$J_z = J_{z+} - J_{z-}$$

where it can be shown (for example, Glasstone and Edlund, *The Elements of Nuclear Reactor Theory*, Chapter 5) that

$$J_{x+} = \frac{1}{4}\phi - \frac{1}{2}D_0\frac{\partial\phi}{\partial x}$$

$$\tag{B.8}$$

$$J_{x-} = \frac{1}{4}\phi + \frac{1}{2}D_0\frac{\partial\phi}{\partial x}$$

with analogous expressions for the other components J_y and J_z, and that

$$D_0 = \frac{\lambda_{tr}}{3} \tag{B.9}$$

B.2 Neutron Leakage Rate

The neutron leakage rate from a volume element dV can now be calculated as the difference of the neutron flow out of and into the volume dV. Consider the volume element in a Cartesian coordinate system

$$dV = dx\,dy\,dz$$

The net leakage rate of neutrons from the volume element is given by Fig. B.1

in x direction:

$$[J_x(x + dx) - J_x(x)]\,dz\,dy = \left(\frac{\partial J_x}{\partial x}\,dx\right)dz\,dy \qquad \text{(B.10)}$$

in y direction:

$$[J_y(y + dy) - J_y(y)]\,dz\,dx = \left(\frac{\partial J_y}{\partial y}\,dy\right)dz\,dx \qquad \text{(B.11)}$$

in z direction:

$$[J_z(z + dz) - J_z(z)]\,dx\,dy = \left(\frac{\partial J_z}{\partial z}\,dz\right)dx\,dy \qquad \text{(B.12)}$$

$$\text{Total leakage rate} = \left(\frac{\partial J_x}{\partial x} + \frac{\partial J_y}{\partial y} + \frac{\partial J_z}{\partial z}\right)dx\,dy\,dz$$

$$= -D_0\left(\frac{\partial^2 \phi}{\partial x^2} + \frac{\partial^2 \phi}{\partial y^2} + \frac{\partial^2 \phi}{\partial z^2}\right)dV$$

$$= -D_0\nabla^2\phi\,dV \qquad \text{(B.13)}$$

$\nabla^2 \equiv \partial^2/\partial x^2 + \partial^2/\partial y^2 + \partial^2/\partial z^2$ is the Laplacian in rectangular coordinates. In spherical and cylindrical coordinates it is given by

$$\nabla^2 = \frac{1}{r^2}\frac{\partial}{\partial r}\left(r^2\frac{\partial}{\partial r}\right) + \frac{1}{r^2\sin^2\theta}\left[\frac{\partial^2}{\partial\phi^2} + \frac{\partial}{\partial\theta}\left(\sin\theta\frac{\partial}{\partial\theta}\right)\right] \quad \text{(spherical)} \quad \text{(B.14)}$$

$$\nabla^2 = \frac{1}{r}\frac{\partial}{\partial r}\left(r\frac{\partial}{\partial r}\right) + \frac{1}{r^2}\frac{\partial^2}{\partial\theta^2} + \frac{\partial^2}{\partial z^2} \qquad \text{(cylindrical)} \quad \text{(B.15)}$$

B.3 Boundary Conditions and Extrapolation Length

In order to determine the two constants of integration that arise in the general solution of the second order diffusion equation 8.6, certain boundary conditions must be assumed to apply. The following conditions,

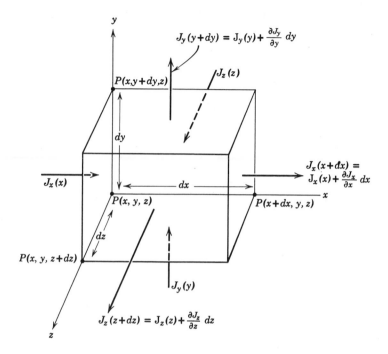

FIG. B.I. Neutron current flow components and neutron leakage rate from volume element dV.

which follow from the physical nature of the problem that the equation describes, are imposed:

A. The neutron flux cannot become negative anywhere in the medium in which the diffusion takes place.

B. The neutron flux must be finite everywhere (except at points that are neutron sources).

In addition, we can show that at the boundary between two different regions

C. The flux must be continuous, and

D. The neutron current component normal to the boundary must be continuous.

If we denote the quantities referring to the two adjacent regions by subscripts (1) and (2), we can deduce conditions C and D from the fact that the total neutron current entering region (2) from region (1) must be equal to the total neutron current leaving region (1) in the same direction. Similarly, the total currents in the opposite directions must be also equal. Hence

$$J_{(1)x+} = J_{(2)x+}$$

Therefore
$$\frac{\phi_1}{4} - \frac{D_{0(1)}}{2}\frac{\partial \phi_1}{\partial x} = \frac{\phi_2}{4} - \frac{D_{0(2)}}{2}\frac{\partial \phi_2}{\partial x}$$

and

$$\frac{\phi_1}{4} + \frac{D_{0(1)}}{2}\frac{\partial \phi_1}{\partial x} = \frac{\phi_2}{4} + \frac{D_{0(2)}}{2}\frac{\partial \phi_2}{\partial x}$$

Addition and subtraction of the two equations lead to the result that

$$\phi_1 = \phi_2 \tag{B.16}$$

and
$$D_{0(1)}\frac{\partial \phi_1}{\partial x} = D_{0(2)}\frac{\partial \phi_2}{\partial x} \tag{B.17}$$

in agreement with conditions C and D laid down previously.

If region (2) is a vacuum, then no neutrons can enter region (1) from region (2); thus we can set the neutron current in the $(x-)$ direction J_{x-} equal to zero. Therefore

$$J_{x-} = \frac{\phi}{4} + \frac{D_0}{2}\frac{\partial \phi}{\partial x} = 0$$

Therefore
$$-\left(\frac{\partial \phi}{\partial x}\right)_0 = \frac{\phi_0}{2D_0} \tag{B.18}$$

If we extrapolate the neutron flux ϕ linearly from the boundary (Fig. 9.1) we have the linear extrapolation distance d given by

$$\frac{\phi_0}{d} = -\left(\frac{\partial \phi}{\partial x}\right)_0 = \frac{\phi_0}{2D_0} \qquad \text{Therefore} \quad d = 2D_0 = \tfrac{2}{3}\lambda_{tr} \tag{B.19}$$

This result provides an additional boundary condition, which is that

E. The flux ϕ must be zero at the extrapolated boundary of the moderator.

Clearly, this derivation is only approximate, since we assumed in it the validity of diffusion theory at the boundary which is not correct. As pointed out in Chapter 9, transport theory leads to the correct result for the extrapolation distance

$$d = 0.71\lambda_{tr}$$

B.4 Solution of Diffusion Equation for Thermal Neutrons from a Point Source

We start with Eq. 8.9

$$\nabla^2 \phi - \frac{1}{L^2} \phi = 0$$

Because of the spherical symmetry of the physical conditions, ϕ will depend only on r, the radial distance from the point source. The Laplacian, therefore, will be reduced to one term.

$$\nabla^2 \phi = \frac{1}{r^2} \frac{\partial}{\partial r} \left(r^2 \frac{\partial \phi}{\partial r} \right) \tag{B.20}$$

so that the differential equation becomes

$$\frac{1}{r^2} \frac{\partial}{\partial r} \left(r^2 \frac{\partial \phi}{\partial r} \right) - \frac{1}{L^2} \phi = 0 \tag{B.21}$$

With the substitution $R = r\phi$, we get

$$\frac{1}{r^2} \frac{d}{dr} \left(r \frac{dR}{dr} - R \right) - \frac{1}{L^2} \frac{R}{r} = 0$$

or

$$\frac{d^2R}{dr^2} - \frac{R}{L^2} = 0 \tag{B.22}$$

This equation has the solution

$$R = Ae^{r/L} + Be^{-r/L} \tag{B.23}$$

which gives, for $\phi = R/r$

$$\phi = \frac{A}{r} e^{r/L} + \frac{B}{r} e^{-r/L} \tag{B.24}$$

The constants A and B are determined from the boundary conditions. As ϕ must remain finite for all values of r, the constant A must be zero.

Therefore

$$\phi = \frac{B}{r} e^{-r/L} \tag{B.25}$$

To determine B we can make use of the physical condition of the problem, that the total neutron absorption rate for the medium (which is assumed to be of infinite extension) must be equal to the source strength Q. Therefore

$$Q = \int_0^\infty \phi \Sigma_a \, dV \tag{B.26}$$

where we choose as our volume element the spherical shell $dV = 4\pi r^2\, dr$ concentric with the source. Therefore

$$Q = \int_0^\infty \phi \Sigma_a 4\pi r^2\, dr \tag{B.27}$$

Substituting the value of ϕ as found for our solution, we get

$$Q = 4\pi\Sigma_a B \int_0^\infty e^{-r/L} r\, dr$$

$$= 4\pi\Sigma_a B L^2 \tag{B.28}$$

Therefore

$$B = \frac{Q}{4\pi\Sigma_a L^2}$$

$$= \frac{3Q}{4\pi\lambda_{tr}} \qquad \text{by 8.8} \tag{B.29}$$

The solution is therefore

$$\phi = \frac{3Q}{4\pi\lambda_{tr} r} e^{-r/L}$$

in agreement with 8.10.

B.5 Solution of Diffusion Equation for Thermal Neutrons from a Plane Source

The diffusion equation for this geometry is formally identical with the differential equation for R in the previous example.

The solution is therefore given by the same expression as was found for R, so that we can set

$$\phi = Ae^{x/L} + Be^{-x/L} \tag{B.30}$$

Again, A must be zero, if ϕ is to remain finite for all values of x. Therefore

$$\phi = Be^{-x/L} \tag{B.31}$$

To evaluate B, we make use of the fact that the neutron current J_x across a unit area parallel to the source plane is

$$J_x = -\frac{\lambda_{tr}}{3}\frac{d\phi}{dx}$$

$$= +\frac{\lambda_{tr}}{3}\frac{B}{L} \qquad \text{by B.31}$$

As we let the unit area approach the source plane, i.e., $x \to 0$, J_x becomes

$$J_x = \frac{B\lambda_{tr}}{3L} \tag{B.32}$$

From the physical conditions of the problem we know that the neutron source plane emits Q neutrons per sec per cm² in both the positive and negative x directions, so that $Q/2$ is the emission rate in the positive x direction. This must be equal to the net neutron flow J_x, as any neutron flow in the positive x direction due to neutron diffusion is balanced by an equal neutron diffusion flow in the opposite direction, by virtue of the symmetry of conditions on both sides of the source plane. We can therefore set

$$J_x(x = 0) = \frac{B\lambda_{tr}}{3L} = \frac{Q}{2} \tag{B.33}$$

Therefore
$$B = \frac{3QL}{2\lambda_{tr}} \tag{B.34}$$

The solution for ϕ is therefore

$$\phi(x) = \frac{3QL}{2\lambda_{tr}} e^{-x/L} \qquad \text{in agreement with 8.13}$$

The solution for a plane source may also be derived from the solution of a point source by integration (see Glasstone and Edlund, *op. cit.*, section 5.52).

Comparing the solution for the plane source distribution just obtained with the previously found solution for the point source distribution, we are led to the important result that the solution $\phi_0(r)$ for a point source may be derived from the plane source solution $\phi_p(r)$ by differentiation. Thus, for equal source strengths Q

$$\phi_0(r) = -\frac{1}{2\pi r} \left| \frac{d\phi_p(x)}{dx} \right|_{x=r}$$

For an extended source of arbitrary shape the solution can then be obtained from the point source solution by integrating over the source shape or volume. Thus

$$\phi(r) = \int \phi_0(|r - r'|) \, dV' Q(r')$$

$$= \int \frac{3e^{-\frac{|r-r'|}{L}}}{4\pi\lambda_{tr}|r - r'|} Q(r') \, dV'$$

where $Q'(r) \, dV'$ is the source strength of the volume element dV'.

In principle it is, therefore, always possible to reduce problems of arbitrary source distributions to plane source distributions, and this device is frequently used in transport theory. (See R. E. Marshak, H. Brooks, and H. Hurwitz, *Nucleonics*, **4**, No. 5, May 1949.)

Appendix C

C.1 One-Group Calculation for Reflected Reactor

The neutrons are assumed to be produced, to diffuse, and to be absorbed at a single energy which we take to be the thermal energy.

The core and reflector regions, denoted by suffixes c and r respectively, must be considered separately because of their different material and nuclear properties, and the solutions obtained for each region must be fitted at the boundary interface. If we take the origin to lie on an axis of symmetry of the system, the necessary boundary conditions to be imposed on the solutions are:

1. ϕ to be symmetrical about the origin.
2. ϕ to be finite and non-negative at all points of the system.
3. ϕ to be zero at the extrapolated boundary of the reflector.
4. ϕ to be continuous at the core-reflector interface.
5. the normal neutron current J_n to be continuous at the core-reflector interface.

When we start with the diffusion equation 8.6 and replace q by $k_\infty \Sigma_a \phi$, which is the rate at which thermal neutrons are produced per neutron absorbed, the equation for the core region becomes after a simple algebraic manipulation

$$\nabla^2 \phi_c + \frac{k_\infty - 1}{L_c^2} \phi_c = 0 \qquad (C.1)$$

Better numerical results are obtained if L_c^2 is replaced in this equation by the migration area $M_c^2 = L_c^2 + \tau_c$, a modification which emerges automatically from a more accurate derivation of C.1. We shall use the more correct version of Eq. C.1, which is

$$\nabla^2 \phi_c + B_c^2 \phi = 0 \qquad (C.1a)$$

with $B_c^2 = \dfrac{k_\infty - 1}{M_c^2}$, the material buckling of the core.

For the reflector region, the neutron source term in Eq. 8.6 is absent

since no neutron production occurs in the reflector region, so that the diffusion equation 8.6 reduces to

$$\nabla^2 \phi_r - \frac{\phi_r}{L_r^2} = 0 \tag{C.2}$$

We shall next apply Eqs. C.1a and C.2 to two simple reflected reactor shapes, namely, *one* the infinite slab reactor and *two* the spherical reactor.

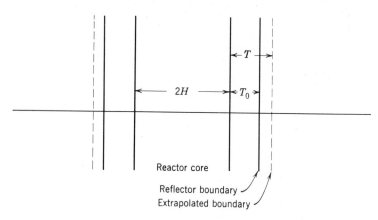

FIG. C.I. Infinite slab reactor with reflector.

Example C.I. Infinite Slab Reactor with Reflector. Let the thickness of the slab in the x direction be $2H$, and the reflector thickness on either side be T. T includes the extrapolation length, so that if T_0 is the geometrical reflector width $T = T_0 + 0.71\lambda_{tr}$ (Fig. C.1).

The core equation C.1a reduces to the one-dimensional equation

$$\frac{d^2\phi_c}{dx^2} + B_c^2\phi_c = 0 \tag{C.3}$$

which has the general solution

$$\phi_c = a_c \cos(B_c x) + b_c \sin(B_c x) \tag{C.4}$$

This expression can be symmetrical about the origin (boundary condition a) only if $b_c = 0$. Hence, the desired solution is

$$\phi_c = a_c \cos(B_c x) \tag{C.5}$$

In the reflector region the diffusion equation has the simple form

$$\frac{d^2\phi_r}{dx^2} - \frac{1}{L_r^2}\phi_r = 0 \tag{C.6}$$

which has the general solution

$$\phi_r = a_r \exp\left(\frac{x}{L_r}\right) + b_r \exp\left(-\frac{x}{L_r}\right) \tag{C.7}$$

[The solution is frequently written in the form

$$\phi_r = a_r{}' \cosh\left(\frac{x}{L_r}\right) + b_r{}' \sinh\left(\frac{x}{L_r}\right) \qquad (C.7a)$$

which is equivalent to C.7 with $a_r = \frac{1}{2}(a_r{}' + b_r{}')$ and $b_r = \frac{1}{2}(a_r{}' - b_r{}')$.]

Equating ϕ_c and ϕ_r at the boundary $|x| = H$ (condition d), we have from C.5 and C.7 for $x = H$:

$$a_c \cos(B_cH) = a_r \exp\left(\frac{H}{L_r}\right) + b_r \exp\left(-\frac{H}{L_r}\right) \qquad (C.8)$$

Similarly, equating the normal neutron currents (Appendix B, Eq. B.17) at the boundary (condition e), we find that

$$D_{0c}a_cB_c \sin(B_cH) = D_{0r}\frac{b_r}{L_r}\exp\left(-\frac{H}{L_r}\right) - D_{0r}\frac{a_r}{L_r}\exp\left(\frac{H}{L_r}\right) \qquad (C.9)$$

Application of the boundary condition (c) leads to a relation between the constants of integration a_r and b_r of C.7 as follows:

By (c),

$$\phi_r(H + T) = 0 \qquad (C.10)$$

Hence, substituting $x = H + T$ in C.7, we have

$$a_r \exp\left(\frac{H+T}{L_r}\right) + b_r \exp\left(-\frac{H+T}{L_r}\right) = 0 \qquad (C.11)$$

Therefore $\qquad\qquad b_r = -a_r \exp\left[\frac{2(H+T)}{L_r}\right] \qquad (C.12)$

Substituting this value of b_r in C.8 and C.9 and then dividing C.9 by C.8, we arrive after some intermediate algebraic steps at the following result:

$$D_{0c}B_c \tan(B_cH) = \frac{D_{0r}}{L_r} \coth\left(\frac{T}{L_r}\right) \qquad (C.13)$$

This equation relates the critical half-thickness H of the reflector to the reflector thickness T and the material and nuclear properties of the assembly, and it represents the critical equation for the reflected slab reactor.

By setting $T = 0$ in Eq. C.13 we arrive at the critical condition for a bare reactor. Thus, for $T \to 0$, $\coth(T/L_r) \to \infty$ and hence also $\tan(B_cH) \to \infty$, i.e., $B_cH \to \frac{1}{2}\pi$. Consequently, for $T = 0$

$$B_cH_0 = \frac{1}{2}\pi \qquad (C.14)$$

It should be noted that H_0 in C.14 is now the extrapolated half-width of the bare reactor as can be seen from C.10 if we allow $T \to 0$. The extrapolated critical half-thickness H_0 of the bare reactor is, therefore,

$$H_0 = \frac{\pi}{2B_c} \qquad (C.15)$$

From the description of the reflected reactor in section 9.10 and in view of the function and purpose of the reflector it is clear that the critical half-thickness of

the bare reactor exceeds the critical half-width of the reflected reactor. This excess is known as the **reflector savings** and we shall denote it by δ. Thus

$$\delta = H_0 - H \tag{C.16a}$$

$$= \frac{\pi}{2B_c} - H \qquad \text{by C.15} \tag{C.16}$$

If we substitute the value of H as given by C.16 in C.13, we can calculate the reactor savings δ directly. Thus,

$$D_{0c}B_c \tan\left(\tfrac{1}{2}\pi - B_c\delta\right) = \frac{D_{0r}}{L_r} \coth\left(\frac{T}{L_r}\right) \tag{C.17}$$

or,

$$\tan\left(B_c\delta\right) = \frac{D_{0c}B_cL_r}{D_{0r}} \tanh\left(\frac{T}{L_r}\right) \tag{C.18}$$

When $B_c\delta$ is small, $\tan\left(B_c\delta\right) \simeq B_c\delta$, and C.18 simplifies to

$$\delta = D_{0c}\frac{L_r}{D_{0r}} \tanh\left(\frac{T}{L_r}\right) \tag{C.19}$$

If, in addition to $B_c\delta$ being small, we also have that $T \ll L_r$, we can set $\tanh\left(T/L_r\right) \simeq T/L_r$, and C.19 can be further simplified to

$$\delta = \frac{D_{0c}}{D_{0r}}T \tag{C.20}$$

This shows that, within the limitation of the preceding assumptions, if the diffusion constants for the reactor core and reflector are equal, the reflector savings is equal to the reflector thickness: therefore, if $D_{0c} = D_{0r}$

$$\delta = T \tag{C.21}$$

If, on the other hand, $T \gg L_r$ with $B_c\delta$ still assumed to be small, then $\tanh\left(T/L_r\right) \simeq 1$, and C.19 reduces to

$$\delta = \frac{D_{0c}}{D_{0r}}L_r \tag{C.22}$$

For $D_{0c} = D_{0r}$, the reflector savings in this case follows from C.22 to be given by

$$\delta = L_r \tag{C.23}$$

The maximum possible reactor savings under this condition would be achieved with a reflector of infinite thickness for which it would be given by the diffusion length in the reflector L_r.[†]

Fig. C.2 and Fig. C.3 show the critical core thickness $2H_0$ and the reflector savings δ as a function of the reflector thickness T.

Example C.2. Spherical Reactor with Reflector. Let the core radius be R and the augmented reflector thickness be T. We again start with Eqs. C.1a and

---

[†] For a more detailed discussion see Glasstone and Edlund, *Elements of Nuclear Reactor Theory*, 8.25 to 8.30.

C.2 and now express ∇^2 in spherical coordinates. Because of the spherical symmetry of the system the flux will be a function of r only. Since by Eq. 9.33

$$\nabla^2\phi = \frac{d^2\phi}{dr^2} + \frac{2}{r}\frac{d\phi}{dr}$$

we get from C.1a that for the flux in the reactor core ϕ_c

$$\frac{d^2\phi_c}{dr^2} + \frac{2}{r}\frac{d\phi_c}{dr} + B_c^2\phi_c = 0 \tag{C.24}$$

By making the substitution $P_c = \phi_c r$, we transform Eq. C.24 into

$$\frac{d^2P_c}{dr^2} + B_c^2 P = 0 \tag{C.25}$$

which has the general solution

$$P_c = a_c \sin (B_c r) + b_c \cos (B_c r) \tag{C.26}$$

or, since $P_c = \phi_c r$, this becomes in terms of ϕ_c

$$\phi_c = \frac{a_c}{r} \sin (B_c r) + \frac{b_c}{r} \cos (B_c r) \tag{C.27}$$

Because ϕ_c must be finite everywhere (condition b), b_c must be set equal to zero as, otherwise, for $r \to 0$ the $\cos (B_c r)$ term would become infinite. Hence, the appropriate solution is

$$\phi_c = \frac{a_c}{r} \sin (B_c r) \tag{C.28}$$

The substitution $P_r = \phi_r r$ in C.2 leads to the equation

$$\frac{d^2P_r}{dr^2} - \frac{1}{L_r^2}P_r = 0 \tag{C.29}$$

which has the general solution

$$P_r = a_r \exp \left(\frac{r}{L_r}\right) + b_r \exp \left(-\frac{r}{L_r}\right) \tag{C.30}$$

or, in terms of ϕ_r,

$$\phi_r = \frac{a_r}{r} \exp \left(\frac{r}{L_r}\right) + \frac{b_r}{r} \exp \left(-\frac{r}{L_r}\right) \tag{C.31}$$

Since for $r = R + T$, $\phi_r = 0$ (condition c), we obtain from C.31 by setting $r = R + T$, a relation between a_r and b_r which is

$$0 = a_r \exp \left(\frac{R+T}{L_r}\right) + b_r \exp \left(-\frac{R+T}{L_r}\right)$$

therefore

$$b_r = -a_r \exp \left[\frac{2(R+T)}{L_r}\right] \tag{C.32}$$

Substituting this value for b_r in C.31, we get:

$$\phi_r = \frac{a_r}{r} \exp \left(\frac{R+T}{L_r}\right) \sinh \left(\frac{r-R-T}{L_r}\right) \tag{C.33}$$

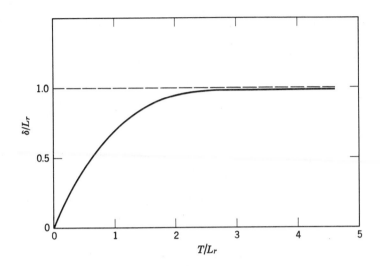

FIG. C.2. Reflector saving shown as a function of reflector thickness. The reflector saving and reflector thickness are shown in units of L_r.

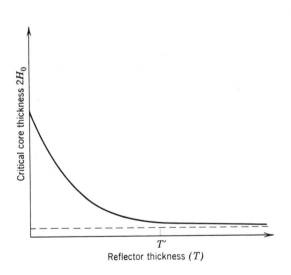

FIG. C.3. The critical core thickness decreases with increasing reflector thickness. After the reflector has reached a certain thickness T' very little reduction in critical core thickness can be gained by a further increase of reflector thickness.

Equating now C.28 and C.33 at the core-reflector interface (condition d), we obtain

$$a_c \sin (B_c R) = -a_r \exp \left(\frac{R + T}{L_r}\right) \sinh \left(\frac{T}{L_r}\right) \tag{C.34}$$

Next, calculating and equating the normal neutron current at the interface according to Eq. B.17 of Appendix B (condition e), we find that

$$Ra_c B_c D_{0c} \cos (B_c R) - D_{0c} a_c \sin (B_c R)$$

$$= D_{0r} a_r \exp \left(\frac{R + T}{L_r}\right) \left[\frac{R}{L_r} \cosh \left(\frac{T}{L_r}\right) + \sinh \left(\frac{T}{L_r}\right)\right] \tag{C.35}$$

Division of C.35 by C.34 leads to the result

$$\frac{D_{0c}}{D_{0r}} [1 - RB_c \cot (B_c R)] = 1 + \frac{R}{L_r} \coth \left(\frac{T}{L_r}\right) \tag{C.36}$$

This is the critical equation for the reactor. If R_0 is the critical radius of the corresponding bare reactor, the reflector savings δ is:

$$\delta = R_0 - R$$

$$= \frac{\pi}{B_c} - R \qquad \text{by Eq. 9.38} \tag{C.37}$$

Substituting the value of $R = (\pi/B_c) - \delta$ as given by this relation in C.36, the reflector savings can be obtained. In particular, if $D_{0c} = D_{0r}$, we find that

$$\tan (\delta B_c) = B_c L_r \tanh \left(\frac{T}{L_r}\right) \tag{C.38}$$

Therefore $\qquad\qquad \delta = \frac{1}{B_c} \tan^{-1} \left[B_c L_r \tanh \left(\frac{T}{L_r}\right)\right] \tag{C.39}†$

† For a more detailed discussion, see Glasstone and Edlund, *The Elements of Nuclear Reactor Theory*, 8.32 to 8.35.

Physical Constants

Fundamental Constants

c	Velocity of light	2.99793×10^{10} cm/sec
N_A	Avogadro's number	6.0249×10^{23} gram mole^{-1}
h	Planck's constant	6.62517×10^{-27} erg sec
$h/2\pi$		1.05443×10^{-27} erg sec
k	Boltzmann's constant	1.38044×10^{-16} erg/degree
m_e	Electron rest mass	9.1083×10^{-28} gram
		$= 5.4876 \times 10^{-4}$ amu
		$= 0.51098$ Mev
m_p	Proton rest mass	1.6724×10^{-24} gram
		$= 1.007593$ amu
		$= 938.232$ Mev
m_n	Neutron rest mass	1.67470×10^{-24} gram
		$= 1.008982$ amu
		$= 939.526$ Mev
m_H	Hydrogen atom mass	1.6733×10^{-24} gram
		$= 1.008142$ amu
		$= 938.722$ Mev
e	Electronic charge	1.60206×10^{-19} coulomb
e/m	Specific charge of electron	1.7589×10^{8} coulomb/gram

Derived Constants

Classical electron radius	$r_0 = e^2/m_e c^2$	2.8178×10^{-13} cm
Thomson cross section	$\sigma_0 = \frac{8}{3}\pi r_0{}^2$	0.665196×10^{-24} cm^2
Compton wavelength of electron	$\lambda_{\text{Comp}} = h/m_e c$	0.0242625×10^{-8} cm
de Broglie wavelength of electron of energy E(ev)	$\lambda_e = h/m_e v$	$1.22638 \times 10^{-7} \times E^{-\frac{1}{2}}$ cm

de Broglie wavelength
of neutron of energy
E(ev) $\lambda_n = h/m_n v$ $2.8601 \times 10^{-9} \times E^{-1/2}\,\text{cm}$

Wavelength corre-
sponding to the
energy E(ev) $\lambda_E = hc/E$ $12397.67 \times 10^{-8} \times E^{-1}\,\text{cm}$

Conversion Factors

	1 erg	1 Mev	1 amu
1 erg	1	6.24196×10^5	670.33
1 Mev	1.60209×10^{-6}	1	1.07393×10^{-3}
1 amu	1.4918×10^{-3}	931.161	1

Slow-Neutron Cross Sections of the Elements
(in barns)

Element	Absorption Cross Section $\sigma_{a(2200)}$	Scattering Cross Section (thermal) $\sigma_{s(th)}$	(epithermal) $\sigma_{s(epith)}$
$_1$H	0.332	38	20.4
$_1$D	0.00046	7	3.4
$_2$He	0.0070	0.8	0.83
$_3$Li	71.0	1.4	0.9
$_4$Be	0.010	7	6.11
$_5$B	755	4	3.7
$_6$C	0.0034	4.8	4.66
$_7$N	1.88	10	9.9
$_8$O	0.00019	4.2	3.75
$_9$F	0.009	3.9	3.6
$_{10}$Ne	<2.8	2.4	2.6
$_{11}$Na	0.505	4.0	3.1
$_{12}$Mg	0.063	3.6	3.4
$_{13}$Al	0.230	1.4	1.4
$_{14}$Si	0.16	1.7	2.2
$_{15}$P	0.20	5	3.4
$_{16}$S	0.52	1.1	1.1
$_{17}$Cl	33.6	16	~4
$_{18}$A	0.66	1.5	0.68

Element	Absorption Cross Section $\sigma_{a(2200)}$	Scattering Cross Section (thermal) $\sigma_{s(th)}$	(epithermal) $\sigma_{s(epith)}$
$_{19}$K	2.07	1.5	2.1
$_{20}$Ca	0.44	3	3.0
$_{21}$Sc	24.0	24	
$_{22}$Ti	5.8	4	4.2
$_{23}$V	4.98	5	4.9
$_{24}$Cr	3.1	3.0	3.9
$_{25}$Mn	13.2	2.3	1.9
$_{26}$Fe	2.53	11	11.4
$_{27}$Co	37.0	7	5.8
$_{28}$Ni	4.8	17.5	17.4
$_{29}$Cu	3.77	7.2	7.7
$_{30}$Zn	1.06	3.6	4.0
$_{31}$Ga	2.80	4	7.3
$_{32}$Ge	2.45	3	8.7
$_{33}$As	4.3	6	7.8
$_{34}$Se	12.3	11	7.8
$_{35}$Br	6.7	6	6.0
$_{36}$Kr	31	7.2	
$_{37}$Rb	0.73	12	5.4
$_{38}$Sr	1.21	10	9.8
$_{39}$Y	1.31	3	
$_{40}$Zr	0.180	8	6.2
$_{41}$Nb	1.15	5	6.5
$_{42}$Mo	2.7	7	6.0
$_{43}$Tc	100		
$_{44}$Ru	2.56	6	6.5
$_{45}$Rh	156	5	5.5
$_{46}$Pd	8.0	3.6	4.7
$_{47}$Ag	63	6	6.4
$_{48}$Cd	2450	7	
$_{49}$In	196	2.2	
$_{50}$Sn	0.625	4	4.8
$_{51}$Sb	5.7	4.3	4.1
$_{52}$Te	4.7	5	4.4
$_{53}$I	7.0	3.6	3.7
$_{54}$Xe	35	4.3	
$_{55}$Cs	29.0	20 ± 10	6.9
$_{56}$Ba	1.2	8	5.9
$_{57}$La	9.3	15 ± 5	9.2
$_{58}$Ce	0.73	9 ± 6	2.8

Element	Absorption Cross Section $\sigma_{a(2200)}$	Scattering Cross Section	
		(thermal) $\sigma_{s(th)}$	(epithermal) $\sigma_{s(epith)}$
$_{59}$Pr	11.6		3.9
$_{60}$Nd	46		16
$_{61}$Pm	60		
$_{62}$Sm	5600		
$_{63}$Eu	4300	8	
$_{64}$Gd	46,000		
$_{65}$Tb	46		
$_{66}$Dy	950	100	
$_{67}$Ho	65		
$_{68}$Er	173	15	
$_{69}$Tm	127		
$_{70}$Yb	37	12	
$_{71}$Lu	112		
$_{72}$Hf	105	8	
$_{73}$Ta	21.3	5	6
$_{74}$W	19.2	5	5.6
$_{75}$Re	86	14	
$_{76}$Os	15.3	11	15
$_{77}$Ir	440		
$_{78}$Pt	8.8	10	12
$_{79}$Au	98.8	9.3	
$_{80}$Hg	380	20	
$_{81}$Tl	3.4	14	10
$_{82}$Pb	0.170	11	11.3
$_{83}$Bi	0.034	9	9.28
$_{84}$Po	7.0		
$_{85}$At			
$_{86}$Rn	0.7		
$_{87}$Fr			
$_{88}$Ra	20		
$_{89}$Ac	510		
$_{90}$Th	7.56	12.5	12.5
$_{91}$Pa	40		
$_{92}$U	7.68	8.3	
$_{93}$Np	180		

ANSWERS TO PROBLEMS

Chapter 1

(1) 5.75×10^9 years
(2) 4.23×10^3 sec^{-1};
  4.87×10^{-18} sec^{-1}
(3) 400
(4) 6×10^9 years
(5) 0.36 curies
(6) 6.5×10^{-9} gm; 3000 gm
(7) 4.95 curies; 9.65 curies;
  0.159 curie; 0.308 curie
(8) 0.65×10^{-4} sec^{-1};
  1.26×10^{-4} sec^{-1}
(9) 2.48×10^5 years
(10) 48 days

Chapter 2

(1) 1.8×10^{11} kg/cm^3
(3) 32.5 Mev
(4) 4.5×10^{-12} cm
(5) 1.98 Mev
(6) 20.56 Mev; 15.60 Mev
(7) 8.942 Mev
(11) 3.08 Mev; 3.24 Mev
(12) 1.24 Mev
(14) 830.5 Mev; 828.8 Mev;
  826.2 Mev
(15) 2.1 Mev

Chapter 3

(1) 12×10^{-22} sec
(3) 9.54 Mev; 7.48–11.86 Mev
(5) 19.35 Mev
(6) -6.92 Mev; -7.87 Mev;
  -8.57 Mev
(8) 2.64×10^{-6} ev

Chapter 4

(1) 1.31×10^{10}
(2) 5.6×10^{-4} cm^{-1}
(3) 10 cm
(4) 8.5 days
(5) 2 barns
(6) 99 barns
(7) 4.55×10^8 neutrons/cm^3;
  1.8×10^{-11} atm

(10) 0.010 cm^{-1}
(11) 110 cm
(14) 0.148; 0.852

Chapter 5

(1) 0.179; 0.099; 0.81; 0.38
(2) 2.07
(3) 3570 kw/m^3; 416 kw/kg
(4) 189 kw
(5) 450 gm
(6) 4000 kw
(7) 0.72 Mev; 2 Mev
(8) 213 Mev

Chapter 6

(1) 507; 503 000; 1340; 652; 6230;
  57.5; 1.21; 92.1; 106; 176
(2) 1.81 Å
(3) 0.86 Mev
(4) 2760 barns
(5) 0.010 ev; 0.0033 ev
(6) 0.06 cm
(7) 6%
(11) 200
(14) $\frac{1}{2}\phi$
(15) $\frac{1}{2}E$
(16) 0.209
(17) 0.171
(20) 7.6 cm
(21) 19.8

Chapter 7

(1) 0.835
(2) 1.026
(4) 29; 109; 875; 752; 45; 48
(5) 1.115; 1.008
(7) 0.704
(10) 1:900

Chapter 8

(1) 2.66 cm
(2) 6.8 cm
(3) 2945 cm^2; 530 cm^2; 39 cm^2;
  28,025 cm^2
(5) 7.4%; 0.28%

(11) 0.2775
(12) 60 cm^2

Chapter 9

(2) 0.0065
(3) 67.4 cm
(5) 37,000 liters
(6) 3055 gm
(7) 2.8%, 36.2%; 43.6%, 1.9%
(9) 0.75 × radius
(12) 0.015; 25.7 cm; height 47 cm
(13) 16 cm
(14) height < 15 cm; or, side < 22 cm

Chapter 10

(1) 2.3 × 10^{-8} sec; 1.8 × 10^{-8} sec
(2) 120 sec
(3) 1.33 × 10^{-5}%
(4) 0.2–2 sec
(5) 34 min
(7) 1025
(8) 1.6 × 10^{-4} sec
(10) 28
(13) 7

Chapter 11

(2) 7 × 10^{-6}
(3) 390 years
(4) 230 gm
(5) 1.84 kg
(6) −0.012
(8) −5 × 10^{-5}/°C
(10) 17 × 10^{-5}/volume of coolant
(11) 0.27

Chapter 12

(1) 2.5 cm

(2) 4.5 × 10^{-5} cm
(3) 4.3 × 10^{-5} cm
(5) Al: 1.43, 0.76, 0.75;
1.57 mgm/cm^2
Cu: 2.70, 0.65, 0.61;
2.35 mg/cm^2
Au: 5.75, 0.51, 0.42;
3.89 mg/cm^2
(6) 2.03 Mev
(7) 0.16 cm; 0.023 cm
(8) 0.9%; 5.7%
(9) 827 mg/cm^2
(10) 9.75 Mev; 27.5 Mev
(13) 4.4 cm; 0.577 cm^2/gm

Chapter 13

(1) 1.4 × 10^{-11} amp
(2) 93%
(3) 0.8 volts
(4) 37 mv
(5) 5.4 mv
(6) 1.83 × 10^{-14} coulomb;
1.66 × 10^{-14} coul
(7) 2280 volts
(8) 66 c/min
(9) 10; 0.002 cm
(10) 1.08 × 10^{-3} cm
(11) 0.3%

Chapter 14

(1) 4.4 × 10^5 Mev/cm^2
(2) 0.65 r/hr
(3) 3 sec
(6) 0.22 cm
(7) 11 m
(8) 2.3 cm

Index of Tables

Index